People today have so extended their domination over the forces of nature that, thanks to that sovereignty it has become very easy for them to exterminate one another to the finish.

Sigmund Freud

I dedicate this book to Professor Werner Greûter who has offered so much to the study of the Cretan flora.

G. Sfikas

George Sfikas

Wild Flowers
of
Crete

With 450 illustrations in colour

EFSTATHIADIS GROUP

Efstathiadis Group S.A.
Agiou Athanasiou Street.
GR - 145 65 Anixi. Attikis

ISBN 960 226 052 1

© Efstathiadis Group S.A. 1995

Printed and bound in Greece by Efstathiadis Group S.A.

INTRODUCTION

Crete is one of the largest Mediterranean islands. From a geographical point of view it constitutes a self-contained unit, like Cyprus, Corsica, Sardinia, and Sicily.

This large island, dubbed by the rest of the Greeks the "Megalonissos" (Big Island), with an area of 8,311 sq. kilometres is well-known for its equable climate, farm produce, sunshine and beautiful seas. It is also well-known for its rare flora which is the subject of this book. Yet, today's visitor to Crete will be hard-pressed to come across any of the island's rare wild flowers, as they can be found only in out-of-the-way localities where man's meddling is either limited so far or, as yet, completely absent. It must be pointed out, however, that such areas where Nature has remained intact up to the present are very few indeed. And that is exactly where the problem lies.

This once well forested island has been so tampered with in our days and Cretan Nature so impaired, that we can speak of its being truly a tragedy. For it is a foregone conclusion that, if human interference continues at the same rate without immediate steps being taken to protect Nature in Crete, it will soon be ecologically destroyed.

The drafting of this book, which has two aims, has meant repeated trips to Crete to collect the specimens and photographic material needed, let alone having to wade through dozens of books and through dozens of learned articles in various publications, all on the subject of Cretan flora.
One of the aims is to put on record the present pressing problems of Cretan Nature on the one hand, and on the other to put forward certain suggestions concerning the measures that should be taken to ensure its conservation. The other aim is to make an inventory of the island's flora, an attempt which is being essayed for the first time. The fact is that although many experts have studied Cretan Nature, concentrating on certain groups of plants, no complete "Flora Cretica" has ever been published.

In this book almost the entirety of the higher plants has been recorded. The exceptions are the gramineae, and the ferns, as well as certain groups of plants that are of no special decorative interest. Plants found on the islets around Crete (Gavdhos, Gramvoussa, Thodhorou, Dia, Coufonissi, etc.) have also been included.

GEOLOGICAL UPHEAVALS

In the early Miocene Period, about 26 million years ago, great geological upheavals occurred in the region of Europe and the Mediterranean. One of the results was the emergence of Aegeis, a continuous stretch of dry land that connected S.E. Europe with Asia Minor.

In the mid-Miocene, 18 million years ago, there were on Aegeis both high mountains and depressions where many lacustrine basins of fresh water were formed. At that time Crete was linked to Greece, Turkey, and the Aegean Islands forming an almost unbroken stretch of dry land. Towards the end of the Miocene, circa 14 million years ago, we know that large herbivorous animals dwelt in the region of Aegeis - elephants, hippopotami, etc.

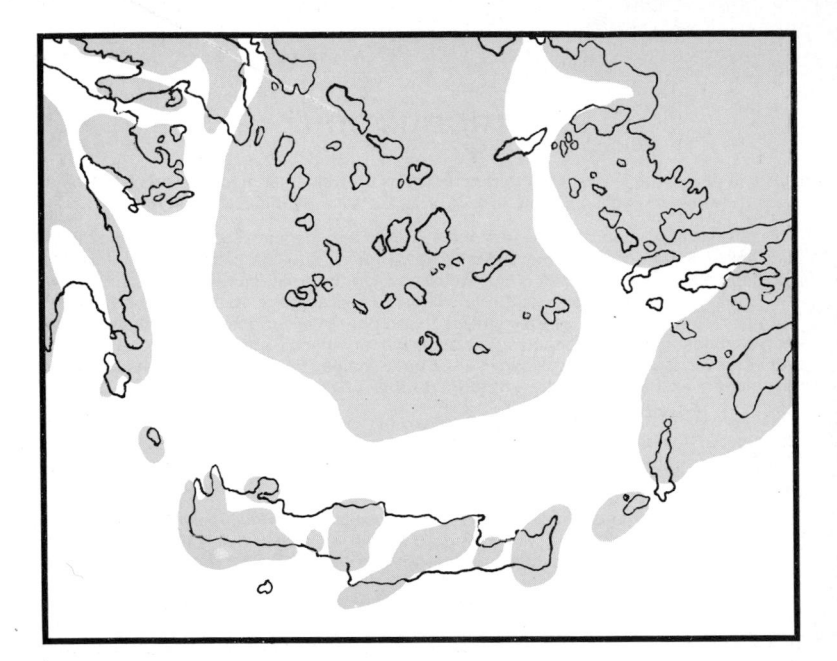

Crete and the South Aegean as they were during the Upper Pliocene 1-2 million years ago according to a map by Greutzburg.

- which, to survive, needed a very extensive living space with rich pastures and plentiful water.

Towards the end of the Tertiary Period, some 10 million years ago, the face of Aegeis began to change. Subsidences and precipitations, some sudden and others occurring over a considerable span of time, led to an ever-increasing encroachment of the Mediterranean Sea, and the consequent dissection of the land-mass of Aegeis. Thus 8 million years ago Crete, at the time divided up into two or three smaller islands, was already surrounded by sea.

Further geological upheavals occurred during the Pliocene, 1 to 3 million years ago, when there were continual subsidences and uplifts. This geological activity created a deep tectonic rift that brought into being the open seas of Crete which were very much like what they are today. But still Crete was not one whole island: it continued to be fragmented into several smaller islands. However, in time as the uplift continued these merged and Crete took on approximately the shape it has at present.

Towards the end of the Pliocene and the beginning of the Pleistocene (about 1 million years ago) the configuration of the Aegean Sea began finally evolving into a shape

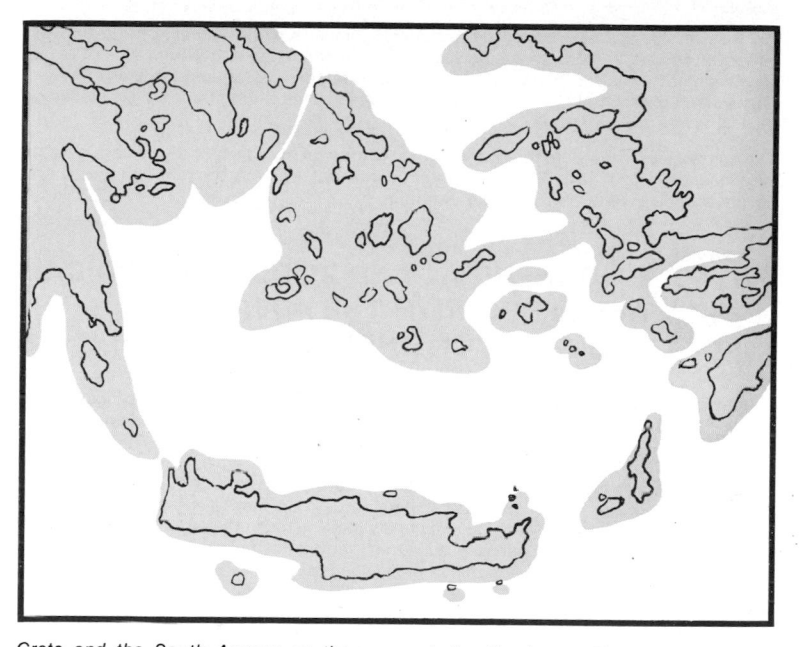

Crete and the South Aegean as they were during the Lower Pleistocene 750,000-1,000.000 years ago according to Greutzburg's work.

strongly resembling that of today. Nevertheless, there continued to be unbroken stretches of dry land in the region of Aegis. One such was that linking together the Cyclades Islands. In the South Aegean the islands of Crete, Carpathos, Cassos and Rhodes stood out clearly.

The geological upheavals in the Aegeis region went on in the Pleistocene as well(1,000,000 to 25,000 years ago); they were, however, on a smaller scale. For all that, their role in the development of the fauna and flora of Crete was of very great importance since, as a result, Crete was once more attached to the adjacent continents as well as to remnants of the old dry land of Aegeis, such as the Cyclades.

The Pleistocene Period was marked by alternating periods of heat and cold due to the fluctuations of. ice ages and interglacials. The great climatic changes in the Mediterranean did not leave the Cretan fauna and flora unaffected. But in the main, they influenced them indireclty as every time the ice spread from the poles to the temperate zones the sea level dropped thus forming land-bridges which linked Crete to the neighbouring landmasses, and resulted in its being colonised by animal and plant species.

It has been estimated that during the first three glacier periods; the Gunz, the Mindel, and

7

the Riss, the sea level dropped by hundreds of metres. For instance, during the Riss period there was a 200m. drop. Only during the last ice-age, the Würm, when the ice-sheets did not spread so much was the drop considerably less, about 90m. The number of animals and plants that crossing the land-bridges formed during the ice-ages settled on the island was considerable.

The point of view regarding the connection of Crete with the adjacent dry lands during the Pleistocene Period has, of course, been contested, yet the phytogeographical and zoogeographical data on the whole uphold it.

PHYTOGEOGRAPHICAL AND ZOOGEOGRAPHICAL AFFINITIES WITH THE ADJACENT CONTINENTS

During the Pleistocene Period there were great numbers of mammals on the island, such as the huge *Elephas antiquus,* the dwarf *Elephas creticus,* the dwarf *Hippopotamus pentlandi,* the deerlike *Anaglochis cretensis,* the *Capra aegagrus,* the *Wild Cow (Bos primigenius),* the *Bison,* and other smaller animals. Did these beasts cross over to the island when it was attached on the one hand to Europe by way of Antikythera, Kythera, and the Peloponnese, and on the other to Asia through Carpathos and Rhodes? Or could they be the direct descendants of the mammals that existed in the region of Crete when it was still part of Aegeis? That is a question that cannot be answered with absolute certainty. What is a fact is that some of these species, such as the dwarf elephants and hippopotami, were endemic to Crete and had evolved *in situ,* while other species were common to the neighbouring continents as well. For instance, *Bos primigenius* and the *Bison* are typical European mammals, while *Capra aegagrus* is typically Asian.

The view that Crete was joined to the adjacent continents is further supported by the phytogeographic data. For example, in Crete there are 61 Asiatic species of plants which do not appear in any other European regions, not even on the mainland of Greece; 33 species exclusive to Cyranaica and Crete. 18 other plants one can find in the S. Balkans, that is, chiefly on the Greek mainland; and another 28 of West European origin reaching down to Crete via the Ionian Islands and mainland Greece.

There are also flowers which are common to both Crete and the Cyclades. In fact, the distribution of these species is limited to just those two regions. Such are: *Campanula laciniata; Athemis ammanthus* - subsp. ammanthus; *Erysimum candicum* -subsp. candicum; *Anthyllis aegea;* to mention but a few.

However, besides the mammals and the plants, there are other groups of living organisms that provide us with invaluable information about the geological past of the island. It is noteworthy that out of the 150 species of snails to be found on Crete not one is to seen in the Peloponnese, while there are species among them that are common to Kythera, Antikythera, Carpathos, and Rhodes. Moreover, the affinity between the butterflies of Crete and the Asiatic species is unmistakable.

From all the above we can conclude that Crete was for longer or shorter periods linked both to the neighbouring continents and to the Cyclades. More frequent and of greater duration must have been the island's connection with Asia, less frequent and less protracted that with Europe, while the connection with Africa must have been both less

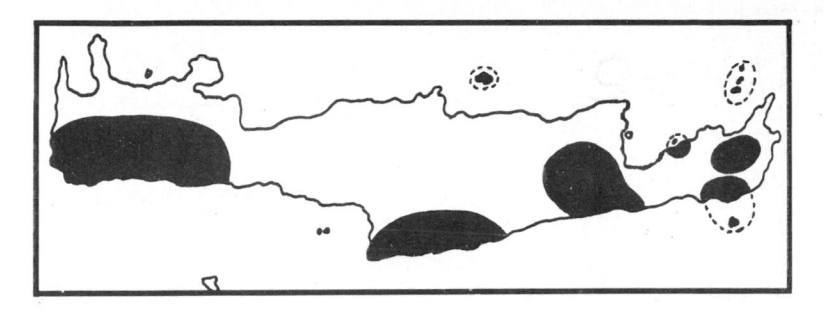

The regions in Crete where most endemics can be found are, according to Sven Snogerup, those marked in black on the map.

frequent and of much shorter duration. On the other hand, one land-bridge joining Crete with the Cyclades appears to have lasted a long time, and that in relatively recent times. Another relatively recent separation seems to have been that of Crete from Carpathos and Rhodes at the east end, and from Antikythera and Kythera at the west end.

ENDEMIC PLANTS AND ANIMALS

Among the animals and plants of Crete many are endemic species or subspecies that are not to be found anywhere else in the world. As regards the plants it has been estimated that there are 210 species and subspecies. These constitute the 44% of all the endemic plants on the Aegean Islands. The percentage of the endemic species and subspecies of snails (molluscs) comes to the 60% of the total number of species on Crete (90% out of a total of 150); 42% in the case of Coleoptera (18 out of 43); and, finally, 10% of all the butterflies are endemics.

Naturally, evolution is a more gradual process where mammals are concerned, and that is why the differentiation of the species is usually on a smaller scale not going beyond the level of a subspecies. Therefore we have *Capra aegagrus-cretica* which is a subspecies of the Asiatic *Capra aegagrus; Martes foina-bunites,* a subspecies of the widespread M*artes foina; Felis silvestris-agrius,* a subspecies of the Eurasian *Felis silvestris;* and so forth. Endemism is, of course, rare in birds, limited only to species that reside permanently on the island, such as the local golden eagle (Aquila chrysaetus, subsp. hoemeyeri).

The large number of endemic plants and animals is due to the fact that Crete though repeatedly joined to the adjacent continents also enjoyed long periods of time in complete isolation. Consequently, under the influence of such geographical seclusion many species differentiated to such an extent as to produce new species or, at least, new subspecies.

Another characteristic of Crete is that its endemic plants are concentrated largely in certain regions, like West Crete with its White Mountains, the end of east Crete, in the mountains of Sitia, and in those lying west of the plain of Messara.

Some endemics are common to the whole island, while others are restricted either to East Crete or to West Crete only. For instance, *Scabiosa albocincta* is to be found in W. Crete,

9

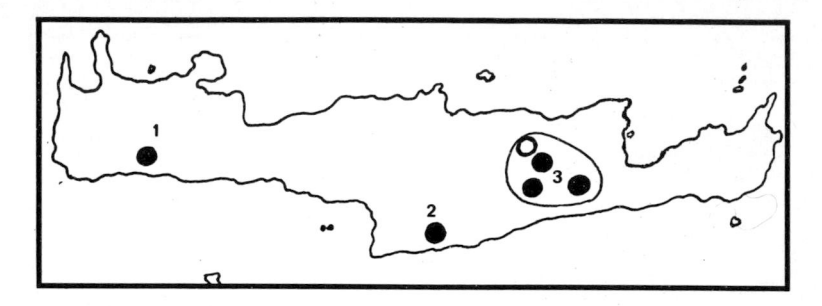

The regions of distribution of three endemic species and sub-species of the Scabiosa genus: 1 Scabiosa albocincta. 2 Scabiosa minoana - subsp. asterusica 3 Scabiosa minoana - subsp. minoana.

but its relation *Scabiosa minoana* is an E. Crete endemic; we have *Anthemis glaberrima* in W. Crete, and the related *Anthemis tomentalla* and *Anthemis ammanthus* in E. Crete; E*rysimum* raulinii in W. Crete and *Erysimum creticum* in E. Crete.

The phenomenon of a restricted, local appearance of endemics can be observed in the land molluscs (snails) too, just as in the case of the plants. Of course, this phenomenon has its roots in geohistorical causes, and leads us to believe that Crete was in the remote past broken up into two or more separate islands for a very long time. Geological research is proving this view to be correct.

NATURE IN CRETE IN ANTIQUITY

Practically the same species of animals and plants existed on Crete during the Minoan era as those to be found there today. But, in addition there were also species that have since disappeared. For example, we know that there were deer on Crete at that time for their antlers have been discovered in the repository of the Temple dedicated to the Goddess of Serpents. There must also have been wild sheep similar to those on Cyprus and Sardinia (ovis musimon), since such survived up to the time of the Venetian Rule. The numerous helmets made of wild boar tusks, found largely in graves of the later Minoan era, are a convincing piece of evidence that the boar, too, was once a resident of the island.

Regarding the plants at any rate, certain species of limited distribution probably existed at that time but disappeared later because their habitats were destroyed. Besides, this phenomenon can be observed even in our own time; certain plants mentioned last century as existing on Crete have never been seen again in recent years. A typical example of a recent disappearance is the case of the wild Madonna Lily (Lilium candidum), which had been discovered in a certain spot near Chania.

Generally speaking, however, the fauna and flora of Crete were about the same in antiquity as they are today. But the same thing is not true of the vegetation. Today's bare Cretan mountains must have at that time been covered with forests; dense forests of conifers as well as of platyphyllous trees. This conclusion has been reached by both direct and indirect evidence. We know, for example, that Crete at that time exported

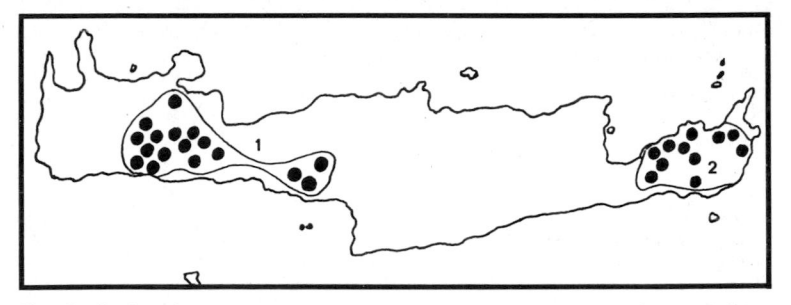

The distribution of two endemic plants belonging to the Erysimum genus: 1) Erysimum raulinii. 2) Erysimum creticum.

cypress timber to all the surrounding countries. We also know that Crete was forest-clad even in much later years.

The name of Mount Idha (today's Psioloritis) is derived from the doric word 'idha' meaning a forest, a forest of tall trees or an afforested mountain. Besides which Herodotus speaks of Crete as: «χώρη υψηλή τε και ίδηοι ουνηρεφή», namely, as being covered with umbriferous trees.

The species of trees that made up the Cretan forest were no different from those found today, that is wherever there are any still preserved. The cypress (Cypressus sempervirens), the Calabrian pine (Pinus brutia) would have been the principal conifers, while the Holm Oak and the other platyphyllous shrubs of the Mediterranean Maquis must have populated large expanses of land, especially on the lower slopes of the mountains. On the other hand, the ravines and wet places must have been covered with perennial plane-trees.

Undoubtedly, there must have been great numbers of both mammals and birds living in this paradise, and as only the most primitive of weapons were used in hunting this could have had no disastrous effect on these populations.

When we compare the Crete of today with that of Minoan times we cannot but grieve over the terrible degradation of its natural world. However, we must not forget that the present state of affairs is almost entirely the result of man's activities and not that of some minor change in climatic conditions.

Yet the climate of Minoan Crete must have been somewhat colder and more humid than at the present day, a fact that would certainly favour still more the development of forests, and this is a view the author has upheld in his book "Greek Nature through the Centuries".

NATURE IN CRETE UNDER VENETIAN AND TURKISH RULE

Even in much later times, when the island's climate differed in no way from today's, Crete preserved a large part of its ancient forests. Indeed, it appears that under Venetian Rule those forests were protected and so flourished once more on many mountains. The protection of forests and their exclusive exploitation by the State was an undeviating policy on the part of the Venetian Government in any country conquered. The reason being that timber was a material of vital military importance for the maintenance of the Venetian Navy. It was therefore not at all strange that the Duke of Naxos, Jacobus Crispus, had to apply for a special licence to bring out of Crete timber needed for the Cyclades at the beginning of the 15th Century.

A century later, in 1518, the Frenchman Jean Palerne was greatly impressed by the cypress forests surrounding Candia (Heracleion). At about the same time it seems there were still plentiful birds of prey on Crete - another indication of the vitality of Cretan Nature. The Cretans used to kill these birds and sell their feathers to the fletchers, while their skins were bought by the tanners, so wrote André Thevet after visiting the island in 1549. During the same period there were still Wild Sheep to be found on the island's mountains. The exact time of their disappearance is unknown.

Still more convincing, however, is the evidence given by Henri Castella who passed through Crete in 1600. He writes that Crete was the happiest Mediterranean island, fertile, enjoying a mild climate and with all its mountains covered with cypresses.

As for the Wild Goats of Crete, they were numerous when Belon passed through in 1554. But even much later, foreign naturalists were impressed by their large numbers. In 1717, Tournefort wrote that they lived in herds, and Savary that the high mountains on the island were inhabited only by Wild Goats.

The rapid degradation of Cretan Nature appears to have set in after the Venetians left the island, and the island was subjugated by the Ottoman Empire in 1669. Though there is no positive documentary evidence to prove it we can conjecture that the main reasons for this degradation were due, on the one hand, to the migration of the islanders from the lowlands and coast up to the highlands for greater safety and, on the other, the indifference of the Turkish authorities regarding the preservation of the forests, coupled with the uncontrolled development of stockbreeding which led to the firing of the forests in order to create new pasture-lands.

Thus the greater part of the Cretan mountains were denuded and when the union of Crete with Greece 1908 came about, it found the island badly scarred, largely because of the stock-breeders' activities. Even after the Union, that sorry state of affairs persisted and, unfortunately, it is still doing so up to the present; the reason is the conviction that a forest is useless and must be got rid of so that the land be left free for the grazing of sheep and goats, a conviction which is firmly rooted in the Cretan shepherds' minds. A fact that should be stressed is that even bushes and phrygana often fall victims to the arsonists so that on many Cretan mountains nothing has been left save the bare rocks and the turbulent torrents, while the forest-covered areas have so dwindled that they occupy less than one-tenth of the island's total surface.

CRETAN NATURE TODAY

Did we not know what Crete's natural world was like but a few centuries ago, we might be tempted to term the current state of the island's natural environment tolerable. But since we do know what it was in much earlier times we cannot but describe it as tragic. It does not take much for the naturalist's experienced eye to realise that if certain activities are not restricted the consequences will be irreparable.

The slopes of Mt Psiloritis (Idha) above the village of Anoyia look like a moonscape. This is the result of uncontrolled grazing which has led to the deplorable state of the Cretan mountain today.

Most of the mountains in Crete lost their forest cover a long time ago, often making them look like bare skeletons, denuded of every shred of vegetation and handed over as they have been to stock-breeding which is ever-declining and futureless. The few plains and rounded hills have, in their turn, been ceded to intense farming where again the uncontrolled use of herbicides, insecticides and other chemical substances is causing the disappearance of wild plants, birds and every living organism non-lucrative to man.

The sandy beaches are either packed with hot-houses or overrun by tourists, thus narrowing the strips that constitute the habitats of the coastal fauna and flora. It is only along the rocky coastline, which is practically inaccessible, that the natural environment remains as yet undisturbed. For the very few wet places that exist are being drained or changed to such an extent that they can no longer act as refuges either for plants or for animals. One result of this is that many migratory birds have stopped coming to the island. Then again, there is all the harm done to fauna through the ever-increasing numbers of gun licences and of sportsmen, not to mention the rise in poaching on the one hand, and the menace caused by the opening up of more and more roads leading to the most inaccessible mountains and shores, on the other.

Under such circumstances it is not strange that dozens of plants of Crete, known to exist

13

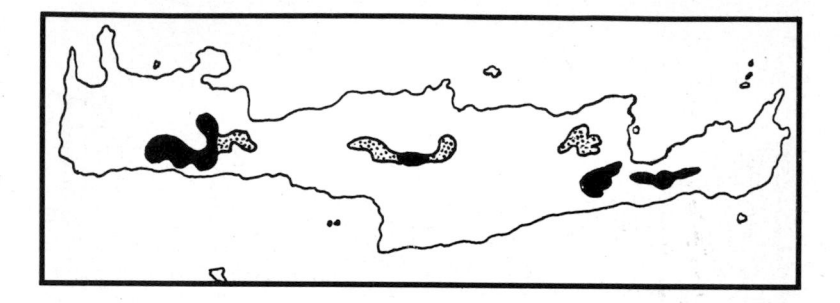

The forests of Crete as they are today. The black areas denote dense forests, and the dotted ones the sparse.

in the recent past, now have a quesion-mark after them when mentioned. Of course, the same thing applies to certain mammals too, such as the Cretan Wildcat (Fourogatos), as well as to birds. There is no doubt that a great many more species would have been lost to us but for the numerous famous Cretan gorges, in which not only do some of the rarest and most threatened Cretan plants find shelter, but also several species of mammals and birds, as well as entire forests of Cypresses, Pines, and other trees.

HABITATS

Actually, Crete is a chain of mountains emerging from the depths of the Eastern Mediterranean sea. The great difference in altitude between the summits of the high mountains and the sea, the existence of many gorges and gullies, the north winds blowing from the open Aegean sea, and the hot winds coming up from North Africa are all factors that influence the climate of Crete and create a variety of habitats.

This diversity of habitats, coupled with the very dissimilar micro-climates naturally do not leave the fauna and flora of the different regions unaffected. The plants especially are affected more, for not being motile, they are forced to adapt to the local climatic conditions in order to survive. But both mammals and birds have their special preferences also, and choose to settle in places where they can find their food easily.

The main types of habitat of Crete are eight in number. The Lowlands, the Submontane, the Montane, the Subalpine and the Alpine zones are largely subject to altitude and difference of temperature. The littoral zone is the one next to the sea, and is directly influenced by it. Wet places again constitute a different kind of habitat, being impervious to both altitude and their proximity to the sea.

The same applies to the very numerous gorges and gullies where completely different conditions of temperature, humidity and light are created.

A characteristic type of seaboard habitat. Tufts of leaves of the Sea Daffodil (Pancratium maritimum) and many malcolmias (Malcolmia flexuosa) can be distinguished.

Littoral Zone

This zone is a narrow strip of land extending from the high water mark up to a few tens of metres inland. Depending on the configuration of the ground, the littoral may be less than 10m. wide, where the coast is rocky and precipitous, to 50m. or more on the saltings, which are areas approximately on a par with the sea-level.

The plants growing in this zone depend to a greater or lesser degree directly on the salinity and amount of humidity of the sea air. On sandy shores we come across the *sea-lily (Pancratium maritimum)*, *Anthemis rigida*, *Centaurea aegialophylla*, *Centaurea pumilio*, *Malcolmia flexuosa*, *Matthiola tricuspidata*, *Calystegia soldanella*, *Ipomoea stolonifera*, *Otanthus maritimums*, *Sedum caespitosum*, *Cakile maritima*, *Cynara cornigera (sibthorpiana)* and many others.

On the sea-cliffs grow: *Crithmum maritimum*, *Malcolmia flexuosa*, *Hypericum aegypticum*, *Convolvulus oleifolius*, *Capparis spinosa*, *Mesembryanthemum crystallinum*, *Teucrium brevifolium* and other plants.

A few metres off the beach, at the point where the sand ends and the lowland zone begins, we find *Cardopatium copymbosum*, *Convolvulus dorycnium*, *Cichorium spinosum*, *Cionura erecta*, the jujubetree *(Elaeagnus angustifolia)*, *Eryngium maritimum*, *Myrtus*

Landscapes such as the above are becoming rarer and rarer in the lowlands. Mechanical cultivation plus weed-killers have annihilated the wild flora.

communis - subspecies tarentina, Oxalis corymbosa, Inula crithmoides, Mesembry-anthemun nodiflorum, various *tamarisks (Tamarix), Limonium sinuatum* and a host of other plants which are only indirectly influenced by the sea.

Another feature of the littoral is the number of various birds nesting or finding their food along the sea-shore. And first and foremost the well-known gulls, such as: *Larus argentatus,* a permanent resident that nests on sheer cliffs, and especially on those of the uninhabited islets around Crete, or such as *Larus ridibundus, Larus canus* and *Larus fuscus* that descend to the Cretan coast to spend the winter.

The rare hawk (Falko eleonore) also makes its nest on the rocky islets around Crete when it comes up north from Africa during the summer months. While the kingfisher (Alcedo atthis) digs out its nest with its long bill in perpendicular earthy coasts, and catches fish in shallow roadsteads and in enclosed calm seas.

The woodpigeon also makes its nest in crevices on the sheer sea-cliffs, but it is in grave danger of extinction due to the brutal way it is being hunted.

It is almost certain that in earlier times the caves round the coast must have sheltered the

Among fields, close to fences and along the roadsides where neither the plough nor the weed-killers reach, a whole multitude of wild flowers grow, such as the Turban buttercup (Rannunculus asiaticus).

Mediterranean seal, while on the sandy Cretan beaches the different kinds of sea-turtles must have laid their eggs. Nowadays, the latter no longer lay their eggs on the island while the former frequent only a very few places of East and South Crete.

Lowlands

This zone begins at the point where the littoral ends, and stops at a height of about 300m. inland. The lowlands contain the main plains of Crete, the low hills and the lower parts of the mountains.

Wherever mechanised cultivation, herbicides and insecticides have not destroyed the natural environment, one can find many interesting plants. First of all there are all the shrubs of the Mediterranean garrigue which often reach right down to the water edge, such as the lentisk *(Pistacia lentiscus)* the Phoenician juniper *(Juniperus phoenicea),* the holm oak *(Quercus coccifera)* and the terebenthine tree *(Pistacia terebinthus).* In the same zone one can also find *Cistus incanus-creticus, Cistus parviflorus, Ebenus cretica,* the oleander *(Nerium oleander), Rannunculus asiaticus, Capparis ovata,* the squirting cucumber, *(Ecbalium elaterium),* the common poppy *(Papaver rhoeas), Daucus carotta, Roemeria hybrida, Matthiola incana, Lunaria annua, Reseda alba, Lupinus albus,* with white flowers (subspecies albus), and with dark blue flowers (subsp *graecus), Lupinous*

17

angustifolius, Chrysanthemum coronarium, Tetragonolobus purpureus, Securigera securidaca, and many others. Equally common are: Anemone coronaria, various annual geraniums, Euphorbia helioscopia, the castor-oil plant (Ricinus communis) Lavatera arborea, and Lavatera cretica, the wild cotton plants, Gossypium herbaceum and Gossypium hirsutum, Hypericum empetrifolium, different species of Eryngium, Ferula communis, Ferulago nodosa, Tordylium apulum, Periploca laevigata, Comphocarpus fruticosus, Convolvulus arvensis, different species of Heliotropium, Borago officinalis, Anchusa azurea and Anchusa undulata, subsp. hybrida. We can also find the Chaste Tree (Vitex agnus-castus), Lavandula stoechas, the rare Withania somnifera, Mandragora autumnalis, Acanthus spinosus, chamomile (Chamomilia recutita), Tragopodon porrifolius, Allium neapolitanum and Allium roseum, Narcissus tazetta, and Narcissus serotinus, Giadiolus italicus, Dracungulus vulgaris with their strikingly large reddish-purple spathes, several species of Serapias, and a host of other perennial and annual plants.

Hares, badgers, weasels and ferrets, that have their nests in the thickets of the surrounding hills and low mountain slopes descend to the Lowlands. There are also many hedgehogs and the usual small mammals of the plains, rodents and chiroptera (bats), such as the wild rat (Apodemus sylvaticus-creticus), the small bat (Myotis oxygnathus), the long-winged bat (Myniopterus schreibersii) and others. The commonest among the birds are: swallows (Hirundo rustica, Delichon urbica) sparrows (Passer domesticus, Passer hispaniolensis), goldfinches (Carduelis carduelis), crows (Corvus corone), and many others. In wintertime many more species come down from the mountain regions such as finches (Fringila coelembs), robins (Erithacus rubooula) and tlts (Parus), or from the north such as starlings (Sturnus vulgarus).

Sub-Montane Zone

Directly above the Lowlands comes the sub-Montane Zone, rising to approximately 800m. in height. These lower mountain slopes are covered largely by shrubs and Mediterranean phrygana such as Kermes or Holly Oak, the Terebinth Tree, the Lentisk, the Phoenician Juniper, Strawberry-Tree (Arbutus unedo) and Eastern Strawberry-tree (Arbutus adrachne), the Heath Tree (Erica arborea), Erica manipuliflora, Euphorbia dendroides, Thymus capitatus, Rhamnus alaternus, Thymelaea hirsuta and Thymelaea tartonraira, Acer sempervirens, Euphorbia acanthothamnos, Medicago arborea, Calicotomevillosa, Sarcopoterium spinosum, Clematis flammula and Clematis cirrhosa, Lonicera implexa, Phlomis cretica, Phlomis tanata and Phlomis fruticosa, Prasium majus, Teucrium microphyllum, Cistus salvifolius, Cistus monspeliensis, Cistus incanus-creticus.

Of the herbaceous and bulbous plants the following should be noted: Cyclamen creticum, Iris inguicularis, Allium subhirsurum, Asphodeline lutea, Asphodelus aestivus and Asphodelus fistulosus, Anthyllis vulveraria-subs. prepropera, Trigonella corniculata and Trigonella balansae, Anemone heldreichii, various species of Vicia and Lathyrus, Tremastelma palaestinum, Urginea maritima, Ballota nigra, Convolvulus althaeoides with its two subsps. (althaeoides and tenuissimus), Cyclamen graecum and many orchidaceous of the Ophrys, Orchis and Serapias genera.

Among trees, those most frequently met with are the Carob or Locust Tree (Ceratonia siliqua) and locally the Eastern Calabrian Pine (Pinus brutia) and the Judas Tree (Cercis siliquastrum).

18

Mediterranean bush (Maquis) in East Crete in the district of Mourniés.   19

One of the last cypress forests on the mountains of East Crete (in the district of Mourniés). Such forests once covered all the mountains on the island.

This is also the realm of hares, badgers and ferrets. There are also numerous weasels, hedgehogs and all the birds of the Lowlands. In the sub-montane zone one can come across different birds of prey such as the Kestrel *(Falco tinunculus)* as well as Crows, Ravens *(Corvus corax)*, Greenfinches *(Carduelis chloris)*, Blackbirds *(Turdus merula)*, Island Partridges *(Alectoris chukar)*, and so on.

Montane Zone

This zone begins roughly from 800m and reaches to approximately 1800 m. above sea-level. The three large Cretan plateaux - Omalos, Lassithi, and Nidha- belong to this zone.

In the past, arboreous vegetation prevailed in the montane zone. There were vast forests of conifers, such as Cypresses, Eastern Calabrian Pines (Pinus brutia) and, in the higher reaches, possibly Black Pines (Pinus nigra) as well. On the lower reaches there were forests of platyphyllus trees also, like the Kermes or Holly, Oak, the Cretan Maple (Acer sempervirens), and others. This zone is the habitat of the rare endemic - Zelkova abelicea, too. Today, these forests of old have vanished and only in certain places do their relics survive.

Many rare herbaceous plants occur in this montane zone. In fact, many of them are

The Lassithi Plateau with the peaks of Mt. Dhikti in the background. The windmills that were formerly the symbol of the region no longer exist today.

endemic to the island. To mention but a few: *Tulipa bakeri, Smyrnium apifolium, Erysimum raulinii, Centaurea idaea, Centaurea redempta, Achillea cretica, Viola cretica, Alyssoides cretica, Onosma erecta, Valeriana asarifolia, Arum idaeum, Tulipa cretica, Chionodoxa cretica, Arum creticum, Crocus oreocreticus, Paeonia clussii,* etc.

Besides plants, this zone is the natural habitat of great birds of prey such as the Lammergeyer *(Gypaëtus barbatus),* the Golden Eagle *(Aquila chrysaëtus),* and the Griffon Vulture *(Gyps fulvus).*

Other birds of the montane zone are: the Alpine Swift *(Apus melba),* the Stonechat *(Saxicola torquata),* the Black-eared Wheatear *(Oenanthe hispanica),* the Blackbird *(Turdus merula),* the Blue Rock Thrush *(Mondicola solitarius),* the Sardinian Warbler *(Sylvia melanocephala),* the Blue Tit *(Parus caeruleus),* the Chaffinch *(Fringilla coelebs),* the Cirl Bunting *(emberiza cirlus),* the Scops Owl *(Otus scops),* the Wood Pigeon *(Columba palumbus),* the Jay *(Garrulus glandarius)* and others.

The most important mammal of the montane zone is, of course, the Cretan Wild Goat which has in our days almost vanished, only a small population surviving in the regions round the Samaria Gorge. Other resident mammals are: the hare, the Dormouse, the Acomys minus, the Cretan Ferret, the Cretan Wild Cat, and varius rodents and bats.

21

The site Xylóscalo whence the Samaria Gorge begins. In the back-ground the bare and eroded slopes of Psiláphi and Ghinghilos Peaks, the last sanctuaries of the Cretan Wild Goat.

Subalpine Zone

This zone begins at about 1800m. and reaches up to 2200m. At this height the winter snowy period is shorter, and the summer is warmer and more prolonged than in the higher alpine zone.

Naturally there should have been forests in the subalpine zone. But these have disappeared from everywhere, and we can make only conjectures as to the species of trees that once grew there. For instance, in this zone there could have been trees such as *Abies cephalonica, Pinus nigra,* and *Juniperus foetidissima* which on mainland Greece and in the Peloponnese grow at an altitude of 1900m., but in Crete they could have existed at an even greater height.

In the subalpine zone a host of herbaceous or bulbous plants grow, as well as small shrubs, well-adapted to the cold: these are *Crocus sieberi, Chionodoxa nana, Anchusa caespitosa, Arabis alpina, Astragalus angustifolius, Corydalis rutifolia, Prunus prostrata, Viola fragrans,* and others. Besides, these many species from both the montane and alpine zones are to be found here also.

From among the bird world the great birds of prey inhabit the zone, so too, do the Alpine Swift *(Apus melba),* the Wheatear *(Oenanthe oenanthe),* the Chough *(Pyrrhocorax*

The bare peaks of the White Mountains, the legendary "Madares" are the most characteristic landscapes of the alpine zone of the mountains of Crete.

pyrrhocorax), and others. The montane mammals rarely climb so high. Only the Wild Goat can be seen in summer on the precipitous summits of Ghinghila, above the Samaria Gorge.

Alpine Zone

This zone extends from 2200 m. up to the highest peaks. An Alpine Zone is to be found only on the two highest mountains of Crete: Psiloritis (Idhi) and the White Mountains, whose summits top the 2200m. limit. Naturally, the area of the Alpine Zone is small.

In this zone most of the subalpine plants grow, as well as certain others that flourish in the cold, such as *Acantholimon androsaceum, Veronica thymifolia, Draba cretica, Thymus leucotrichus subsp. creticus, Cynoglossum sphacioticum, Dianthus sphacioticus,* and others. In this zone one also finds the same birds that exist in the subalpine zone.

The Moni Capsa Gorge in South-East Crete.

Gorges, Precipitous Mountainsides and Castles

What strikes one as regards the Cretan landscape (besides its high mountains) is the large number of gorges that traverse the island, usually from north to south; for instance the Samaria Gorge, the Imbriotico Gorge, the Courtaliotico Gorge etc. These gorges which start from the montane and the sub-montane zones and usually end somewhere near the sea, offer ideal refuge to hosts of rock plants (chasmophytes), such as *Campanula pelviformis, Campanula tubulosa, Petromarula pinnata, Verbascum arcturus, Symphiandra cretica, Staechelina fruticosa, Staechelina arborea, Linum arboreum, Centaurea argentea, Scabiosa minoana, Ebenus cretica, Nepeta melissifolia, Scutellaria sieberi* and many others.

Most of the above plants are endemic to Crete, or else, they have a very limited distribution in the South Aegean. Therefore the gorges are considered veritable paradises for wild flowers. In addition, the gorges have undergone either very slight effects from human activity or even none at all, leaving their rich flora practically untouched.

Similar flora is to be found on all rocky cliff faces, as well as on the walls of the island's old castles, no matter what the altitude may be. Still there are species that prefer, almost exclusively, old walls or even any walls such are: *Erysimum candicum* and *Hyoscyamus aureus*.

The gorges are ideal sanctuaries for mammals such as ferrets, weasels, bats and rodents. However, many birds as well build their nests among the rocks or on the trees in the gorges, for instance the Kestrel *(Falco tinunculus)*, the Vulture *(Gyps fulvus)*, the Wild Pigeon *(Columba livia)*, the Crag Martin *(Ptynoprogne or Hirundo rupestris)*, the Alpine Swift *(Apus melba)*, and others.

Wet Places

If we except Lake Courna in the province of Chania, the sole lake on the island, the wet places of Crete are limited to small coastal marshes, to the estuaries of small rivers (most of which run dry in the summer), to the banks of said rivers, and to various small swamps. Nevertheless, these small damp areas are of great interest, as much for their flora as for their fauna.

Of the plants, one comes across *Iris pseudacorus, Oenanthe pimpineloides, Oenanthe prolitera, Epilobium hirsutum,* several species of the genera *Lythrum* and *Tamarix* etc. On the banks of the wet places, particularly of those close to the sea, the rare Cretan palm grows *(Phoenix theophrastii)* which is endemic to the island.

The role the wet places of Crete play is of immense importance for the preservation of the migratory birds that come up from Africa to Europe each summer and use this island as an intermediate resting place. Such birds are the Pratincole *(Glareola pratincola)*, the Crane *(Grus grus)*, the Glossy Ibis *(Plegalis falcinellus)*, the Ruff *(Philomachus pugnax)*, the White Stork *(Ciconia ciconia)*, the Great White Heron *(Egretta alba)*, and many more.

Wet places are equally important for the other birds too, that either reside on the island the whole year round, such as the Stone Curlew *(Bourhinus oedicnemus)*, the Grey Heron *(Ardea cinerea)*, the Coot *(Fulica atra)*, and the Moorhen *(Gallinula chloropus)* or come in

Wetlands near Georgoupolis.

The palm forest of Vai grows on the banks of a small river bed ending by the sea.

winter only, such as the Curlew *(Numenius arcuata)*. These small wet places are their last and only sanctuaries which, if destroyed, means that those birds, too, will disappear from the island.

THE PLANTS

That such a large number of different plant species should be contained within so relatively small a region as Crete cannot but command the expert's respect.

It has been estimated that, not counting subspecies, there are about 2000 species of the higher plants on the island. This number represents a little under a third of the whole range of the species of Greek flora. But what is still more astonishing is the number of the endemic plants which are not to be found anywhere else in the whole world. Out of the circa 700 Greek endemic species about 250 are to be found in Crete, and of these some 160 are exclusively endemic to it. This number is constantly increasing as new rare species are, even in our day, coming to light growing out of sight in some isolated gorge or some remote mountainous region.

Of the Cretan endemics it has been estimated that 6 are threatened with immediate extinction because they are so few, and because their habitats are being destroyed; 15 others are endangered but not immediately; 78 are rare, and of another 4 we possess but vague information. It is only the remainder that are to some degree abundant and in no danger.

Besides the endemics, there are many more non-endemic plants of Crete which are threatened, because their populations on the island are very small and their habitats are under intense pressure. As it seems, approximately 50 species are on the verge of disappearance or have already disappeared. On the other hand, however, new species are being added to the Cretan Flora as plants common in the surrounding countries of the East Mediterranean are being discovered; these plants had never been observed on the island up to the present. It is noteworthy that during the author's trips to Crete for the collection of material for this book, 2 species of Poppy which are not mentioned in Flora Europaea were observed, as wells as 4 new plants, first introduced as cutivated species, but now completely naturalised.

Coniferales

Pinaceae Family

Trees, rarely shrubs, always resinous with needleshaped leaves, solitary or in clusters of 2-5 on a common short-shoot. Cones of various shapes. Male flowers in small cones which fall after releasing the pollen.

Pinus (Pines)

Evergreen trees, with leaves (needles) in clusters of 2-5. Cones usually ripen the second or third year. Scales permanent.

1. Pinus brutia: A tree up to 20m. tall, with rather rounded top and somewhat columnar trunk. Needles fine and long, 1-1,5mm wide and 80-120mm. long, in twos on a common short shoot. Ovate cones, slightly curved, almost sessile, and vertical to the branch they grow on, 5-11cm. long. Sub-montane and montane zones. **2. Pinus pinea.** Big round-topped or umbrella-shaped tree. Needles in twos, 100-200mm. in length. Large cones 8-14 cm, spherical-elliptical, with big edible seeds. Rarely found in the littoral and lowland zones.
Pinus nigra mentioned as existing on the Cretan mountains, seems to have disappeared in our day.

Cupressaceae Family

Resinous trees or shrubs, leaves small bract-like or spinys-needlelike. Small cones, more or less spherical. Tiny male inflorescences (cones).

Cupressus (Cypresses)

Leaves bract-like, opposite. Cones round or slightly elliptical, with few scales and seeds.

1. Cupressus sempervirens: Dark green tree reaching up to 30m. in height. Diameter of cones 25-40mm. Erect columnar trunk with top narrowly or broadly pyramidal. There are two distinctive forms. The true native cypress *(forma horizontalis)* has spreading branches and a wide flat-topped crown. Conversely the *forma sempervirens* met with on the island only in a cultivated form, has nearly erect branches, but shorter and denser, and a narrowly pyramidal top that is almost cylindrical.

Pinus brutia

Pinus pinea

Cupressus sempervirens

Juniperus oxycedrus -s.sp. oxycedrus

Juniperus (Junipers)

Bract-like leaves, similar to those of the cypress, or needleshaped like hard spines, opposite or in groups of 3. Small round cones, with few scales and seeds.

1. Juniperus oxycedrus - subspecies oxycedrus: A dioecious shrub or small tree. Pointed, needlelike leaves, up to 25mm. long and 2mm wide. Cones 8-10mm. brown and shiny. Sub-montane and montane zones. **2. Juniperus oxycedrus-subspecies macrocarpa:** Very similar to 1 but with slightly wider leaves and larger fruit 12-18mm. across, covered before ripening with a wax-like coating. Littoral and lowland zones, but always near the sea. **3. Juniperus phoenicea:** Monoecious shrub or small tree, up to 8m. high, usually with somewhat a pyramidal top. Leaves like scales, similar to those of the cypress. Russet-coloured cones. Found on hills and stony slopes of the lowland and sub-montane zones.

4. Juniperus excelsa: Similar to 3 but bigger, reaching a height of 20m. At first pyramidal, later when old with a spreading crown. Cones 8mm., dark brown when ripe. Rarely met with in the montane zone.

Gnetales

Ephedraceae Family

Dioecious shrublike plants, leaves opposite or verticillate. Small leaves, usually like small sheaths. Small fruit with 1-2 seeds surrounded by 2 pairs of fleshy bracts.

Ephedra (Sea grape)

Green shoots. Leaves like small sheaths. Fruit reddish and fleshy.

1. Ephedra fragilis - subspecies campylopoda: Stems climbing, creeping, or more usually pendulous. Fruit red, 8-9 mm. Montane and sub-montane zones, in rocky and stony places.

Salicales

Salicaceae Family

Deciduous and dioecious trees or shrubs. Leaves alternate, with small stipules. Flowers erect or in hanging catkins.
Male flowers composed of 1 bract and 2 or more stamens. Female flowers composed of one oblong ovary and 1 bract.

Salix (Willows)

Leaves more or less oblong, more long than wide. Tree-like or shrub-like plants.

1. Salix alba - subspecies alba: Tree can reach 25m. in height, with rounded top. Lanceolate leaves 5-10cm., very pointed, greenish on top and whitish-silvery underneath. Small stipules that fall off easily. Montane and sub-montane zones, on river banks, in ditches and wet places in general.

Populus (Poplars)

These plants are always trees, with broad leaves approximately as long as they are wide.

1. Populus alba: Large tree, up to 30m. in height, with a wide bushy crown. Two kinds of leaves; on developed stems three-lobed or five-lobed, on short ones dentate-wavy. The leaves are dark green on top, and silver and downy underneath. River and stream banks, lakes and swamps. Montane, sub-montane and lowland zones. **2. Populus nigra.** Similar to 1 but leaves of developed stems rhomboid-ovate and of smaller stems broader, deltoid. Uniform-coloured green leaves. River banks and gullies of the montane and submontane zones.

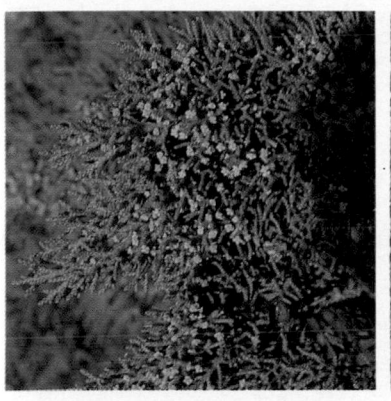

Juniperus phoenicea

Ephedra fragilis -s.sp. campylopoda

salix alba - s.sp. alba

Populus alba

Juglandales

Juglandaceae Family

Deciduous trees with alternate pinnate leaves. Many male flowers in catkins. Few detached female flowers. Fruit either drupes or nuts.

Juglans (Walnut trees)

Trees with large aromatic leaves. The fruit are large drupes. Male flowers in solitary catkins.

1. Juglans regia: A tree up to 30m. high with a spreading crown. Large leaves, with 7-9

31

ovate-elliptic leaflets. Its well-known fruit, the walnut, is almost globose, with a fleshy green outer covering and an inner woody one. Both native and cultivated in the montane zone, mainly in ravines and gullies where there is plenty of water.

Fagales

Fagaceae Family

Trees or shrubs with simple, alternate leaves. Male flowers in catkins or heads. Female flowers from 1-3, enclosed in a cup. Fruit composed of 1 or more nuts in a cup, at least at their base.

Castanea (Chestnut trees)

Deciduous trees with crenate leaves. Erect male catkins, flowers composed of 6-segmented perianths, and of 10-20 stamens. Female flowers usually in groups of threes, each group in a common cup. The fruit are large and consist of a large spiny cup that ordinarily contains 3 chestnuts.

1. Castanea sativa. Tree up to 30m. high, leaves oblong-lanceolate 10-25cm. long, mucronate at tip. Its fruit edible, in wild form up to 2,5cm. cultivated may reach 4cm. Both native and cultivated in the montane zone, usually in non-calcareous soils.

Quercus (Holm and Oak trees)

Deciduous or evergreen trees with pinnate leaves, dentate or entire. Male flowers in small pendulous catkins. Few famale flowers in sparse catkins. The fruit an ovate or elliptic nut, the well-known acorn surrounded, at least at its base, by a cup. The cup is covered with hard scales of varied shapes.

1. Quercus ilex. An evergreen tree or shrub with a broad bushy crown. Its leaves are 3-7 cm. long, oblong-ovate or lanceolate, spine-toothed or, more rarely entire, dark green on top and whitish silvery underneath. The acorns are relatively small. The cup has small adpressed scales. Sub-montane zone. **2. Quercus coccifera.** Similar to 1 but usually a low shrub, rarely a tall tree in old age. Leaves toothed and spiny, dark green on both sides. 1,5-4cm. long. Larger acorns, with scales of cup prickly and spreading. **3. Quercus macrolepis:** Semi-evergreen tree, (shedding its leaves at the end of winter). Leaves 6-10 cm. long, light green and pubaescent underneath, upper surface sparsely downy and dark green, obovate-oblong, dentate with very pointed teeth. Fruit: acorns, Invested in a large cup with elongated scales, the outer ones spreading or curved downwards. On hills and mountain-slopes of the sub-montane and lowland zones. **4. Quercus cerris.** A deciduous tree growing up 35m. high. Leaves fairly large, oblong or ovate, roundish or nearly cordate at the base, pinnate with 4-7 pairs of lobes, glabrous above and downy underneath. Acorn medium sized, cup fairly large. Scales of cup oblong and spreading. Rarely found in the montane zone. **5. Quercus brachyphylla:** A small tree or large shrub, deciduous or semi-evergreen. Stems pubescent. Leaves small and pinnate with lobe-like lobes, cordate at base. Medium-sized acorn, cup 15-20 mm. in diameter. Scales on cup small. Sub-montane and Montane zones.

Juglans regia

Quercus coccifera

Castanea sativa

Quercus macrolepis

Urticales

Ulmaceae Family

Deciduous trees with simple alternate leaves, usually asymmetric (somewhat unequal) at the base. Small flowers. Fruit drupes or samarae.

Ulmus (Elms)

Leaves at base asymmetric, dentate. Small flowers appearing before leaves, bell-shaped perianth with 4-8 lobes, 4-8 stamens. Fruit a samara, more or less disk-like, bipartite at apex, membraneous, with one seed near centre.

33

1. Ulmus minor. Tree up to 30m. high. Young shoots slender and glabrous. Leaves obovate, ovate or oblanceolate, with 7-12 pairs of lateral nervatures. Samarae 7-17mm. with the seed above centre. Found in wet places from the lowland to the montane zones. Rare. **2. Ulmus canescens.** Similar to 1 but young stems covered with dense white down, and leaves ovate-elliptical, densely downy with 12-18 pairs of lateral nervatures. Montane and sub-montane zones. Tree native to Mediterranean countries around Crete, it has now become sporadically native to the island after its introduction as a decorative tree.

Zelkova

Small trees, similar to Ulmus but with smaller leaves, not asymmetric, and their fruit are small hard drupes.

1. Zelkova abelices. A tree 3-5m. high, with slender pubescent branches. Leaves about 2,5cm. ovate with 7-9 teeth. Small white aromatic flowers. Pubescent drupes. Grows on rocks of the montane zone. A West Asian plant, it does not appear in any other European country, and in Greece only on Crete.

Celtis (Nettle Tree)

Trees with two kinds of flowers, male and bisexual. The perianth segments are free down to the base. The fruit is a fleshy drupe.

1. Celtis australis. A deciduous tree reaching 25m. in height. Leaves lanceolate or ovate-lanceolate, mucronate crenate, dark green and smooth on uppper surface, light green and pubescent underneath, 4-15cm. long. Globular drupes, 9-12mm across brownish-black, sweet and edible. Rarely met with in the montane and sub-montane zones. **2. Celtis tournefortii.** Similar to 1 but a small tree or shrub with smaller leaves 5-7 cm., and a yellowish-brown drupe. Found in gorges at a low altitude (500-600m.). Rare. To be found in West Crete (Imbriotico Gorge).

Moraceae Family

Trees or shrubs either monoecious or dioecious. Leaves usually alternate. Small flowers in dense, spike-like or head-like inflorescences, or enclosed in a fleshy receptacle (Fig Tree).

Morus (Mulberry Tree)

Trees with heart-shaped leaves, crenate, often palmate. Flowers of both sexes on the same short dense spike. Aggretate fruit consists of many fleshy drupes. The well-known mulberry.

1. Morus nigra. Leaves 6-18 cm. entire or palmate. Fruit dark purple, juice crimson, edible only when completely ripe, prior to that it is very acid. Habitat: from the montane zone right down to the lowlands. Both cultivated and sparsely self-growing. It is an Asiatic plant introduced into the Mediterranean countries in antiquity. **2. Morus alba.** Very similar to 1 but the berries are white, pink or crimson, edible long before they are entirely ripe. Both, cultivated and sparsely self-growing. From the montane zone to the lowlands. A Chinese plant introduced into the Mediterranean lands during the Byzantine era.

Ficus (Fig Trees)

Trees with entire or palmate leaves. Flowers enclosed in a fleshy, pear-shaped receptacle which later develops into a sweet fleshy fruit. (Fig).

Ulmus minor

Ficus carica

Osyris alba

Aristolochia clematitis

Ficus carica

Tree with palmate leaves, 10-20 cm. long. The fruit (fig) is 5-8 cm. long, greenish or dark violet, sweet and edible in the cultivated varieties, non-edible that of the wild trees. Montane, sub-montane and lowland zones. Both cultivated and wild.

The Urticaceae family is represented in Crete by certain species of the Urtica (Nettle) genera, and Parietaria, which are not of any decorative interest and are namely: **Urtica dubia, Urtica pilulifera, Parietaria officinalis, Parietaria diffusa, Parietaria lusitanica** and **Parietaria cretica.**

Santalales

Santalaceae Family

Woody or herbaceous plants with alternate leaves, simple, linear, oblong or lanceolate. Small flowers with no petals. The calyx from 3-lobed up to 5-lobed. Ovary semi-inferior. Fruit one small green nut or a fleshy drupe.

Osyris

Phrygana-like dioecious plants. Flowers with a 3 or 4-lobed calyx. Fruit a globular drupe.

1. Osyris alba: Slender stems up to 100cm. long with many short forks. Leaves small, linear-lanceolate. 3-segmented flowers. Red drupe, 5-7mm. across ripening in autumn. Habitat: sub-montane and montane zones in shrubby and stony places.
The Thesium genus of plants, insignificant and of no decorative interest, also belongs to the Santalaceae Family; in Crete one can find **Thesium humile, Thesium bergeri** and **Thesium divaricatum.**

The **Viscum album** is a semi-parasitic plant belonging to the Loranthaceae Family, and is known as mistletoe. In Crete the subspecies **austriacum,** growing on pine trees is mentioned. It differs from the subspecies growing on fir trees in having smaller and narrower leaves, and from the colour of its berries which are yellowish instead of white.

Aristolochlaceae

Herbaceous or woody plants, often climbers. Leaves alternate, entire. Flowers from 1 to many, usually growing in the axil of the leaves. Flowers actinomorphic or zygomorphic, ovary inferior. Perianth composed of three clearly divided segments in the actinomorphic species, but fused into a single blade, lingulate or funnelshaped in the zygomorphic flowers.

Aristolochia (Birthworts)

Perennial herbaceous or woody climbing plants. Zygomorphic flowers. Perianth lingulate or funnel-shaped, either erect or curved.

1. Aristolochia sempervirens: An evergreen plant with climbing stems up to 5m high. Leaves traingular-ovate, cordate at base, glabrous up to 10cm. Flowers from 1-3 yellowish flushed with purple funnelshaped, 2-5cm long, with lip one-sided and flattened. Habitat: littoral and lowlands. Flowers in spring or beginning of summer. **2. Aristilochia cretica:** Similar to 1 but pubescent, with stems reaching only from 30-60cm. Leaves up to 5,5cm and flowers purplish-brown, large 5-12cm., markedly curved. Habitat: Stony places in sub-montane and lowland zones. Flowers April-May. A West Asian plant found only on Carpathos and Crete. **3. Aristolochia clematitis.** Similar to 1 but with a deep rhizome, creeping, with a simple erect stem, up to 1m. Leaves broad, ovate, rounded at the tip. Smaller flowers (2-3cm.), yellowish, with brown ligulate from 2-8 in the axils of leaves. Habitat: in cultivated and fallow fields at a low altitude. Flowers in spring. **4. Aristolochia rotunda:** One or many stems 15-60cm. high. Tuberous root, globular or ovoid. Leaves ovate - disk-like, and cordate and amplexicaul at the base. Flowers solitary, yellowish with dark brown ligule, 3-5cm. long. Habitat: Fallow or cultivated fields from the montane zone down to the lowlands. Flowers April-May. **5. Aristolochia pallida:** Similar to 4 but with one simple or forked stem. Leaves with stalks up to 2cm. Flowers greenish, yellowish or light

Aristolochia rotunda

Aristolochia longa

Cytinus hypocistis - s.sp. orientalis

Polygonum maritimum

brown with dark parallel stripes and ligule of a deeper shade. Habitat: Sub-montane zone. Flowers April-May. **6. Aristolochia longa:** Similar to 4 and 5 but with leaves smaller, ovate-triangular. Stalk up to 1cm. Habitat: Fields of the sub-montane and lowland zones. Flowers April-May. **7 Aristolochia parvifolia:** Similar to 4 but plant small, with smaller leaves and flowers. Found in West Asia and on the East Aegean islands. Discovered recently on the shores of Elounda (Crete)

Rafflesiaceae Family

Perennial herbs without chorophyll, parasitic on the roots of various other plants. Flowers with perianth usually 4-lobed. Inferior ovary.

Cytinus

Parasites on the plants of the Cistaceae family. Stem simple, short and thick. Leaves small, fleshy bract-like. Flowers sessile in densely clustered spikes, with a 4-lobed perianth. 8 stamens, fused.

1. Cytinus hypocistis - subspecies orientalis: Stem 3-7cm. Leaves bract-like, reddish. Flowers yellow, about 18mm. Long, Parasitic on the roots of **Cistus parviflorus.** A plant of W. Asia, found in Europe only on Crete and Gavdho. Habitat: lowland and submontane zones. Flowers May-June.

Cynomorium coccineum, of the Balanophoraceae family. It is an open question whether this plant grows in Crete. It is like Cytinus, but its flowers either have no perigone (female) or else they have only 1-5 linear scales (male). It is a parasite on plants of salt-rich soils in the littoral zone.

Polygonales

Polygonaceae Family

Herbs or shrubs with simple, alternate leaves. Flowers green, yellow, pink or white in racemes, spikes or panicles, dioecious or monoecious or bisexual without petals but only with a petal-like calyx. Ovary superior, adpressed or triangular.

Polygonum (Knot grass)

Herbs or shrubs with alternate leaves. Flowers small in axillary spikes or racemes, or single. Calyx greenish or coloured, with 4-6 sepals. 3-9 stamens.

1. Polygonum maritimum: Perennial with thick woody base. Stems 10-50cm. thick, spreading, branched. Leaves 5-25mm. narrow, elliptic, glaucous, with curved lips. Flowers pink or white, from 1-4 in the axils of leaf-like bracts. Habitat: Sandy beaches. Flowers April-October. **2. Polygonum idaeum:** Very similar to 1 but more crowded with stems only 3-6cm., and leaves denser, ovate, rounded at tip. Endemic to Crete and possibly to Euboea (Evia). Habitat: Rocks in the montane zone. Flowers May-July. **3. Polygonum salicifolium:** a perennial with creeping, rooting stems up to 70cm., with ascending ends. Leaves 7-15cm. linear-lanceolate, glabrous, with hairs only at the lips and underneath nervatures. Flowers pink on long, sparse and slender spikes. Habitat: Wet places and banks of rivers and streams in the montane and sub-montane zones. Flowers July-October. **4. Polygonum longipes.** A sturdy perennial with lanceolate leaves and small greenish-pink flowers in small racemes in the axils of leaves. Habitat: Lowland zone, in cultivated fields and gardens. Flowers in summer. Rare in West Crete. Other plants of the Polygonaceae family to be found in Crete are: **Bilderdykia convolvulus, Rumex acetosela, Rumex pulcher, Rumex bucephalophorus, Emex spinosa** and **Atraphaxis billardieri,** plants without any special decorative importance.

Centrospermae

The plants of the Chenopodiaceae family of the Centrospermae are not described here because they are of no special decorative interest. Only the following species are mentioned as existing in Crete: **Beta vulgaris, Beta adamensis, Beta macrocarpa, Chenopodium vulvaria, Chenopodium giganteum, Atriplex halimus, Atriplex hortensis, Atriplex rosea, Arthrocnemum parenne, Arthrochemum fruticosum, Arthrocnemum glaucum, Salicornia europaea, Suaeda vera, Suaeda maritima, Salsola kali** and **Salsola aegaea.** The same applies to the plants of the **Amaranthaceae** family. Apart from certain cultivated species, the self-seeding do not present any decorative interest. They are

Phytolaca americana (fruits)

known as pigweed and some species are edible when boiled. The following are the Cretan species: **Amaranthus hybridus, Amaranthus cruenthus, Amaranthus retroflexus,** (all three established American species), **Amaranthus graecizans,** and **Amaranthus lividus.**

Phytolacaceae Family

Herbs, shrub, or trees with alternate entire leaves. The flowers which are in racemes are small with 5 petal-shaped segments and the ovary is superior.

Phytolaca (Pokeweeds)

Plants with racemes, usually opposite leaves. Flowers with 10 staments. Fruit berry.

1. Phytolaca americans: Glabrous perennial herb, with stems 1-3m. usually reddish. Leaves ovate-lanceolate 12-25cm. Racemes about 10cm. rather erect. Flowers whitish-green. Fruit blackish-purple berry with violet-coloured juice. A N. American plant which has become naturalised on Crete. Habitat: Wet places, swamps, banks of rivers and pools in the lowland and littoral zones. Flowers June-September.

Aizoaceae Family

Herbs or shrubs with succulent, usually opposite, leaves. Fleshy calyx. Petals numerous or absent. Ovary half-inferior. Fruit dry, or fleshy.

Aizoon

Annual plants with leaves usually alternate. Flowers without petals. 20 stamens.

1. Aizoon hispanicum: Densely papillose plant. Leaves oblong-lanceolate, rounded at tip. Flowers single at the base of the dichotomous stems. Calyx conical with 5 mucronate lobes, yellowish on the upper surface. Habitat: Barren, gravelly places of a low elevation.

Mesembrianthemum

Succulent herbs. Flowers with numerous linear petals. Leaves opposite.

1. Mesembrianthemum nodiflorum: Annual plant with spreading stems up to 20cm. Leaves cylindrical-semicylindrical. Flowers small, about 1,5cm., with white or whitish-yellow petals. Habitat: Sandy beaches and salt marshes of littoral zone. Flowers May-July. **2. Mesembrianthemum crystallinum:** Like 1 but covered with dense crystalline papillae. Leaves spathulate to broadly ovate. Flowers larger with white petals. Habitat: Beaches and salt marshes or stony slopes, always near the sea.

Portulacaceae Family

Annual or perennial herbs usually glabrous and fleshy. Leaves simple, entire. Flowers with 2 sepals and 4-6 petals. 3 or more stamens.

Portulaca (Purslanes)

Fleshy herbs with alternate or opposite leaves. 7-12 stamens.

1. Portulaca oleracea - subspecies oleracea: a branched, spreading annual with oblong-obovate leaves. Flowers small, yellow, with 5 obovate petals. Habitat: Fallow or cultivated fields, at a low altitude.

Caryophyllaceae Family

Herbs or small shrubs. Leaves usually opposite, rarely alternate or whorled, entire, with or without stipules. Petals 4-5 free. Sepals 4-5 free, or fused at base, or else forming a tube with 4-5 teeth. Ovary superior.

Arenaria (Sandworts)

Annual, biennial or perennial herbs. Leaves opposite, varying from disk-shaped to awl-shaped. Flower solitary or in sparse cymes. Petals 5 entire, white rarely pink. 5 free sepals.

Mesembrianthemum nodiflorum

Mesembrianthemum crystallinum

Portulaca oleracea - s.sp. oleracea

Arenaria filicaulis - s.sp. graeca

1. Arenaria fragillima: Perennial with many stems 5-10cm., greyish-green and covered, like the leaves, with very small hairs. Lower leaves ovate, upper leaves elliptic-linear. Flowers white. Sepals and petals about 5mm. long. Endemic to Crete and Carpathos. Habitat: Rocky sites of montane and sub-montane zones. Flowers May-June. **2. Arenaria cretica:** Similar to 1 but stems 2-10cm., dense, tufted, slender, glandular towards apex. Leaves crowded, oblong-elliptic or oblanceolate, green. Sepals 2,5-4,5mm. Petals twice, or more longer than the sepals. Habitat: Rocky sites in alpine and subalpine zones. Flowers June-July. **3. Arenaria serpylliflora:** A rather sturdy annual with stems up to 13cm., erect, branched. Leaves up to 8mm. broadly ovate to ovate-lanceolate, pointed or mucronate. Flowers in sparse dichasia, sepals 3-4,5mm. Petals smaller. Habitat: Dry places, usually sandy, in lowland and littoral zones. Flowers April-May. **4. Arenaria leptoclados:** Very like 3 but more delicate and with smaller flowers. Insignificant weed.

Habitat: Sandy and sandy-clayey fields of low altitude. Flowers April-June. **5. Arenaria muralis.** Like 3 and 4 but pubescent-glandular, stems shorter, leaves obovate and petals a little longer than the sepals, but very narrow. A plant of W. Asia, it does not occur in any other part of Europe except Crete. Habitat: Rocks of the montane zone. Flowers May-June. **6. Arenaria fillicaulis - subsp graeca.** Hairy-glandular, tufted, perennial. Leaves 5-10mm. Elliptic or ovate. Stems 5-15cm. Flowers 3-10 in sparse inflorescences. Petals double the calyx, white. Habitat: Stony places of the montane zone in W. Crete. Flowers June-July. **7. Arenaria guicciardii.** Annual, somewhat glandular, with many stems, 3-20cm. Leaves ovate or ovate-oblong. Flowers 5-20 in crowded inflorescences. Sepals mucronate. Petals slightly smaller than sepals. Habitat: Montane zone of W. Crete. Flowers April-May.

Moehringia (Three-nerved Sandworts)

Plants similar to Arenaria, but leaves ovate to linear.

1. Moehringia trinervia. Annual or perennial, with pubescent stolons or ascending stems, up to 40cm. Leaves about 25mm., ovate, pointed, ciliate. Flowers with 5 sepals and 5 petals, in ones, in axils of leaves, or in sparsely-flowering cymes. Sepals 4-5mm. and petals smaller, white. Habitat: Forests of the montane zone. Flowers May-June.

Minuartia (Sandworts)

Plants similar to Arenaria, but leaves usually subulate or thread-like, rarely narrow lanceolate.

Group A. Plants of lowland and littoral zones.

1. Minuartia thymifolia. Annual, with stems up to 6cm., usually branching from the base. Leaves 3-6mm., succulent. Inflorescences cymose, crowded, with more than 10 flowers. Sepals 2,5-3,5mm. and petals a little larger, white. Observed only once in Crete. A plant of the shores and islands of the E. Mediterranean. Habitat: Sandy seaside areas of the littoral zone. Flowers April-May. 2. Minuartia hybrida-subsp hybrida. Annual, pubescent, glandular, with erect stems 3-10cm., branching from base. Sepals 3-4mm. Petals somewhat longer. Leaves linear-subulate. Sparse inflorescences, many-flowered. Habitat: Dry sandy places of the littoral and lowland zones. Flowers April-May. **3. Minuartia hybrida - subsp lydia.** Very like 2, but stems are higher (up to 17cm.) and more slender. Sepals a little longer. Its occurence on Crete is not certain. A plant of W. Asia and Euboea. Habitat: In places similar to 2. **4. Minuartia mediterranea.** Similar to 2 and 3, but glabrous, with denser inflorescences. Sepals 3-5mm. Petals about half the length of sepals. Habitat: Lowland and littoral zones. Flowers April-May.

Group B. Plants of alpine and sub-montane zones.

1. Minuartia verna - subsp verna. Perennial plant, sparsely tufted, with stems 5-10cm., pubescent, glandular, with 1-7 flowers. Petals slightly larger than sepals. Leaves linear-subulate or thread-like. Anthers purple. Habitat: Rocks in the montane zone. Flowers May-June. **2. Minuartia verna - subsp attica.** Similar to 1, but woody at base. Leaves up to 10mm. Inflorescences with 3-15 flowers. Petals of the same length as sepals. Habitat: Rocky places of the montane and submontane zones. Flowers May-June. **3. Minuartia verna - subsp idaea.** Like 1 and 2, but stems shorter, more glandular, with 1-5 flowers, leaves up to 5mm. and petals smaller than sepals. Endemic to the mountains of Crete and to Mount Olympus. Habitat: Alpine and sub-alpine zones. Flowers June-July. **4. Minuartia wettsteinii.** A glabrous tufted perennial, with linear, glaucous-green leaves. Inflores-

Minuartia verna -s. sp. verna

Minuartia verna s. sp. attica

Cerastium ligusticum - s. sp. ligusticum

Gypsophylla nana

cences with few flowers. Sepals 4-5mm., slightly fleshy. Petals distinctly larger than sepals. Endemic to E. Crete (mountains east of Ierapetra). Habitat: Rocks of montane zone. Flowers May-June.

Cerastium (Mouse-ears)

Annual or perennial plants. Flowers in dichasia, white, with 5 sepals and 5 petals. Petals more or less bi-lobed at tip, rarely absent.

1. Cerastium illyricum - subsp comatum. Annual, up to 140cm., densely hairy, with erect branches. Leaves up to 14mm., the lower spathulate or obovate. Petals smaller than sepals. Habitat: Littoral sites. Flowers April-May. **2. Cerastium scaposum.** Similar to I, but much smaller, up to 11cm. Leaves smaller, petals longer than sepals, deeply bi-lobed. Endemic to Crete. Habitat: Rocks of montane and sub-alpine zones. Flowers May-June. **3. Cerastium brachypetalum - subsp doerfleri.** Like 1, but stems up to 7cm. and petals longer than sepals. Endemic to Crete. Habitat: Montane zone. Flowers May-June. **4. Cerastium brachypetalum - subsp roeseri.** Similar to I, and about the same size, but petals and sepals of equal length. Habitat: medium and low altitude. Flowers April-June. **5. Cerastium ligusticum - subsp ligusticum.** Similar to 1, but up to 15cm., rarely bigger. Leaves up to 20mm. Petals almost double the size of sepals. Habitat: Medium and low altitudes. Flowers April-May. **6. Cerastium semidecandrun - subsp semidecandrum.** An annual plant, spreading or erect, up to 20cm. Lower leaves oblanceolate, upper leaves ovate or elliptic. Stems with glandular hairs. Petals smaller than sepals, not very deeply bi-lobed. Habitat: Sandy beaches and fields of low altitude. Flowers April-May. **7. Cerastium pumilum - subsp litigiosum.** Annual, up to 14cm., with stems branching towards upper end. A hairy plant with glandular hairs. Petals slightly longer than sepals. Habitat: Fallow and cultivated fields at a low altitude. Flowers April-May. **8. Cerastium dichtotomum.** Annual, densely glandular-hairy, with simple stem, up to 18cm. Leaves linear or ovate-lanceolate. Sepals 9- 12mm. Petals half the length of sepals and somewhat bi-lobed. Habitat: Fields of sub-montane and Montane zones. Flowers April-May.

Gypsophila (Gypsophilas)

Annual or perennial herbs, with leaves small, narrow, opposite. Flowers in dichasia. Calyx bell-shaped, with 5 teeth and 5 parallel veins, without epicalyx scales. Petals 5, emarginate, usually white, rarely pink.

1. Cypsophila nana. Dwarf perennial, pubescent-glandular, tufted, with many slender stems, 2-4cm., rarely higher. Leaves linear-oblong, 5-10mm. Flowers up to ten on each stem. Calyx 4-5mm. Petals double the size of the calyx, pink. Endemic to Crete and S. Greece. Habitat: Rocks of alpine and sub-alpine zones. Flowers May-June.

Saponaria (Soapworts)

Perennial or annual herbs with leaves opposite and flowers in dichasia. Calyx tubular with 5 teeth and without epicalyx scales. Petals 5, entire bipartite or emarginate, with or without scales on inner surface.

1. Saponaria officinalis: Perennial, with many strong stems, 30-90cm., erect, glabrous, simple or branching. Leaves large, ovate or ovate-lanceolate, with 3 parallel veins. Dense inflorescences, with large flowers. Calyx about 20mm. greenish or reddish. Petals 10mm., entire, pale pink. Both self-seeding and cultivated. Habitat: Montane zone, in hedges and stony ground, on the edges of forests. Flowers July-September. **2. Sapenaria glutinosa.** Annual or biennial, hairy-glandular. Stem 20-50cm., branching towards top with large, pyramidal inflorescences. Basal leaves spathulate. Stem leaves ovate-lanceolate. Calyx 20-25mm. Petals 5mm, purple bipartite. Habitat: Sporadically occurring in stony places of the lowland and sub-montane zones. Flowers May-June. **3. Saponaria calabrica.** Annual, with many spreading, hairy-glandular branches. Lower leaves spathulate. Upper leaves oblong-ovate. Sparse inflorescences. Calyx 6-10mm., hairy-glandular. Petals emargina-te, pinkish-purple 3-5mm. Habitat: Rocky and sandy places of montane zone. Flowers May-June.

Saponaria officinalis

Bufonia (Bufonias)

Plants similar to Minuartia but succulent.

1. Bufonia stricta. Perennial, with stems erect-arc-shaped, slender and usually non-branching. Flowers few, usually 1 on each stem. Sepals and petals 3-4mm. Endemic to Crete and Attica (Hymettos). Habitat: Montane and sub-montane zones. Flowers May-June.

Stellaria (Stitchworts)

Annual or perennial herbs. Flowers white, in dichasia. Sepals 5. Petals 5, deeply bifid, sometimes absent. Leaves opposite, simple.

1. Stellaria media - subsp media. Annual, with tender stems, up to 40cm. Leaves glabrous, the lower are ovate, pointed, long-stalked. The others are more or less sessile. Inflorescences glandular. Flowers with sepals 3-5mm. Petals as long as the sepals, bifid, almost to the base. A common weed, its habitat is the cultivated fields of the sub-montane and montane zones. Flowers January-May. **2. Stellari media - subsp postii.** Like 1, but up to 60 cm. Leaves pubescent beneath. Inflorescence denser. Flowers a little larger. Habitat: Cultivated and fallow fields in the sub-montane and lowland zones. Flowers Jan.-May. **3. Stellaria pallida.** Like 1, but more delicate, with all the leaves stalked and with small flowers, usually without petals. Habitat: Sandy tracts near the sea.

Holosteum (Chickweeds)

Annual plants, with umbrella-shaped inflorescences. Petals dentate.

1. Holosteum umbellatum. Erect, with stem simple or branched, glandular, glaucous-green, up to 20cm. Leaves oblong, the lower forming rosettes. Flowers small, white or pink, with petals smaller than sepals. Habitat: Sub-montane and lowland zones. Flowers March-May.

Silene (Campions or Catchflies)

Annual or perennial herbs or shrubs of various shapes. Flower with sepals fused to form a tube, (calyx) of various shapes with 5 teeth. Petals 5, free, ending in a claw, and with 1 scale inside. Stamens 10. Inflorescences of various shapes, usually cymose or dichasia.

Group A. Perennial or biennial plants with woody base. Lower leaves lanceolate to spathulate. Inflorescence with opposite viscid limbs, that produce dichasia with 3-7 flowers, rarely with 1 flower. Flowers large, erect or nodding.

1. Silene italica - subsp nemoralis. Biennial plant, hairy. Stem simple, 20-80cm. Basal leaves lanceolate-spathulate, rounded at tip. Rather crowded inflorescence. Calyx 14-21mm., pubescent-glandular. Petals deeply bilobed, white on upper surface, reddish or greenish beneath, with very small scales. Habitat: Glades in the montane zone. Flowers May-June. **2. Silene sieberi.** Similar to 1, but up to 30cm., with fewer flowers. It is considered a variety of the previous plant, endemic to the Cretan mountains. Habitat: Alpine and sub-alpine zones. Flowers June-July. **3. Silene dictaea.** Dwarf plant, perennial, with stems up to 15cm., usually with 1 flower, calyx 8-11mm. pubescent-glandular. Petals white or pink. Endemic to E. Crete. Habitat: Montane and sub-alpine zones. Flowers May-July. **4. Silene fruticosa.** A sturdy perennial plant, with glabrous erect stems, 20-50cm. Lower leaves obovate or narrowly spathulate. Dense inflorescence. Flowers large, erect. Calyx about 25mm, with glandular hairs. Petals pink or purple, not very deeply bifid. Habitat: Stony and rocky places of sub-montane and lowland zones. **5. Silene gigantea.** A biennial plant with sturdy stem, simple, up to 1m. Basal leaves spathulate, forming rosette. Flowers not very big. Calyx 8-12mm. Petals bifid, white, pink or greenish. Inflorescence with short and dense ramifications. Habitat: Stony places of submontane zone. Flowers May-June.

Group B. Perennial plants. Flowers are in ones or in rather sparse dichasia. Calyx inflated with 10-20 veins, with distinctly netted secondary veins.

1. Silene vulgaris - subsp angustifolia. Perennial, glaucous-green, glabrous, with narrowly lanceolate leaves, 4-7cm. and with long stolons. Flowers in sparse dichasia, pink or greenish. Calyx inflated, with 20 veins. Petals bifid. Habitat: Common in fields of the

Saponaria calabrica

Silene italica -s. sp. nemoralis

Silene gigantea

Silene vulgaris - s. sp. angustifolia

submontane and low-land zones. Flowers April-May. **2. Silene vulgaris - subsp suffrutescens.** Like 1, but plant resembling a small shrub. Endemic to Crete, first made public only in 1984. Habitat: Rocks of montane and sub-montane zones. Flowers April-May. **3. Silene variegata.** Dwarf plant, with long creeping roots and short stems up to 10cm., with 1-5 flowers. Leaves succulent, the lower spathulate-ovate, those of the stem small, elliptic or obovate. Calyx with 10 veins, not very inflated. Petals greyish-violet, deeply bifid. Endemic to Crete and Samothrace. Habitat: Rocks of montane and submontane zones. Flowers May-July.

Group C. Perennial plants with a more or less woody base and ovate, lanceolate or linear leaves. Calyx not inflated, without secondary netted veins. Inflorescence with few, or solitary flowers.

47

1. Silene succulenta. Fleshy perennial, with woody base and numerous simple, or even ascending, stems, pubescent and glandular. Leaves obovate or oblanceolate. Flowers large, in ones or twos, in axils of upper leaves. Calyx 15-20mm., narrow club-like. Petals white, bifid. Habitat: Sandy shores. Flowers May-June. **2. Silene saxifraga.** Rather low and rather tufted, with numerous slender, viscid, stems, up to 20cm. Leaves linear or linear spathulate. Flowers in ones or twos. Calyx club-like, 8-13mm. Petals whitish or greenish above and greenish or reddish beneath, bifid. Habitat: Montane zone. Flowers May-July. **3. Silene multicaulis - subspecies cretica.** Similar to the other 2, but less crowded, with flowers purple on greenish and leaves linear or linear-lanceolate. Endemic to Mt Dhikti. Habitat: Montane and sub-alpine zones.

Group D. Annual, or perennial plants, often dioecious, with large flowers, in ones or in dichasia. Petals bilobed or bifid, with large scales. Leaves rather wide and big.

1. Silene noctiflora. Annual, hairy and glandular towards the top. Stems up to 40cm., erect. Leaves ovate or ovate-lanceolate. Inflorscence with few flowers, hermaphrodite. Calyx 20-30mm. Petals bilobed, pink on top and yellowish beneath, closed, inrolled during the day, open and scented at night. Habitat: Cultivated sites of montane and sub-montane zones, Flowers April-May. **2. Silene alba.** Dioecious plant, annual or perennial, up to 80cm. Leaves ovate or ovate-lanceolate, hairy. Calyx hairy-glandular, inflated. Petals white, large, deeply bilobed. Flowers in dichasia. Habitat: Cool, wet sites of montane zone. Flowers May-July.

Group E. Annual plants. Stems pubescent or viscid towards the top. Calyx not constricted at lips.

1. Silene pinetorum. Stems 5-20cm., branching, viscid towards the top. Basal leaves spathulate, rounded at tip, the other leaves linear-lanceolate, pointed. Lax inflorescence. Calyx 4-7mm. Petals pink, bifid. Endemic to Crete. Habitat: Pine-woods of littoral zone. Flowers March-April. **2. Silene sedoides.** Like 1, but more branched, thickly pubescent-hairy, with petals emarginate, small, pink or white. Habitat: Lowland and sub-montane zones. Flowers March-May. **3. Silene greuteri.** Annual 4-10cm., leaves ovate or elliptic and flowers pink, slightly bilobed at tip. Has been found only in the Kourtaliotiko Gorge. Habitat: Go rges of South-Central Crete.

Group F. Annual plants, glabrous or almost so. Calyx constricted at lips.

1. Silene cretica. Stems 30-60 cm., usually branched, erect, pubescent-hairy at base. Flowers in sparse dichasia. Calyx 9-16mm. Petals bilobed or bifid, purple. Basal leaves obovate, the others narrow, linear. Habitat: Cultivated and fallow fields at a low altitude. Flowers April-May. **2. Silene behem.** Stems 15-20 cm., simple or branched. Leaves glaucous-green. All the plant is glabrous. Flowers in lax dichasia. Calyx. 11-17mm., whitish, with reddish veins. Petals small, pink, bipartite. Habitat: Meadows and fallow fields at a low altitude. Flowers March-May.

Group G. Annual plants, pubescent or pubescent-glandular. Calyx constricted at mouth.

1. Silene pendula. Stems spreading, pubescent, branched, 15-40cm. Very sparse inflorescence. Calyx 13-18mm. Petals pink, large, emarginate. Lower leaves oblong-obovate, the others ovate-lanceolate. Habitat: Cultivated or fallow fields in the sub-montane and lowland zones. Flowers April-May. **2. Silene dichotoma - subsp racemosa.** Pubescent stems, 20-100cm., branched towards the top. Lower leaves spathulate or lanceolate, forming rosette at the base of the plant. Stem leaves lanceolate. Flowers white, with bifid petals arranged in double curl-like racemes. Habitat: Cultivated and fallow fields at a low altitude. Flowers April-May. **3. Silene gallica.** Stems 15-45cm., erect, simple or branched, pubescent, glandular towards the top. Leaves pubescent, the lower oblong-

Silene alba

Silene gallica

Silene bellidifolia

Silene colorata

obovate, the upper linear.
Flowers in one or more racemes. Calyx 7-10mm. Petals entire or emarginate, pink, or rarely, white. Habitat: Meadows of the lowland zone. Flowers May-June. **4. Silene bellidifolia.** Stems 30-60cm., erect, branched, towards the top, pubescent. Leaves pubescent-hairy, oblong-obovate or lanceolate. Flowers in double spikes. Calyx 14-17mm. Petals 3-5mm. pink, bifid. Habitat: Cultivated and fallow fields at a low altitude Flowers April-May. **5. Silene conica - subsp sartorii.** Pubescent 5-20 cm. Lower leaves obovate-spathulate. Calyx 8-13mm. cylindrical, ovate whilst maturing. Petals pink, bifid. Habitat: Littoral and lowland zones. Flowers March-April.

49

Group H. Annual plants. Calyx open (not constricted) at mouth.

1. Silene nocturna - subspecies nocturna. Stems 10-60cm., erect, usually branched. Lower leaves obovate or lanceolate-spathulate, rounded at tips, pubescent. Flowers from 5-15 in raceme-like inflorescences. Calyx 9-13mm. Petals bipartite, white above and greenish-yellow beneath. Habitat: Vineyards, sandy soil, roadsides in the sub-montane and lowland zones. Flowers April-May. **2. Silene colorata.** Pubescent plants. Stems 10-50 cm., erect or spreading, branched. Leaves ovate-spathulate, the upper linear. Calyx 11-13mm., cylindrical. Petals large, bifid, 5-9mm., pink, rarely white. Habitat: Fallow fields, hills and meadows of sub-montane and lowland zones. Flowers March-April. **3. Silene apetala.** Similar to 2, but upper leaves wider than the lower, and petals small or absent. Habitat: Fallow and cultivated fields at a low altitude. Flowers March-April. **4. Silene ammophila - subsp ammophila.** Small plant, up to 15cm., branched from the base and covered with grey-green pubescence. Stems viscid towards edges. Calyx cylindrical, 5-7mm. Petals small, 1-2mm., slightly notched at tips, pink. Lower leaves oblong-spathulate, rounded at tip.

Vaccaria (Cow Basils)

Plants similar to Silene but the calyx has 5 parallel wings.

1. Vaccaria pyramidata. Annual, glabrous, with 1 or more erect stems, height 30-60cm. Leaves glaucous-green, ovate or lanceolate, sessile, about 5cm. Sparse, mutli-branched inflorescence. Calyx 12-17mm., inflated. Petals 3-8mm., pink, emarginate. Habitat: Sporadic occurrence in cultivated fields and at waysides. Flowers June-July.

Petrorhagia (Proliferous Pinks)

Annual or perennial herbs, similar to Dianthus but with a short calyx, often without epicalyx scales.

1. Petrorhagia candica. Perennial, glabrous or slightly pubescent, up to 20cm. Sparse inflorescence. Calyx 3-4,5mm. Petals 4,5-7mm., oblong-spathulate, emarginate, white, with pink veins. Endemic to Crete. Flowers May-June. **2. Petrorhagia dianthoides.** Perennial, with many stems and crowded inflorescences, head-like, with 1-8 flowers, surrounded by purple veins, 6-10mm. long. Endemic to Crete. Habitat: Rocky places in the sub-montane zone. Flowers May-June. **3. Petrorhagia velutina.** Annual, up to 50cm., with pubescent, glandular stems. Inflorescence head-like, with very wide, brown, membranous, pointed bracts. Petals 10-13mm., pink or purple, obcordate. Habitat: Montane zone. Flowers June-August. **4. Petrorhagia glumacea.** Similar to 3 but glabrous. Head bracts rounded at tip. Petals 12-18mm., entire, serrate or fringed. Habitat: Stony places at a low altitude. Flowers May-June.

We note **Petrorhagia illyrica - subs illyrica,** as occurring in Crete, but with certain reservations.

Lychnis (Catchflies)

Perennial plants with tall, erect stems. Sepals fused together in a calyx tube, and dentate margin, with no epicalyx scales at its base. 5 free petals with a long claw and scales on inner surface. Dichotomous inflorescence flowers at the apex and in the axils of upper leaves. Leaves opposite.

Vaccaria pyramidata

1. Lychnis flos-cuculi - subsp. subintegra: Stems 20-90cm., high, often branched, sparsely pubescent-glandular towards apex. Stalked basal leaves oblong-spathulate. Stem leaves linear-lanceolate, joined at base. Flowers in calyx, 6-10mm., across, white-petalled, bipartite, with oblong lobes rounded at tip. Habitat: A rare plant, found in montane forests. Flowers May-June.

Agrostema (Corn Cockles)

Plants similar to Lychnis, but annuals. Calices with long linear teeth (awns).

51

1. Agrostema githago: Erect stems, usually branched, 30-100cm. high. Plant covered with thick greenish-green hairs. Leaves usually linear, lower ones broader. Calyx 3-7cm. long. Large pinkish-purple obovate to obcordate petals. Habitat: A rare plant found in montane glades. Flowers May-July.

Moenchia

Glabrous, glaucous-green plants, usually annuals. Leaves linear to lanceolate. Flowers of 4-5 sepals and petals, solitary or few. Petals either entire or slightly bilobed at tip. Sepals and bracts have white, membraneous margins.

1. Moenchia graeca: Low, multibranched stem, 8-15cm. high. Leaves pointed, lanceolate-oblong. Flowers white, in few-flowered dichasia; petals slightly smaller than sepals, 5 petals and sepals. Habitat: barren places at low altitude. Flowers April-May. **2. Moenchia mantica - subsp mantica:** Similar to former, but grows to 30cm. in height. Its stem is without branches or very slightly branched. Leaves lanceolate, and the petals of its flowers are double the length of its sepals. Habitat: Barren places of sub-montane zone. Flowers in April.

The following species of the **Sagina** genus grow in Crete: **Sagina maritima, Sagina apetala and Sagina procumbens.** They are insignificant small plants with linear leaves and minute quadri-partite flowers, petals tiny or absent. **Scleranthus annuus** is an insignificant annual with 5-sepaled small flowers and apetalous. Another insignificant species is **Corrigiola litoralis** a small annual with very tiny quintuple flowers, and leaves linear-oblanceolate with little stipules. The **Paronychia** genus is represented in Crete by these species: **Paronychia echinulata, Paronychia argentea, Paronychia kapela** and **Paronychia capitata.** These, too, are small insignificant plants, with minute flowers, often apetalous, surrounded by relatively large membraneous bracts.

Spergula (Spurreys)

Usually annuals, with stems branching from the base. Leaves linear with rounded tips and membraneous stipules. Leaves opposite, from whose axils small leafy twigs grow in such a way that one gets the impression that the leaves are whorled. Flowers with 5 petals and sepals. Petals entire and white.

1. Spergula arvensis: A 5-70cm. high annual. Leaves fleshy, 1-3cm. long. Flowers in sparse inflorescence at the tip of stems. Sepals and petals 4-5mm. Habitat: Sandy tracts near the sea or in the Lowlands. Flowers June-September.

Spergularia (Sea Spurreys)

Herbaceous plants often woody at base. Leaves linear, opposite, with membraneous stipules, fused, forming a single bract beneath leaf. Flowers, with 5 sepals and 5 petals, entire, white, pink or bluish-violet.

1. Spergularia media: A perennial, with stems 5-40cm. high, glabrous or glandular, only at the inflorescence. Pointed leaves. Sepals 4-6mm. White or pink petals about same size as the sepals. Habitat: seaside salt-marshes. Flowers July-October. **2. Spergularia marina:** The same as the former 1, only it is an annual or a biennial. Flowers smaller and always pink. Habitat: seaside salt-marshes plant. Flowers July-September. **3. Spergularia diandra:** Similar to 2 but with a many-branched and many-flowered inflorescence with lilac-coloured flowers. Habitat: seaside salt-marshes. Flowers July-October. **4. Spergularia rubra:** Similar to 2 but smaller. Smaller inflorescence. Flowers pink. Habitat:

Agrostema githago

sandy tracts, but not salty ground. Flowers July-October. **5. Spergularia bocconii:** Annual or biennial. Stems 2-3mm. Petals slightly smaller, pink or white. Habitat: lowlands, usually near the sea. Flowers June-September. **6. Spergularia lycia:** Similar to 5 but a small dwarf plant, growing in the montane and subalpine zones. Flowers in summer. A plant of W. Asia which has been found on the White Mountains.

The species of the **Herniaria** genus are insignificant plants, with small ovoid or disk-like leaves and minute flowers with or without petals. The **Herniaria parnassica** and the

Herniaria hirsuta species can be found in Crete. The **Polycarpon genus** is represented in Crete by a few insignificant species such as **Polycarpon tetraphyllum, Polycarpon diphyllum** and **Polycarpon alsinifolium.** Their leaves are ovoid to disk-like, opposite or in fours. The flowers are minute, quintuple and with translucent petals.

Telephium (Telephiums)

Perennials, woody at base. Flowers in terminal cynes.

1. Telephium imperati - subsp orientale: A glabrous, dwarf shrub with a very thick woody rhizome. Stems from 15 to 35cm. high, simple, spreading. Leaves alternate, rather fleshy, glaucous, ovate with small membraneous stipules. Cymes with few densely massed flowers. 5 sepals with white margins. 5 white entire petals. Habitat: stony places of lowland zone. Flowers May-June. A W. Asia plant sporadically seen in Crete and S. Greece.

Dianthus (Pinks)

Usually perennial herbaceous plants or small shrubs. Leaves opposite, usually narrow linear and with parallel venations. Flowers solitary or in heads. 5 petals, entire, dentate or fringed. Tubular calyx, surrounded at base by epicalyx scales. 10 stamens and 2 styles.

1. Dianthus xylorrhizus: Perennial, up to 15cm. high. Branches closely massed and woody at their base. Basal leaves oblong-linear, pointed or not at tip, up to 4mm. wide, on the whole rather dense and flaccid. Stem leaves in 3-6 pairs, smaller than basal ones. Epicalyx scales usually 4, brown, ovate, pointed, 1/4 of the calyx. Calyx 20-25mm. Petals 4- 6mm. shiny, creamy-white dentate. Endemic to Crete. Habitat: among rocks of submontane zone. **2. Dianthus sphacioticus:** Similar to former, but usually with a thick woody stem at the base. Leaves white, wider and shorter (5mm long). Epicalyx scales 6, 1°3 of calyx. Calyx 13-16mm. Petals 3-4mm., nearly entire, bearded, pale pink. Endemic to Crete. Habitat: Alpine zone. **3. Dianthus strictus:** A glabrous perennial, 30-50cm. high, with simple or many-branched stems arising from woody base. Basal leaves wither at the time of flowering. Stems with 6-12 pairs of leaves. Leaves 1-3mm. wide. Calyx conical 15-18mm. Petals 10mm. dentate, and bearded, 4-scaled epicalyx. Solitary flowers. Habitat: rocky and stony places. It is a S.W. Asia plant. **4. Dianthus tripunctatus:** Similar to 3 but an annual. Calyx 15mm. Flowers yellowish-pink. Habitat: dry places. **5. Dianthus juniperinus - subsp juniperinus:** A woody perennial shrub, closely packed at the base, with many short non-flowering stems. Flowering stems up to 20cm. high, with 2-3 flowers. Pale pink dentate petals 4-8mm and 4-8 epicalyx scales. Calyx 13-20mm. Endemic to Crete in rocky places. **6. Dianthus juniperinus - subsp heldreichii:** Like 5 but smaller. Stems bearing 1, rarely 2 flowers. Flowers smaller, pink, sparsely dotted with purple spots. W. Cretan endemic growing in rocky places. **7. Dianthus pulviniformis:** Similar to 5 but flowering stems are only 3-5cm. long, with 2-3 white flowers. Dentate petals 3-4mm. Endemic to south-central Crete. Habitat: rocky places at a medium altitude. **8. Dianthus aciphyllus:** Also similar to 5 but flowering stems sturdier and with more pairs of leaves, the pink petals are 10mm. Endemic to East Crete. Habitat: calcareous rocks of the montane zone. **9. Dianthus aciphyllus - var. bauhinorum:** A sturdier plant with wide leaves. Endemic to central Crete. Habitat: among rocks at a low altitude (600-800m). **10. Dianthus arboreus:** A small shrub up to 50cm. high. Leaves linear fleshy, glaucous with rounded tips. Numerous scented flowers. 10-20 obovate, pointed epicalyx scales. Calyx 18-22mm. long and 2-3mm. across, narrowing towards tip. Petals pink, dentate, 10mm. Endemic to Crete and to the South-West Peloponnese. Habitat: sub-montane rocks. Flowers April-June. **11. Dianthus fruticosus:** Similar to former but with elliptical or oblanceolate leaves. Flowers

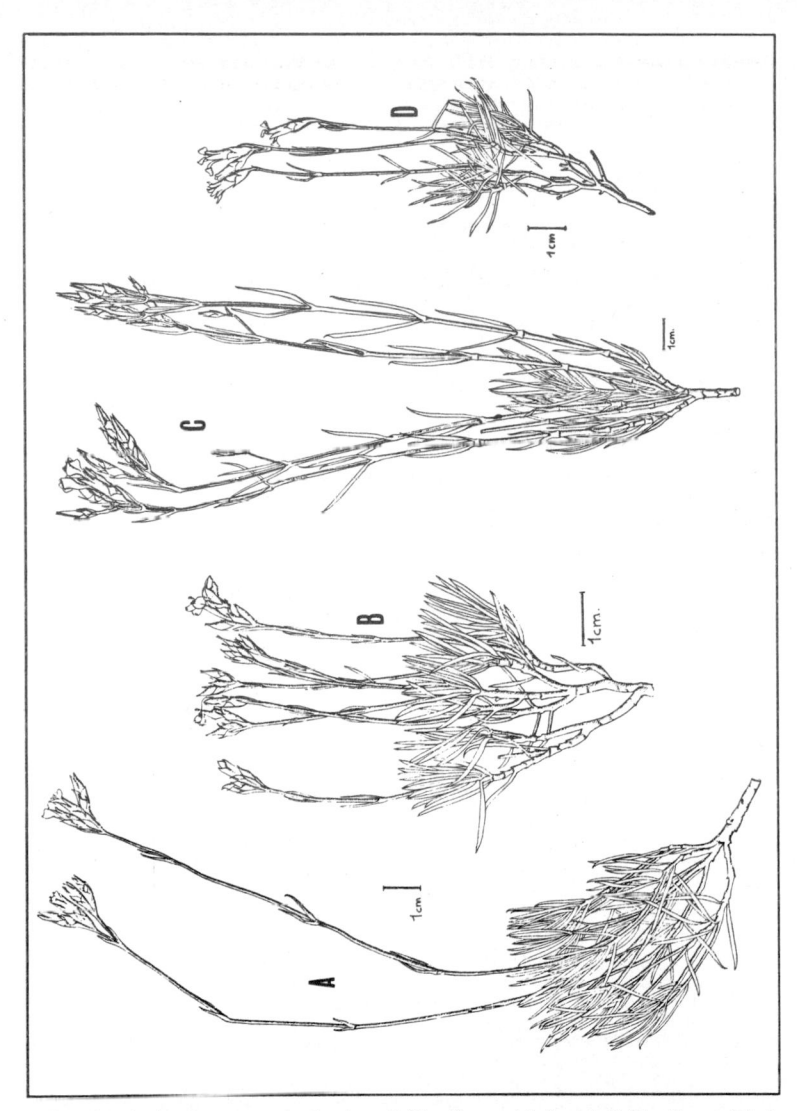

A. *Dianthus juniperinus - s. sp. juniperinus* B. *Dianthus pulviniformis* C. *Dianthus aciphyllus* D. *Dianthus juniperinus - s. sp. heldreichii*

scentless. 8-10 scales, and calyx a little longer. Flowers April-June. Habitat: rocks of sub-montane and lowland zones. This species has become divided into a series of geographical subspecies, of which the following can be found in Crete: **Subsp. sitiacus,** endemic to E. Crete, **subsp. occidentalis,** endemic to W. Crete, and **subsp. amorginus** found on the Dionysiades islets.

Velezia (Velezias)

Annuals with dichotomous branching. Flowers in leaf axils, 1 to 3. Calyx narrow and long with 5 teeth. 5 petals with long claws, and short blades.

1. Velezia rigida: A pubescent-glandular plant up to 15cm. high. Stems hard. Leaves 10-20mm., linear mucronate. Flowers from 1-2. Calyx 10-14mm. very narrow. Small pink petals. Habitat: calcareous hills at a low altitude. Flowers May-June.

Ranales

Nymphaeaceae Family

Aquatic plants with large ovate or orbicular leaves, cordate at the base, long-stemmed and floating. Large flowers on very long stalks, floating with irregular number of sepals, petals and stamens. Ovary superior, to slightly semi-inferior.

Nymphaea (Water Lilies)

Perennial plants with rhizomes, leaves reddish underneath. Many petals, usually white, the outer ones larger than the sepals. 4-5 sepals, whitish on inner surface, greenish on outer. Ovary somewhat semi-inferior. Many stamens.

1. Nymphaea alba: White scented flowers, 10-20cm. Sepals and petals lanceolate. 20-25 white petals. They grow in stagnatnt or slow-running waters. Flower June-September.

Family Ranunculaceae

Herbaceous plants rarely woody, climbing shrubs. Leaves alternate, seldom opposite. Bisexual flowers, with 3-15 sepals, often large, petal-like, in other instances very small or absent, and a corresponding number of petals, or often either without petals or with very small ones, nectariferous. Frequently the sepals and the petals are with spur at the base. Many stamens. Fruit usually polycarpic, composed of many separate achenae or many-seeded ovaries.

Nigella (Love-in-a-mists)

Annuals with bi-or-tri-pinnate leaves with narrows leaflets. Flowers have 5 large, coloured, petal-like sepals and 5-10 very small funnel-shaped, nectariferous petals. Many stamens. Fruit with 5-10 carpels fused at the base, with a beak at the tip and many seeds.

1. Nigella cretica: Plant diverging from the base with spreading stems. Stem leaves have few ovate lobes or else are entire. Small flowers, bluish-green, sepals broadly ovate, ending in claw. Carpels fused up to the middle. A Cretan endemic. Habitat: fallow fields of sub-montane and lowland zones. Flowers April-May. **2. Nigella doerflieri:** Small plant, glabrous with few branches. Small bluish-green flowers. Carpels fused along their whole length. Beaks almost double the length of the carpels, out-curved. Endemic to Crete,

Numphaea alba

Nigella damascena

Anemone coronaria - var. rosea

Anemone coronaria - var. phoenicea

Cyclades and Antikythera. Habitat: low to medium altitude. Flowers April-May. **3. Nigella damascena:** Stem 20-50cm. high, erect, simple or branched. Leaves have linear thread-like lobes. Large pale blue flowers, enclosed in a hypanthium, where leaves are almost similar to those of the stem. Carpels fused dorsally, large inflated, surrounded by involucre leaves. Habitat: Both fallow and cultivated fields of lowlands and sub-montane zone. Flowers April-May.

Caridella (Caridellas)

These plants are like the Nigellas but with caducous sepals and small petals, tubular at base, bilabiates, with outer lip bipartite.

57

1. Caridella nigelastrum: 30-60cm. slender stems, single or with few branches. Flowers 10mm., greenish flushed with red. Habitat: submontane and lowland zones. Flowers March-May.

Anemone (Anemones)

Plants with a perennial rhizome. Leaves at base form rosettes. Stems usually with 1 flower and 3 leaves, forming a subtendingwhorl which is either similar to basal leaves or very different. Flowers without petals but large, coloured, petal-like sepals. Many achenae and many stamens.

1. Anemone coronaria: Basal leaves long-stalked, trifoliate with bi-palmate or bipinnate leaflets with narrow lobes. The leaves of the subtendingwhorl are sessile and much smaller than those of the base, lobed with narrow lobes. Big flowers 3,5-7cm. across and 5-7 sepals of various colours from blue-violet (var. cyanea) to pink (var. rosea), white (var. alba) and red (var. phoenicea). Black anthers. Habitat: lowlands and sub-montane zone, in fallow fields and scrub. Flowers Jan-April. **2. Anemone pavonina:** Very similar to 1 but with basal leaves much less dissected and with much wider lobes, hyphanthium leaves entire, lanceolate or 3-toothed at summit and flowers with 7-9, rarely up to 12, sepals, red or pinkish-purple (var. purpuroeviolacea). Habitat: Meadows and scrub in sub-montane and lower montane zones. Flowers March-April. **3. Anemone heildreichii:** Similar to 2 but basal leaves with narrower lobes, involucral bracts small flowers smaller with about 15 sepals which are narrow, white or very pale pink on inner surface and pale violet or light pink outside: Habitat: montane and sub-montane zones. Flowers Feb-April. Cretan endemic considered also as a subspecies of **Anemome hortensis,** which is a Central Mediterranean species.

Clematis (Clematis)

Woody climber plants with opposite leaves. Scented flowers, 4 big coloured sepals. Petals either very small or absent. Many carpels (achenae) with a long beak, frequently hairy, hairs adpressed.

1. Clematis flammula: Deciduous, with stems 3-5m. Leaves bipinnate leaflets narrow or broad, entire or 3-lobed. Flowers 2cm. creamy-white with narrow sepals, rounded at tip, pubescent outside. Habitat: Montane and sub-montane zones. Hedges, rocks and ditches. Flowers May-July. **2. Clematis cirrhosa:** Evergreen up to 4m. high. Leaves 2,5-5cm. simple, dentate, 3-lobed or bipinnate with dentate leaflets. Flowers 4-5cm. creamy-white, pubescent and pendulous. Habitat: Scrub in sub-montane and montane zones. Flowers Nov.-March. **3. Clematis viticella:** Similar to 2 but deciduous, bigger leaves always pinnate and flowers a little smaller, blue or purple. Habitat: Scrub of the sub-montane zone. Flowers April-June. **4. Clematis elisabathae - carolae:** Evergreen shrub with creeping stems. Inferior leaves simple, ovate-cordate or ovate. Superior leaves trifoliate with ovate or lanceolate leaflets. Flowers in one-sided sparse, many-flowered inflorescences, white, 2,5-3cm. across, scented. Endemic, with restricted distribution on White Mountains. Habitat: Montane zone. Flowers May-June.

Adonis (Pheasant's Eyes)

Perennial or annual herbaceous plants with leaves pinnate, bi-pinnate or three-pinnate, with linear or strap-like lobes. Flowers with 3-20 shiny petals. Sepals smaller, usually 5. Numerous achenes.

1. Adonis aestivalis: Annual with small red flowers up to 2cm. Petals 5-8. Anthers black. Sepals and leaves glabrous. Habitat: Common in fields of sub-montane and lowland

Anemone coronaria - var. cyanea   *Anemone pavonina (typical form)*

Anemone pavonina-var. purpureoviolacea *Anemone heldreichii*

zones. Flowers March-May. **2. Adonis microcarpa:** Similar to 1 but petals usually yellow. Habitat: Sub-montane and lowland zones. Flowers March-May.

Delphinium (Delphineums)

Annual or perennial plants, with flowers usually violet or blue. Sepals 5, coloured, like petals, the topmost ending in a spur. Petals 4, the upper 2 fused into a spur that is situated inside the spur of the topmost sepal. Fruit consisting of 3 capsules.

1. Delphinium peregrinum. Annual plant or rarely biennial, erect, greyish-green, 30-80cm. Leaves palmately or bipalmately lobed, with lobes linear-lanceolate or linear. Upper leaves entire, narrow. Flowers violet or bluish-violet, with sepals 7-10mm. Inflorescence raceme-like, condensed. Common in disturbed habitats and arable fields of the submontane and lowland zones. Flowers June-August. **2. Delphinium staphisagria.** Annual with erect stems 30-100cm., pubescent-hairy. Leaves palmately lobed, with 5-7 lobes, lanceolate, simple or tri-lobate. Flowers dark blue with very short spur. Inflorescence raceme-like. Habitat: Lowland and sub-montane zones. Flowers May-July.

Consolida (Larkspurs)

Similar to Delphinium but always annual. Petals 2. Fruit, a simple capsule.

1. Consolida ambigua. Stem up to 100cm., simple or branched. Basal leaves palmately lobed with oblong lobes. Stem leaves, with linear lobes. Flowers 10-14(-20)mm., usually dark blue or violet. Spur 13-18mm. Crowded inflorescences. Habitat: Fallow and cultivated fields at a low altitude. Flowers April-May. **2. Consolida regalis.** A plant less than 50cm. high, multi branched, with very sparse inflorescences and with few dark blue flowers. Flowers 9-11mm. Spur 12-25mm. Leaves with linear lobes. Habitat: Fallow and cultivated fields at a low or medium altitude. Flowers April-June.

Ranunculus (Buttercups and Crowfoots)

Annual or perennial herbs, sometimes aquatic. Flowers with large coloured petals, and smaller greenish sepals. Many achenes, dense, compressed or inflated, pointed and curved at tip.

Group A. Flowers large, at least 30mm. in diameter, of various colours, red, pink, white or yellow.

1. Ranunculus asiaticus. Pubescent, greyish-green plant with perennial rhizome. Basal leaves entire or trilobate, with dentate lobes. The other leaves almost tripartite with lobes narrow, entire or dentate at apex. Flowers 30-50mm., 1 or more on each stem. There are 3 varieties, a) with yellow flowers, b) with red flowers, and c) with white flowers, rarely purple or pink. Each of these varieties is usually found in different geographical zones. A plant of S.W. Asia, spreading as far as Carpathos, Crete and Kythera. Habitat: Hills and mountain slopes or waysides of the lowland and sub-montane zones. Flowers March-April.

Group B. Yellow flowers. Terrestrial plants that grow in either damp or dry soils.

1. Ranunculus velutinus. Perennial hairy plant, with stems 40-80cm. Leaves broadly ovate at margin, deeply tripartite, with wedge-shaped lobes, obovate, trilobate and dentate. Upper leaves small, linear. Many flowers 15-25mm., with easily-dropping petals. Achenes in spherical heads. Habitat: Damp pastures of montane zone. Flowers May-June. **2. Ranunculus neapolitanus.** Similar to 1 but smaller (20-50cm), and petals do not drop easily. Habitat: Damp and shady places at a low altitude. Flowers April-May. **3. Ranunculus demissus.** Glabrous, perennial, up to 20cm. Rhizome oblique. Basal leaves disk-like at margin, 3 or 5-lobed, with lobes separated into narrow lobules. Stem leaves tripartite, with narrow lobes. Flowers in ones or twos, small with pubescent sepals. Habitat: Sub-alpine and alpine zones. Flowers May-June. **4. Ranunculus bulbosus - subsp aleae.** Similar to 3, but the stem is inflated at its base, as if it were a bulb, but not very thick. Middle lobe of basal leaves stalked. The whole plant hairy. Habitat: Fallow fields and pastures of sub-montane zone. Flowers April-May. **5. Ranunculus sarduus.** Similar to 4, but without a bulbous swelling at the base, annual. Habitat: Damp sites and swamps of sub-montane zone. Flowers April-May. **6. Ranunculus muricatus.** Annual, glabrous, up to 50cm. The basal and the stem leaves are alike, deeply dentated and often with 3 shallow lobes. Flowers small. Achenes in a spherical head. Habitat: Damp sites of medium and low altitude. Flowers April-May. **7. Ranunculus arvensis.** Pubescent annual, 15-60cm. Basal

Clematis cirrhosa

Adonis aestivalis

Consolida ambigua

Ranunculus asiaticus (form)

leaves simple, the others trilobate, with lobes often divided into linear lobules. Flowers 4-12mm., a light greenish-yellow. Habitat: Sub-montane and montane zones. Flowers small, 3-6mm. Habitat: Fields of sub-montane and lowland zones. Flowers March-April. **9. Ranunculus gracilis.** Perennial with ovate, tuberous roots. Basal leaves almost glabrous or slightly hairy, practically orbicular at margin, divided into 3 shallow lobes, dentated at edge. The other leaves with lobes more deeply dissected and narrower with few, and very small, upper leaves. Flowers rather large. Habitat: Montane and sub-montane zones. Flowers April-May. **10. Ranunculus paludosus.** Like 9, but pubescent. Leaves with narrower lobes, divided into narrow lobules. Habitat: Fallow lands of the sub-montane zone. Flowers March-April. **11. Ranunculus cupreus.** Pubescent, perennial, 10-20cm., with ovate tuberous roots. Basal leaves bipinnate, with ovate lobules. Flowers 15mm. yellow inside, brownish-copper outside. Endemic to Crete. Habitat: Stony places of alpine and sub-alpine zones. Flowers May-June. **12. Ranunculus creticus.** Perennial, pubescent, with branched stem. Basal leaves orbicular to reniform, crenate or only just lobate. Stem leaves tripartite with lanceolate lobes. Flowers 25mm., plentiful. Habitat: Rocky and stony places of sub-montane zone. Flowers March-April. **13. Ranunculus subomophyllus.** A perennial, slender and almost glabrous plant, with oblong tubers at root. Basal leaves disk-like at margin, tripartite. Lobes divided into roundish lobules. Flowers 1-2, small. Habitat: Montane and sub-montane zones. Flowers April-May. **14. Ranunculus spruneranus.** Perennial, hairy or pubescent, many-branched plant, 40-80cm., with cylindrical tuberous roots. Basal leaves orbicular-cordate at margin, three or five-lobed. Numerous flowers. Habitat: Fallow fields and meadows of sub-montane zone. Flowers April-May. **15. Ranunculus ficaria - subsp. ficariiformis.** A sturdy plant, glabrous, with wide ovate leaves, cordate at base, slightly crenate, concentrated mainly low down. Stems short. Flowers large, 30-50mm., with 8-12 ovate petals. Sepals 3, yellowish-white. Habitat: Damp places, arable fields and gardens of lowland and sub-montane zones. Flowers February-April. **16. Ranunculus bullatus.** Plant with perennial root and leaves ovate, serrate, hairy beneath, concentrated at base. Flowers about 25mm. with pubescent sepals and 5-12 petals. Habitat: Lowland hills. Flowers October-November. **17. ranunculus brevifolius - subspecies pindicus.** Perennial, dwarf glaucous-green plant, with 4-10 basal leaves, broader than long, with big teeth towards their edge and a similar sessile leaf on stem. Flowers solitary diameter 15-25mm. Habitat: Stony places and moraines of alpine and sub-alpine zones. Flowers May-July. **18. Ranunculus ophioglossifolius.** Annual 10-40cm. Basal leaves ovate or almost disk-shaped, cordate at base. The upper ones are smaller, lanceolate. Many flowers, 5-9mm. Habitat: Muddy ground and marshes. Flowers April-June. **19. Ranunculus lateriflorus.** An unimportant plant, with small leaves, ovate or lanceolate and flowers 2-3mm., sessile, in axils of leaves. Habitat: Swamps and ditches. Flowers April-May. **20. Ranunculus radinotrichus.** Plants with horizontal, perennial rhizome. Leaves small, hairy, deeply trilobed. Stems up to 5cm. during flowering period, up to 12cm. during fructification. Flowers solitary, 15-20mm. in diameter, with hairy sepals. Endemic to the White Mountains. Habitat: Alpine and sub-alpine zones. Flowers June-August.

Group C. Plants floating in pools and swamps. White flowers.

1. Ranunculus peltatus. Annual or perennial. Upper leaves regular, with 3-7 lobes and lower leaves divided into many filiform lobes or else all leaves regular with 3-7 lobes or all with filiform lobes. Flowers usually quintuple with petals more than 10mm. Habitat: Pools and swamps at a low altitude. Flowers May-July. **2. Ranunculus aquatilis.** Similar to 1, but the lobes of the regular leaves are dentate and the flowers have petals smaller than 10mm. Habitat: Swamps at a low altitude. Flowers March-June. **3. Ranunculus trichophyllus - subspecies trichophyllus.** Similar to 1 and 2, but all the leaves always have long filiform lobes, and the flowers have small petals, rarely larger than 5mm. Habitat: Swamps and pools at a low altitude. Flowers July-October.

Thalictrum (Meadow Rues)

Perennial herbs with leaves two, three or four times pinnate, with stipules at base of stem. Sepals 4-5, small that fall easily. Petals absent. Stamens many, with rather long filaments.

1. Thalictrum minus - subspecies minus. Perennial, with glabrous or somewhat glandular stems, 25-50cm., dense and rhizome-like towards base. Basal leaves 3 or 4 times pinnate,

Ranunculus asiaticus (form)

Ranunculus velutinus

Ranunculus spruneranus

Ranunculus ficaria - s. sp. ficariiformis

with small leaflets, almost disk-shaped or broadly ovate, dentate or with not very deep lobes. Long-branched inflorescences Many flowers, small, yellowish, pendulous at first. Habitat: Cool places of montane zone. Flowers May-June.

Paeoniaceae Family

Perennial herbs or shrubs, with alternate leaves. Flowers usually single, large, with 5 sepals and 5-10 (-13) petals. Stamens numerous. Fruit consists of 2-8 free carpels, with few seeds.

Paeonia (Peonies)

Herbs with perennial rhizome. Leaves large, bipinnate or tripinnate. Flowers 6-14cm. Carpels 2-8.

1. Paeonia clusii. Stems 20-30cm., reddish. Basal leaves twice tripartite, with leaflets deeply divided into narrow, pointed lobes. Flowers white (rarely flushed with pink), 7-10cm. in diameter and 6-8 obovate orbicular or almost orbicular petals. Endemic to Crete and Carpathos. Habitat: E. and W. Crete, in the montane and sub-montane zones. Flowers April-May.

Berberidaceae Family

Shrubs or herbs with alternate leaves or all at base. Flowers with 6-9 sepals and 4-6 petals, large and coloured or small and nectariferous. Ovary superior.

Berberis (Berberries)

Yellow-wooded shrubs. Leaves entire, growing in clusters, from the axil of a stout spine. Flowers small in little racemes, with 3 small sepals, 6 larger yellow sepals and 6 small, nectariform petals. Stamens 6.

1. Berberis cretica. A deciduous shrub, 30-80cm. Leaves entire, narrow, 1-2cm. Spines tripartite Flowers small, in small inflorescences. Fruit a black berry. Habitat: Montane and subalpine zones. Flowers May-June.

Leontice (Leontices)

Herbs with perennial rhizomes. Leaves large, twice-thrice tripartite or twice-thrice bipinnate. Sepals 6 large, yellow, petal like. Petals 6, very small. Stamens 6.

1. Leontice leontopetalum. Glaucous-green plant. Stem 30-50cm., erect, branching upwards. Leaves up to 20cm., the lower long-stalked, all twice or thrice tripartite, with leaflets broadly ovate, entire. Many inflorescences in the axils of the upper leaves, with 15-40 yellow flowers, about 2mm. in diameter. Habitat: Lowland and sub-montane zones. Flowers April-May.

Lauraceae Family

Evergreen trees or shrubs, with entire, alternate leaves. Flowers hermaphrodite or male and female on the same plant (monoecious) or on different trees (dioecious). Flowers small. Petals and sepals 2 or 3. Petals and sepals like. Ovary superior. Fruit: berry.

Laurus (Laurels)

Dioecious plants, inflorescence almost sessile. 2 petals and 2 sepals, petal like. 8-12 stamens.

1. Laurus nobilis. A big shrub or small tree; leaves glabrous, oblong-lanceolate, dark green above and a lighter green beneath, 5-10cm. long. Flowers whitish-green, about 1cm. Fruit a black berry that looks like a small olive. Habitat: cool gullies in the lowland and sub-montane zones. Flowers in Spring.

Ranunculus bullatus | Ranunculus brevifolius - s. sp. pindicus

Leontice leontopetalum

Laurus nobilis

Papaveraceae Family

Herbs with actinomorphic flowers, quadripartite, rarely sexpartite or zygomorphic. Stamens: 2, 4, or many. Ovary: superior.

Papaver (Poppies)

Annuals with leaves more or less pinnately-lobed. Single big flowers, with 2 sepals which fall off when the bud opens, and 4 big petals, usually reddish. Fruit, a swollen capsule, round or ablong, with numerous tiny seeds (pod).

Group A. Pod glabrous.

1. Papaver somniferum - subsp. setigerum. A sparsely-haired plant reaching 1m. in height. Leaves ovate-oblong, pinnately-lobed, seagreen. Petals: pink, nearly disk-like, 35-40mm long, with a dark blotch at the base. Pod ovate, 5-6cm. Habitat: fallow fields ditches, and waysides of sub-montane and lowland zones. Flowers April-May. The **subsp. somniferum** with its glabrous leaves and bigger flowers, pink, white, or red, single or double with fringed petals, is often cultivated in Crete, but rarely grows of itself. **2. Papaver rhoeas.** Hairy plant with hairs adpressed, 25-90cm. in height. Leaves: pinnately-lobed or bipinnate, lobes dentate, mucronate. Apical lobe larger than rest. Disk-like scarlet petals, sometimes with a black blotch at their base. Stamens with filaments, and anthers blackish. Pod almost round or broadly ovate, rounded at base. Stigma disc spreading. Habitat: Lowland and sub-montane zones. Flowers March-May. **3. Papaver commutatum** Very similar to 2, but more robust. The petals have a big black blotch at the base, reaching almost to the middle, and the pod is broadly obovate. Habitat: Lowlands, and sub-montane zones. Flowers April-May. **4. Papaver dubium.** Like 2 but adpressed hairs towards base, depressed upwards. Flowers with smaller petals, 15-30mm., orange, red, with a small black blotch at the base of the petals, and basal 1vs. pinnately-lobed to pinnate, with segments ovate, rounded at tip. Pod obovate, 1,5-2cm. Spreading stigma disc. Habitat: Sub-montane and montane zones. Flowers April-June. **5. Papaver laevigatum.** Very like 4 but almost glabrous with few sparse hairs, while petals are smaller, about 15mm. The existence of this species in Crete was doubtful; however, the author discovered it on sandy beaches around Sitia. Habitat: In Eastern Crete on the borders of the littoral and lowland zones. Flowers April-May.

Group B. Pod hairy

1. Papaver argemone. A hairy plant, 20-50cm. high. Leaves pinnate with narrow segments, usually mucronate. Petals 20-25mm., obovate, reddish, with a black blotch at their base, rarely unblotched. Anthers blackish. Pod oblong-obovate, 1,5-2cm. Stigma disc decurved at lips. Habitat: Sub-montane and lowland zones. Flowers April-May. **2. Papaver nigrotinctum.** Similar to 1 but smaller and with more slender stems, 10-20cm. Leaves of base more or less in a rosette with lanceolate segments. Pod 1-1,5cm. Rare in Greece occurring in Corinth and the Cyclades, and noted for the first time in Western Crete by the author. Habitat: sub-montane zone. Flowers April-May. **3. Papaver hydridum.** Like 1 but petals 10-20mm., pod obovate-spherical; leaves bigger with segments broader. Habitat: Both cultivated and uncultivated fields of the lowland and sub-montane zones. Flowers March-June.

Roemaria (Violet Horned-popies)

Annuals similar to Poppies (Papaver), but with a long, narrow capsule, linear, dehiscent. Flowers violet-coloured.

1. Roemeria hybrida. Stems 20-40cm. Leaves trilobate, lobes linear. Flowers either apical or axillary. Petals 1,5-3cm., almost disk-like, violet, with black blotch at base. Anthers yellow; capsule 5-10cm., hairy. Habitat: Lowland and sub-montane fields. Flowers March-June.

Roemeria (Violet Horned-popies)

Glaucous-green plants, with flowers like poppies, yellow or orange-coloured. Fruit: a linear capsule splitting from top to bottom.

1. Glaucium flavum. A biennial or perennial plant. Stems 30-90cm. Basal leaves lyrate-pinnately-lobed, 15-35cm. Stem leaves smaller, stem-clasping. Petals yellow or pale

Papaver somniferum - s. sp. setigerum   Papaver rhoeas

Papaver laevigatum   Papaver argemone

yellow, broadly obovate, 3-4cm. long. Stamens yellow. Sepals glabrous or, frequently, with rare pointed protuberances, like coarse hairs. Capsule either straight or bent, 15-30cm. long. Habitat: Maritime zone. Flowers May-September. **2. Glaucium lelocarpum.** Very like 1 but petals a dark yellow, and the capsule smaller up to 10cm., slightly compressed between seeds. Habitat: Littoral zone, and arid, bare places of lowlands but always close to sea. Flowers May-September. **3. Glaucium corniculatum.** Similar to 1 and 2 but much smaller, and with a hairy capsule. Flowers smaller, with petals up to 3cm., golden-yellow or reddish, with or without a dark blotch at base. Habitat: Lowland cultivated and uncultivated fields. Flowers April-July.

Chelidonium (Celandines)

Plant with orange-coloured sap. Flowers small, with 4 petals and 2 sepals. Capsule linear.

1. Chelidonium majus. A sparsely-pubescent, glaucous-green perennial with pinnate leaves composed of 5-7 ovate or oblong, crenate leaflets. Terminal leaflet usually trilobate. Umbellate inflorescence with 2-6 flowers. Petals 1cm., yellow. Stamens also yellow. Capsule 2-5cm. Habitat: A rare plant, found in the montane zone. Flowers May-September.

Hypecoum (St. John's Worts)

Glaucus-green, glabrous annuals. Flowers consist of 2 small sepals that drop off easily, and 4 small petals, of which one pair, at least, is trilobate. 4 stamens. Fruit an oblong capsule, squeezed between the seeds.

1. Hypecoum procumbens. Stems procumbent. Leaves bipinnately-lobed; lobes linear. Cymose inflorescence. Yellow flowers, 5-15mm. in diameter. Outer petals trilobate. Inner ones deeply trilobate, almost tripartite with central lobe nearly disk-like, fringed. Capsule 4-6cm. curved. Habitat: Sandy tracts in lowland and sub-montane zones. Flowers February-April.

Corydalis (Corydalis)

Usually glabrous plants with compound leaves, and racemose inflorescence, Zygomorphic flowers with 2 free sepals, and 4 converging petals, of which the 2 inner ones are alike, and oblong. The 2 outer ones are dissimilar. The upper petal is spurred at base.

1. Corydalis uniflora. A perennial with a small tuber at the root. Slender stem, 5-15cm. Leaves opposite, usually bipartite. Raceme with 1-2 (-3) flowers, 15-25mm., whitish flushed with purple. Spur 8-12mm. Endemic to Crete, and often considered a kind of subspecies of the Asia Minor species **Corydalis rutifolia** which bears more flowers, and has a shorter spur. Habitat: Alpine and sub-alpine zones. Flowers May-June.

Fumaria (Fumitories)

Annuals, stems long, slender, often climbing. Leaves bipinnate to four times pinnate. Inflorescences racemose. Flowers zygomorphic, small, with two sepals and 4 converging petals, the topmost spurred.

1. Fumaria judaica. Leaves with flat, ovate-lanceolate or oblong lobes. Racemes with 10-20 flowers, white or, rarely, pinkish. Corolla 9-13mm. long. Habitat: Lowland and submontane zones. Flowers March-April. **2. Fumaria macrocarpa.** Like 1 but racemes with 7-11 pale pink flowers, 9-11mm. Habitat: Lowland and sub-montane zones. Flowers March-May. **3. Fumaria capreolata - subsp. capreolata.** Like 1 but corolla creamy or pink, except for the tips of petals which are blackish-red. Habitat: Lowland and sub-montane zones. Flowers March-June. **4. Fumaria flabellata.** Similar to 1 but racemes often with up to 30 flowers. Fruit with protuberances. Habitat: Lowland and montane zones. Flowers March-April. **5. Fumaria Parviflora.** Leaves with narrow, lanceolate, oblong or linear, canaliculate lobes. Clusters up to 20 flowers, white, only rarely flushed with pink. Habitat: Montane and sub-montane zones. Flowers March-May.

Capparidaceae Family

Herbs, shrubs, or trees. Leaves simple, palmately-lobed or palmate, alternate, with or without stipules, or with spines instead of stipules. Flowers zygomorphic or actinomorphic, with 4 petals and sepals. Stamens 6 or many. Ovary superior.

Papaver nigrotinctum

Roemeria hybrida

Glaucium flavum

Chelidonium majus

Capparis (Capers)

Creeping shrubs, leaves simple, and stipules usually spine-like. Flowers big, solitary, more or less zygomorphic, with 4 large petals, and 4 smaller sepals. Stamens numerous. Fruit an oblong big berry, greenish in colour, known as the "caper cucumber".

1. Capparis spinosa. Glabrous leaves, orbicular or ovate-orbicular, rather fleshy, rounded or slightly bilobed at tip. Spines thin and hooked. Flowers white or pink, somewhat zygomorphic, 5-7cm. across. Habitat: Sea cliffs. Flowers May-September. **2. Capparis ovata.** Very similar to 1, but leaves slightly pubescent, ovate, elliptic or oblong, less fleshy, pointed, and slightly awned at tip. Flowers intensely zygomorphic, 4-5cm. Habitat: Rocks, walls, and stony places of lowland and sub-montane zones, usually not close to sea. Flowers May-September.

Cruciferae Family

Annual or perennial herbs, rarely small shrubs. Leaves alternate. Flowers with 4 sepals, free, spreading or converging, and 4 petals, free, ending in a claw. Fruit of varied shape, consisting of 2 fused carpels called siliqua. Inflorescence a dense or sparse simple or, rarely, compound, raceme.

Sisymbrium (Rockets)

Annuals or perennials with simple hairs or glabrous. Leaves entire or palmately lobed. Flowers small in racemose inflorescences. Sepals erect alike. Petals yellow, rarely white. Fruit (siliqua) linear, with a very small beak.

1. Sisymbrium irio. An almost glabrous annual up to 60cm. high. Lower leaves pinnately lobed, with apical lobe bigger. Flowers yellow, 6-10mm. across. Siliquae 25-64mm. Habitat: Ruins, rubble, and rubbish-dumps in the lowland and sub-montane zones. Flowers April-June. **2. Sisymbrium orientale.** Similar to 1 but stem pubescent, many-branched, apical lobe of basal leaves more or less arrow-shaped, flowers creamy, siliquae sparse, spreading, 35-100mm. Habitat: Uncultivated lowland and sub-montane fields. Flowers March-June. **3. Sisymbrium officinale.** Similar to 1 but occasionally biennial. Siliquae erect, 10-20mm., almost touching stem. Flowers smaller. Habitat: Ruins, rubble, rubbish-dumps, and lowland and sub-montane fields. Flowers March-May.

Arabidopsis (Thale-cress)

Annuals or biennials. Leaves entire or pinnately-lobed. Sepals alike. Petals white, pink, or yellow. Fruit linear siliqua.

1. Arabidopsis thaliana. Annual or biennial, up to 40cm., sparsely pubescent. Basal leaves entire or dentate, those of stem entire, wedge-shaped at base. Petals white 2-4mm., entire. Siliqua 5-20mm., glabrous. Habitat: Open sandy tracts in lowland and sub-montane zones. Flowers March-April.

Bunias (Cabbages)

Annual or biennial plants. Leaves entire or pinnately-lobed. Sepals somewhat divergent, almost identical. Petals white or yellow, practically clawless. Siliquae angular, angles with dentate wing.

1. Bunias erucago. A pubescent-glandular annual or biennial, 30-60cm. Lower leaves pinnately-lobed, upper ones entire or dentate. Dense inflorescence, with yellow flowers. Petals 8-13mm. Siliqua 10-12mm. Habitat: Lowland and sub-montane zones. Flowers April-May.

Erysimum (Treacle Mustards)

Usually biennials or perennials. Flowers similar to those of Stock, but yellow. Sepals erect, 2 of them saccate at base. Fruit a linear siliqua.

1. Erysimum candicum - subsp. candicum. A many-branched perennial, with a woody base. Leaves narrowly lanceolate, 2-12cm. long, nearly sessile. Sepals green or greenish-yellow. Petals 19-22mm., either golden or pale yellow. Endemic to Crete and the Cycladian island of Anaphe. Habitat: Rocks in the lowland, sub-montane, and lower slopes of montane zone. **2. Erysimum raulinii.** A 15-50cm. biennial. Stems quadrangular at their base, and slightly winged. Lower leaves oblong-lanceolate, dentate, 4-12mm.,

Capparis spinosa

Capparis ovata

Bunias erucago

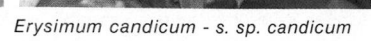

Erysimum candicum - s. sp. candicum

broad. Sepals 6-10mm. Petals yellow, 11-15mm. Siliquae 15-40mm. broad. Sepals 6-10mm. Petals yellow, 11-15mm. Siliquae 15-40mm., erect, with a quadrangular section. A W. Crete endemic. Habitat: Montane zone. Flowers April-May. **3. Erysimum mutabile.** A tufted perennial, stems no higher than 12cm. Lower leaves up to 20mm. oblong-spatulate, long-stalked. Sepals 4-6mm. Petals 7-11mm., yellow above, brownish-yellow or crimson beneath. Siliqua 10-20mm. Endemic to both East and West Crete. Habitat: Montane and sub-alpine zones. Flowers May-June. **4. Erysimum graecum** Biennial, hairy, greyish-green, erect, reaching up to 55cm. Sepals 5-8mm. Petals pale yellow, 8-12mm. x 2-3mm. Stem leaves narrowly linear. Basal leaves broader, dentate. Siliquae 35-75mm. with a square section. Habitat: Hills of sub-montane and lowland zones in W. Crete. Flowers April-May. **5. Erysimum creticum.** Similar to 4, but much more branched, flowers larger, and a bright yellow. Siliquae compressed. Endemic to E. Crete. Habitat: Sub-montane zone. Flowers April-May.

Malcomia (Virginian Stocks)

Annual or perennial plants. Sepals erect, 2 of them usually saccate. Petals pink, violet, or crimson, rarely white with long claw. Siliqua linear.

1. Malcolmia africana. A hairy annual up to 40cm. Leaves lanceolate entire or notched. Sepals 3-5mm., not saccate. Petals small, 8-10mm., violet. Siliquae 25-65mm., spreading, of a more or less quadrangular cut, densely haired. Habitat: Lowland and sub-montane zones. Flowers February-April. **2. Malcolmia chia.** Similar to 1 but a smaller and slenderer plant. Entire or dentate, ovate-oblong leaves, with wedge-shaped base. Both sepals saccate. Violet or pink flowers. Siliquae neither erect nor spreading but ascending. Habitat: Lowland zone near sea. **3. Malcolmia flexuosa.** A rather fleshy annual, with entire, obovate or oblong leaves. Sepals 6-10mm., of which 2 saccate. Petals pale pink, pinkish-violet, or lilac. Siliquae 35-80mm. long, and nearly 3mm. broad. Habitat: Cliffs of littoral zone. Flowers February-April.

Matthiola (Stocks)

Annuals or perennials, hairy plants. Sepals erect, the two saccate. Long-clawed white, purple, violet, or yellowish petals. Siliqua linear, bilobed at tip.

1. Matthiola incana - subsp. incana. A hairy, greyish-green perennial with woody base. Leaves entire, lanceolate, rarely notched pinnately-lobed. Flowers large. Sepals 9-13mm. Petals 20-30mm., purple pink or violet, seldom white. Siliquae 45-160mm. Habitat: Littoral and lowland rocks. Flowers February-May. **2. Matthiola tricuspidata.** An annual. Leaves notched-crenate to pinnate, lobes ovate, rounded at tip. Sepals 7-11mm. Petals purple or lilac, 15-22mm. Siliquae 25-100mm. Habitat: Sandy beaches. Flowers March-May.

Rorippa (Yellow-cress)

Annual or perennial plants, glabrous or sparsely haired. Leaves simple or pinnately-lobed. The two calyx sepals saccate. Petals yellow. Siliquae small, oblong or ovate, compressed.

1. Rorippa sylvestris - subsp. sylvestris. A 20-50cm. perennial, glabrous, producing a creeping stolon. Leaves pinnately-lobed or pinnate, with lanceolate segments, frequently dentate or lobed. Petals 4-5mm. Siliquae 6-18mm., more or less ascending. Habitat: Cultivated and uncultivated fields at a low altitude. Flowers April-May.

Nasturtium (Watercress)

Perennials, glabrous or with few hairs. Leaves pinnately-lobed or pinnate. Petals white, seldom pink. Siliqua linear.

1. Nasturtium officinale. Stems 10-60cm., procumbent, and frequently rooting at base, erect at tip. Leaves pinnately-lobed, lobes more or less entire, disk-like or broadly elliptic. Lower leavs with 1-3 lobes the rest with 5-9. Numerous small flowers, white or rarely pink. Siliqua 13-18mm. Habitat: Streams and pools, the base of the plants usually being in the water; sub-montane and montane zones. Flowers April-May.

Erysimum creticum

Malkolmia flexuosa

Matthiola incana - s. sp. incana

Nasturtium officinale

Cardamine (Bitter-Cress or Coral-Worts)

Annual or perennial herbs, glabrous or with sparse hairs. Leaves simple, pinnately-lobed, or pinnate. Flowers with both sepals slightly saccate. White, pale yellow, or pink petals. Linear siliquae, strongly compressed.

1. Cardamine graeca. An annual or biennial plant, 10-30cm., either glabrous or hairy. Leaves pinnatelis-lobed. The lower with 4-5pairs of obovate-cuneate lobes, the upper with 2-3 pairs of entire or trilobate lobes. Petals white, 4-6mm. long. Habitat: Montane and sub-montane zones. Flowers April-May. **2. Cardamine hirsuta.** Like 1 but always an annual. Lower leaves with 1-3 pairs of lobes, stem leaves with 2-5 pairs of lobes. All leaves

73

hairy on upper surface. Petals white, small sometimes missing. Habitat: Both cultivated and uncultivated fields. Flowers March-May.

Arabis (Rock-cress)

Annual or perennial herbs with simple leaves. Flowers with white, pink, or purple petals, and the two sepals of calyx slightly saccate. Siliquae oblong-linear.

1. Arabis serpillifolia - subsp. cretica. A tufted, biennial or perennial plant, with densely hairy stems, 5-25cm. Leaves hairy, the lower ones long-stalked and oblong. Stem leaves 3-5. oblong-ovate, entire. A 7-16 - flowered inflorescence. Petals pink. 5-7mm. long. Endemic to Crete. Habitat: Montane zone. Flowers June-July. **2. Arabis muralis.** A light-green, erect perennial, often branched from its base. Basal leaves narrowing on short stalks, obovate, dentate, rounded at tip, and hairy. Stem leaves 6-14, oblong, rounded at base. Inflorescence with 8-14 flowers. Petals 6-18mm. erect, white, rarely pink. Siliquae 30-70mm. Habitat: Lowland, sub-montane, and montane zones. Flowers April-June. **3. Arabis recta:** A 10-30cm. pubescent annual. Stem simple or branched. Basal leaves ovate or obovate, stalked. Stem leaves 5-14, sessile, ovate or oblong, rounded at tip, with auricles at base. Flowers pink 7-40. Petals 2-3,5mm. Habitat: Sub-montane and lowland zones. Flowers April-may. **4. Arabis verna.** Similar to 3 but more branched, with few stem leaves (usually 1-2), cordate at base, crenate. Up to 10 flowers. Petals bigger (5-8mm), lilac or white. Habitat: Sub-montane and lowland zones. Flowers March-April. **5. Arabis caucasica.** A densely pubescent perennial, with many leaf rosettes, stems creeping or ascending, 15-35cm. Basal leaves greyish-green with few rounded teeth. Stem leaves auricled or arrow-shaped at base. Big white flowers, petals 9-18mm. Habitat: Montane and sub-alpine rocks. Flowers May-July.

Aubrieta (Aubrietas)

Perennial herbs, hairy; hairs simple or star-shaped. Simple, dentate leaves. Both sepals saccate. Petals pink or violet. Carpel a siliqua, oblong-cylindrical, short with style showing clearly at tip.

1. Aubrieta deltoidea - var. deltoidea. A tufted plant, not very dense; leaves small, spathulate, obovate or rhomboid, with 1-3 pairs of teeth. Sepals 6-10mm. Petals 15-28mm., purple-violet. Siliqua up to 16mm. Habitat: Montane and sub-montane zones. Flowers April-June.

Ricotia (Ricotias)

Annual or perennial plants, glabrous or else with simple hairs. Leaves entire to bipinnate. Two of the erect sepals saccate. Pink or lilac petals. Oblong siliquae, flattened.

1. Ricotia cretica. A 10-25cm. annual. Leaves either bipinnate or bilobate, lobes ovate or elliptic, dentate. Few flowers. 10-20mm. petals. Siliqua 30-50mm. Endemic to Crete. Habitat: Stony places in montane and sub-montane zones. Flowers April-May.

Lunaria (Honestie)

Biennial or perennial plants. Leaves big, simple, dentate. Sepals erect, the 2 of the two saccate. Petals puprle or violet, rarely white. Siliquae large, strongly flattened, membraneous, almost pellucid, with an elliptic or ovate margin.

Cardamine graeca

Arabis caucasica

Aubrieta deltoidea - s. sp. deltoidea

Lunaria annua - s. sp. pachyrhiza

1. Lunaria annua - subsp. pachyrhiza. A biennial with fleshy roots. Stems up to 100 cm. Leaves big, ovate to lanceolate, very sharply dentate, mucronate at apex. Petals 15-25mm., purple or violet. Siliqua 20-70mm., oblong-elliptic or nearly orbicular. Habitat: Ditches, cultivated fields, and hedges, in the lowland and sub-montane zones. Flowers March-May.

Alyssoides

Perennials - with branched or star-shaped hairs. Erect or slightly distant sepals, two of which saccate. Yellow petals. Siliqua spherical, like a little bubble.

1. Alyssoides cretica. A small shrub, with a woody base, multibranched, with many rosettes of greyish-green or silvery leaves, oblanceolate or obovate. Sepals 7-11mm. Petals 12-20mm., entire. Siliqua 10-15mm. Endemic to Crete and Carpathos. Habitat: Rocks of sub-montane and montane zones. Flowers March-May.

Alyssum (Alisons)

Annuals or perennials, usually with yellow flowers. Sepals erect-divergent; not saccated at base. Petals entire or else shallowly bilobate. Fruit are siliquae, disk-shaped, ovate, obovate, or elliptic, compressed two-valved, with 1-6 seeds in each valve.

Group A. Perennials. Crowded inflorescences, simple. 2-4 seeds in each valve of siliqua.

1. Alyssum saxatile - subsp. orientale. A crowded plant, hairy and woody-based with numerous stems, 10-40 (-50) cm. Sepals 2-4mm. Petals 3-6(-8)mm., wavy at tip or bilobed. Glabrous siliquae, orbicular, with wedge-shaped base, and 4-8mm. across. Basal leaves obovate or oblanceolate, pinnately-lobed, either deeply dentate or entire. Stem leaves smaller, usually entire. Habitat: Rocks of middle and lower montane zone. Flowers March-May.

Group B: Annuals. inflorescence one simple raceme or umbel. 2 seeds in each valve of siliqua.

1. Alyssum alyssoides. Multibranched, with stems erect or ascending up to 30-(40) cm., covered with a greyish pubescence. Leaves small, the lower ones obovate or oblanceolate, the others narrower. Petals 3-4mm. undulate at margin. Disk-like, pubescent siliquae. Habitat: Uncultivated places at a low altitude. Flowers in spring. **2. Alyssum follosum.** Like 1, but smaller reaching up to 10cm. high, greyish-green. Lower leaves orbicular and long-stalked. Very narrow petals. Short inflorescences, almost umbellate, surrounded by the upper leaves. Habitat: Barren areas at a low altitude. Flowers in spring. **3. Alyssum minutum.** Similar to 1, but petals smaller and densely pubescent. Siliquae glabrous. Habitat: As 2. Flowers in spring. **4. Alyssum umbellatum.** Like 1 but a dwarf, not over 10cm. in height. Leaves linear or linear-oblong, inflorescences umbellate. Habitat: Fallow fields and barren tracts at low altitudes. Flowers in spring. **5. Alyssum minus.** Similar with 1, up to 40cm. Leaves either oblong-obovate or oblong-lanceolate. Small petals. Pubescent siliquae up to 6mm. Habitat: Low barren regions. Flowers in spring. **6. Alyssum strigosum.** Very similar to 5 but with hairy siliquae. Habitat: Barren regions. Flowers in spring.

Group C. Perennials. 2 seeds to each valve of siliquae. Simple inflorescence.

1. Alyssum sphacioticum. A greyish or silvery plant. Flower-bearing stems 5-10cm. high, erect. Non-flowering stems procumbent. Basal leaves obovate or obovate-orbicular; upper ones linear or oblong, adpressed to stem. Petals up to 6mm. entire. Inflorescence rather dense, becoming slightly oblong as silique mature. Endemic to Crete. Habitat: montane and subalpine zones. Flowers in spring. **2. Alyssum lassithicum.** Like 1 but greyish-white, more shrubby and robust, with flower-bearing stems erect, up to 20cm., while the non-flower-bearing stems are recumbent. Basal leaves obovate, pointed. Stem leaves linear-oblanceolate or obovate, rounded at tip. A Cretan endemic. Habitat: On the montane and alpine zones of Dhikti (Lassithi mountains). **3. Alyssum ideaeum.** A creeping dwarf-plant, greyish-green or whitish with simple stems up to 5cm. Leaves obovate-orbicular to ovate-oblong. Petals 4-6mm. Siliquae almost orbicular. Another Cretan endemic. Habitat: The montane zone, mainly in the region of Idha (Psiloritis).

Group D Perennialy. 1 seed in each cell of siliqua. Compound inflorescences.

1. Alyssum murale. A caespitose perennial with 25-70cm. erect flowering stems, long

Alyssoides cretica

Alyssum murale

Aethionema saxatile

Iberis sempervirens

non-flowering ones, or dense leaf rosettes. Basal leaves obovate-spathulate or oblanceolate. Stem leaves 10-20 x 3-6mm. Pubescent siliquae. All the leaves are greyish-green above and whitish or grey beneath. Small flowers on large inflorescences. Habitat: stony and barren places of montane and sub-montane zones. **2. Alyssum corsicum.** Similar to 1 but stems 30-60cm., numerous non-flower rosettes, basal leaves orbicular-spathulate. Glabrous siliquae. A plant of W. Anatolia established in Crete. Habitat: Stony places. Flowers in spring. **3. Alyssum fragillimum.** A dwarf perennial with stems 1-3cm. Basal leaves similar or narrower. A Cretan endemic. Habitat: Montane and alpine zones. Flowers April-June. **4. Alyssum fallacinum.** Perennial, 20-50cm. high, with long non-flowering stems. Leaves oblanceolate, green on top, white beneath, 15-25mm. long. Flowers small. Siliquae elliptic or oblanceolate. Endemic to Crete and S. Greece. Habitat: Sub-montane zone. Flowers May-June.

Aethionema

Glabrous annuals or perennials. Leaves small, entire. Flowers have erect sepals, and white, pink, or purple petals, darker-veined. Siliqua compressed, winged, with the wing more or less bilobed at tip.

1. Aethionema saxatile. An annual or biennial plant, stems either spreading or erect, up to 30cm. high. Leaves ovate, oblong, or oblong-linear. Little white, pink, or purple flowers. Siliquae obovate or almost orbicular. Habitat: Rocks of montane, sub-alpine, and alpine zones. Flowers May-June.

Iberis (Candytufts)

Plants similar to Aethionema, but differing in flowers which have two large and two small petals.

1. Iberis sempervirens. A perennial plant with few branches, glabrous and spreading, 10-25cm. Oblong-spathulate leaves, 2,5-5mm. broad. Small white flowers in crowded umbels. Siliqua 6-7mm. Habitat: Montane, sub-alpine, and alpine zones. Flowers May-July.

Biscutella (Buckler Mustards)

Herbs or shrublets, yellow-flowered. A very distinctive siliqua consisting of two discoid, flattened segments.

1. Biscutella laevigata. An almost glabrous perennial with 10-50cm. stems. Basal leaves linear or ovate-lanceolate, entire, toothed or notched, glabrous or hairy. Petals 4-8mm. Siliqua 8-14mm. wide. Habitat: Montane zone. Flowers April-May. **2. Biscutella didyma.** Similar to 1 but a hairy annual with 1 or more stems. Basal leaves. Obovate-cuneate, dentate. Petals 4mm. Habitat: Dry places in the sub-montane and lowland zones. Flowers March-April.

Lepidium (Pepperworts)

Annuals or perennials. Flowers small, white or yellow, in crowded clusters. Siliquae flattened, bilobed at apex.

1. Lepidium hirtum. A hairy perennial, with many stems, 10-30cm., spreading or ascending. Basal leaves obovate, entire or slightly undulate. Flowers tiny, crowded, white. Habitat: Sub-alpine and alpine zones. Flowers May-June. **2. Lepidium ruderale.** Annual or biennial, with a strong smell, usually with a single erect stem, 10-30cm. Basal leaves palmately-lobed or pinnate, the upper ones linear. Small petals, yellowish, or they may be absent. Habitat: Uncultivated places at a low altitude. Flowers March-April.

Cardaria (Hoary Cress)

Similar to Lepidium, but the inflorescence is a compound raceme, and the siliquae are heart-shaped.

1. Cardaria draba. A glabrous, or slightly pubescent, annual, 15-90cm. Leaves obovate or ovate-oblong, dentate sinuate, the lower ones wedge-shaped, stalked, the upper sessile, stem-clasping. Petals 4mm. white. Habitat: Roadsides, rubbish-heaps, rubble of submontane and lowland zones. Flowers February-April.

Cardaria draba

Coronopus squamatus is an inconspicuous plant, with pinnate leaves and tiny flowers in small racemes, common in lowland and submontane zones.

Clypeola (Disk Cress)

Hairy annuals. Sepals rather erect, not saccate. Petals yellow. Siliquae orbicular or kidney-shaped, flattened, nodding. Leaves small.

1. Clypeola Jonthlaspi. An erect, pubescent, greyish-green plant, up to 20cm. Leaves linear-oblanceolate or obovate. Raceme oblong. Flowers small, petals 1-2mm. An inconspicuous plant of the lowland and sub-montane zones. Flowers March-April.

Draba (Whitlow Grass)

Annual or perennial herbs. Leaves simple, entire or dentate. Sepals not quite erect, two of them slightly saccate or all uniform non-saccated. Petals white or yellow, entire or a little emarginate at tip. Siliquae compressed, elliptic or oblong.

1. Draba cretica. A dwarf perennial, with stems 1-2cm. Leaves in rosettes, small, ovate, rounded at tip, hairy. Flowers with non-saccated sepals and yellow petals. A Cretan endemic. Habitat: Alpine and sub-alpine zones. Flowers May-June. **2. Draba muralis.** Annual, hairy, erect, up to 30cm. Stem leaves broad, ovate, almost stem-clasping. Basal leaves obovate-cuneate. Crowded inflorescence, small white flowers. Habitat: Sandy, uncultivated places at a low altitude. Flowers March-April.

Erophila (Whitlow Grass)

Annuals similar to Draba, but very small. Small white, pink, or purple flowers. Petals bilobed.

1. Erophila verna. 1 or more stems, up to 20cm. All leaves at base in a rosette spathulate or lanceolate, entire or dentate, hairy. Flower-raceme with small white or purple flowers. Habitat: Barren sandy places in the sub-montane zone. Flowers March-April.

Camelina (Gold of Pleasure)

Hairy annuals or biennials. Yellow or white flowers. Sepals erect. Siliquae obovate or pear-shaped, compressed, Style remaining at tip.

1. Camelina sativa. Annual, erect, hairy or nearly glabrous, 30-80cm. Lanceolate or oblong leaves, 3-9mm. Yellow petals 5mm. Habitat: Appears sporadically at a low altitude. Flowers March-April. **2. Camelina microcarpa.** Similar to 1 but sturdier, hairier, and petals a pale yellow. Habitat: Sub-montane cultivated and fallow fields. Flowers April-May. **3. Camelina alyssum.** Like 1 but branched, smaller, up to 50cm., leaves deeply dentate, flowers pale yellow. Habitat: Lowland and sub-montane zones. Flowers March-April.

Teesdalia (Shepherd's Cress)

Small annuals, leaves pinnately-lobed or dentate, all basal, very seldom 1-3 small leaves on stem. Small white flowers sepals somewhat divergent. Siliquae compressed, orbicular or ovoid.

1. Teesdalia coronopifolia. A small glabrous plant 3-12cm. high. Leaves pinnately-lobed or dentate in a rosette. Small raceme, flowers 2mm. Siliquae orbicular. Habitat: Sandy tracts in lowland and sub-montane zones. Flowers February-April.

Thlaspi (Pennycress)

Annual or perennial herbs. Stem leaves sessile, more or less stem-clasping. Flowers with non-saccate, erect sepals. Petals white or purple. Siliquae compressed, orbicular ovate, or oblong, usually cuneate at base.

1. Thlaspi graecum. A tufted perennial, stems 2-10 (-20)cm. Basal leaves oblong, longstalked. Stem leaves oblong. Sepals 2mm. White petals 6mm. Endemic to Crete and Greek mainland. Habitat: Montane and sub-alpine zones. Flowers May-June. **2. Thlaspi microphyllum.** Similar to 1 but much smaller (1-4cm. high). Basal leaves very small. Sepals violet, petals white. Habitat: Alpine and sub-alpine zones. Flowers May-July.

Thlaspi graecum

Moricandia (Violet Cabbages)

Hairless annuals or perennials. Leaves simple, a little fleshy. Big flowers with erect sepals, two of them saccate at base. Siliquae linear-cylindrical.

1. Moricandia arvensis. A glaucous-green perennial up to 65ch. high. Branched stems. Basal leaves obovate, a little crenate, narrow at base. Upper leaves heart-shaped, entire, stem-clasping. Racemes have 10-20 flowers. Petals bout 2mm. violet. Habitat: In stony places of sub-montane and lowland zones. Flowers April-May.

Brassica (Wild Cabbages and Mustards)

Herbs or shrublets. Leaves entire, pinnately-lobed or pinnate. Sepals erect, or the two

81

biggest slightly divergent. Petals yellow or white. Siliquae oblong, cylindrical, or almost quadrangular, with a short, conical beak at the apex.

1. Brassica cretica - subsp. nivea. Perennial, with fleshy, glaucous-green leaves. Basal leaves large, 10-15cm., lyrate. Stem leaves sessile, smaller, and auricled at base. Tall stem up to 1m. Flowers large, white. Siliquae spreading-divergent. Habitat: Rocks near the sea. Flowers April-May. Plants with distinctive intermediates between the subsp. **nivea** and subsp. **cretica** which can be found in the rest of Greece, have been observed in W. Crete as well. These usually have pale yellow flowers. **2. Brassica tournefortii.** A sea-green annual with lyrate leaves concentrated at base. Stems up to 50cm. Sepals almost erect. Petals 5-7mm., pale yellow, often violet towards base. Siliquae 35-65mm. Habitat: Seashore. Flowers March-April. **3. Brassica nigra.** A bright green annual. Basal leaves lyrate, upper ones oblong-linear. Stems branched. Flowers yellow, petals 7-9mm. Siliquae erect, touching stem. Habitat: Lowland and sub-montane zones. Flowers March-May.

Sinapis (Charlocks or Mustards)

Plants similar to **Brassica,** with yellow flowers. Siliquae with long beak.

1. Sinapis arvensis. An annual, on the whole hairy, with stems up to 80cm. Lower leaves lyrate, with a large dentate apical lobe, up to 20cm. long. Upper leaves small, sessile, lanceolate. Siliquae spreading, 25-45mm. long, and beak 10-15mm. Habitat: Fallow, and cultivated fields in the sub-montane and lowland zones. Flowers March-April. **2. Sinapis alba - subsp. alba.** Like 1 but the leaves stalked. Siliquae 20-40mm. beak reaching 30mm. Habitat: Both cultivated and uncultivated lowland and sub-montane fields. Flowers March-April.

Eruca

Plants similar to Sinapis, but flowers have outer sepals saccate and the siliquae have a lance-shaped beak.

1. Eruca vesicaria - subsp. sativa. An annual, usually hairy, with a hot flavour. Leaves lyrate to pinnate. Petals 15-20mm., white or yellowish, with violet veins. Siliquae erect, 12-25mm. Sepals caducous. Habitat: Lowland and sub-montane zones. Flowers February-April.

Hirschfeldia (Hoary Mustard)

Like **Sinapis** but siliquae have a short, swollen beak.

1. Hirschfeldia incana. Annual or perennial. Stems up to 1m. usually branched, densely hairy towards base. Lower leaves pinnate with one ovate, dentate apical lobe. Upper leaves simple, sessile. Flowers 5mm., pale yellow, often with dark veins. Beak 8-17mm. Habitat: Lowland and sub-montane zones. Flowers March-May.

Erucaria

Annual or biennial plants. Sepals erect. Long-clawed lilac petals. Oblong jointed siliquae.

1. Erucaria hispanica. Annual or biennial. Stem erect, glabrous or slightly hairy at base. Leaves all stalked, pinnate, with linear-oblong or pinnately-lobed segments, rarely found entire. Flowers 10-15mm high. Siliquae 10-20mm. Habitat: Lowland and sub-montane zones in uncultivated and cultivated fields. Flowers April-May.

Neslia (Ball Mustards)

Small-flowered annuals. Non-saccated sepals. Yellow petals. Hard round siliquae.

Brassica nigra

1. Neslia paniculata. A pubescent, 15-60 cm. tall plant, leaves oblong or lanceolate almost entire. The stem-clasping leaves have pointed auricles at base. Sparse inflorescence of small yellow flowers. Habitat: Lowland and sub-montane fields. Flowers April-May.

Capsella (Shepherd's Purses)

Annual or biennial plants, hairy or not. Basal leaves entire or pinnately-lobed, stem leaves arrow-shaped clasping stem. Small flowers. Non-saccate erect sepals. Petals white, pink, or yellowish. Flattened siliquae, wedge-shaped at base.

1. Capsella bursa-pastoris. A sparsely-haired annual. Basal 1vs. pinnately-lobed, rarely entire. Small white flowers. Triangular-cuneate siliquae. Habitat: Lowland and sub-montane fields. Flowers February-May. **2. Capsella rubella.** Very similar to 1, but calyx reddish, petals pink, at least at tip; siliquae deeply bilobed at apex with spreading lobes. Habitat: Fields in lowland and sub-montane zones. Flowers February-May.

Hornungia (Hutchinsia)

Small annuals. Small white flowers. Siliquae constricted, elliptic or ovate-oblong.

1. Hornungia petraea. Stems 3-15cm., slender, bearing few leaves. Leaves pinnately-lobed, with 3-15 lobes that are lanceolate, ovate or obovate, pointed, and mostly found at base. Flowers small, white. Siliquae elliptic, ovate. Habitat Lowland and sub-montane zones. Flowers February-April.

Cakile (Sea Rockets)

Fleshy, hairless annuals. Flowers violet, white, or pink, and siliquae slightly fleshy, indehiscent, oblong, pointed, with two protuberances at base.

1. Cakile maritima - subsp. aegyptica. A plant with spreading stems up to 60cm. Leaves varied, pinnate, dentate or entire; flowers small, lilac. Habitat: Sandy beaches. Flowers March-July.

Rapistrum (Bastard Cabbages)

Annual or perennial herbs. Flowers with slightly diverging sepals, and yellow petals. Siliquae with two joints, the upper one spherical and larger that the lower joint.

1. Rapistrum rugosum. A 15-60cm. annual, hairy, mainly at the base. Lower leaves pinnately-lobed, the upper dentate, stalked. Petals pale yellow, 6-10mm. Siliquae 3-10mm. This species is subdivided into a series of subspecies which differ in the shape of the siliquae, and in the length of the flower-stalks. Habitat: Sub-montane and lowland zones. Flowers March-May.

Didesmus

Plants similar to **Rapistrum** but petals white. The upper part of siliquae broader than the lower, almost quadrangular. Beak long, pointed.

1. Didesmus aegyptius. An erect, sparsely hairy annual, 10-40cm. high. Leaves oblong-elliptic, dentate, lyrate or pinnately-lobed, rarely bipinnatifid. Petals 6-10mm. Siliquae 6-10mm. Habitat: Fields at a low altitude. Flowers March-May.

Enarthrocarpus

Annuals. Sepals slightly lax. Petals yellow with violet veins. Two-jointed siliquae. The lower two-valved, seedless. The upper oblong caducous, with 3-15 seeds, and constrictions among seeds.

1. Enarthrocarpus arcuatus. Hairy stems reaching 50cm. in height, with spreading branches. Lower leaves lyrate-pinnately-lobed, stalked, forming a rosette. Petals 10-13mm. Siliquae 3-9cm., curved, covered with hairs. Habitat: Sandy and stony seashores. Flowers April-June.

Sinapis alba - s. sp. alba

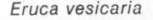

Eruca vesicaria

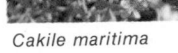

Cakile maritima

Reseda alba

Raphanus (Radish)

Annual or perennial herbs. Sepals erect. Petals tapering to a narrow claw. Siliquae oblong, pointed, more or less constricted between seeds.

1. Raphanus raphanistrum - subsp. raphanistrum. An annual or biennial hairy, plant. Stem erect, branched, up to 150cm. Lower leaves large, lyrate, upper ones smaller, entire. Flowers with sepals 5-10mm. and petals 12-20mm., white or yellowish, dark-veined. Siliquae 30-90mm. Habitat: Cultivated ground in the lowlands. Flowers March-May. **2. Raphanus raphanistrum - subsp. rostratus.** Similar to 1 but always annual. Flowers lilac, 15-25mm. Siliquae 30-130mm. Coastal zone. Flowers March-May.

Resedaceae Family

Annuals or perennials with alternate leaves. Flowers in terminal racemes or spikes. 4-8 sepals. Petals 4-8 free, entire or fringed. 7-25 stamens. Fruit a capsule, splitting downwards, or divided into 4-7 carpels.

1. Reseda alba. Annual or perennial with erect stem, branching upwards, 30-80cm. Leaves pinnately-lobed, with 5-15 lobes on either side Flowers small, white, in dense clusters. Petals 5 or 6, fringed to about the middle. Habitat: Sub-montane and lowland zones. Flowers March-May. **2. Reseda lutea.** Similar to 1, but flowers smaller, yellowish, on more oblong clusters. Leaves with 1-4 lobes on either side. Hab. Bushy places and slopes of lowland and sub-montane zones. Flowers March-May. **3. Reseda luteola.** Similar to 1 but a biennial, with yellowish flowers and entire leaves. Hab. Lowland and sub-montane zones. Flowers March-May. **4. Reseda orientalis.** Like 1 but basal leaves entire, the upper ones palmately-lobed with 1 or 2 pairs of lobes Flowers white. It is a W. Asia species. A rare plant in Crete; it has been met with only in Chora Sphakion, and on the islet of Gavdhos.

Rosales

Crassulaceae Family

Annual, biennial, or perennial herbs, with entire, and more or less fleshy leaves. Inflorescences usually cymose, rarer to come across in clusters or spikes. Sepals 3-20, either fused or free. Petals 3 or many, also either fused or free.

Crassula (stonecrops)

Small, hairless annuals with leaves opposite, fused at base, frequently reddish. Flowers tiny, deeply divided into three, four, or five segments.

1. Crassula tillaea. Shoots small and spreading. Ovoid leaves dense, 2mm. Flowers three or four-segmented, white or pink. Habitat: Cool, sandy sites at a low altitude. Flowers springtime. **2. Crassula vailantii.** Stems 2-6cm. Sparse leaves. Flowers cleft into 4 segments, pink. Habitat: Damp, sandy places at a low altitude. Flowers springtime.

Umbilicus (Pennyworts)

Perennials with rhizome or tuber. Basal leaves usually shield - shaped, hairless, stalked. Stem leaves much smaller. Flowers 5-segmented, in racemes. Small calyx. Corolla tubular or campanulate.

1. Umbilicus parviflorus. Basal leaves 2-5cm. across, palmately-lobed, lobes not very deeply cleft. Stem 10-35cm. Small, yellow flowers, 4-6mm. Habitat: Shady, rainy sites, and walls in the lowland and sub-montane zones. Flowers April-May. **2. Umbilicus chloranthus.** Like 1 but with leaves more deeply cleft and flowers smaller, spreading or a little pendulous, in a fewer-flowered raceme. Habitat: In shady ruins, and rocks, in lowland and sub-montane zones. Flowers April-May. **3. Umbilicus erectus.** Like 1 and 2 but stems are strong, up to 60cm., leaves deltoid-arbicular, cordate at base, margin crenate-undulate, and flowers numerous, yellow, in crowded racemes, 8-25cm. long.

Πθοοda lutoa

Umbilicus rupestris

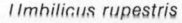

Sedum praesidis

Sedum litoreum

Corolla 9-13mm. The Cretan plants belong to the **lassithiensis var.,** with flowers opening out of big, dentated bracts. Habitat: Shady rocks in montane and sub-alpine zones. Flowers May-June. **4. Umbilicus rupestris.** Similar to 3 but leaves orbicular-shield-like, flowers drooping, 7-20mm. Habitat: Shady rocks of sub-montane and lowland zones. Flowers April-May. **5. Umbilicus horizontalis.** Similar to 4 but with a smaller raceme, leaves more numerous and denser and smaller flowers. Habitat: Rocks, ruins, in lowland and sub-montane zones. Flowers April-May.

Sedum (Stonecrop)

Leaves fleshy, usually alternate; sometimes concentrated in dense rosettes. Cymose

87

inflorescence. Flowers divided into 5 to 8 segments. Petals free or a little fused at base. Stamens usually 10.

Group A Perennials.

1. Sedum sediforme. Robust plant with flower-bearing shoots 25-60cm., and sterile ones short, densely-leafed. Leaves oblong, small, glaucous-green. Crowded inflorescence with branches strongly deflexed. Flowers a whitish-green or straw-coloured. Petals 4-7mm., spreading. Habitat: Sub-montane rocks. Flowers May-June. **2. Sedum ochroleucum - subsp. ochroleucum.** Like 1 but slightly smaller, up to 30cm. Leaves linear-cylindrical, very pointed. Inflorescence branches not very deflexed. Petals 8-10mm., whitish-green. Habitat: Submontane rocky places. Flowers April-May. **3. Sedum tenuifolium.** A slender plant. Flower-stems 7-20cm. erect. Leaves of non-flowering stems dense glaucous-green, pointed. Leaves of flowering stems more or less amplexicaul at base. Lax, one - sided, cymose inflorescence. Petals 6-8mm., yellow with a red central vein (midrib). Habitat: Stony and sandy sites in submontane and lowland zones. Flowers April-May. **4. Sedum acre.** Glabrous, sparsely tufted; Flower-stems 5-12cm.; sterile stems short. Leaves 3-6mm., elliptic, broader towards base, rounded at tip. Bright yellow flowers with spreading petals. Inflorescences on the whole few-flowered. Habitat: Stony areas of montane and sub-montane zones. Flowers May-July. **5. Sedum idaeum.** Similar to 4 but leaves linear, reddish. Densely-leafed flower-stems only 4cm. Creamy flowers few and crowded. Habitat: Sub-alpine and montane zones. Flowers June-July. A Cretan endemic. **6. Sedum athoum.** A tufted plant. Flower-stems 5-30cm. Leaves, reddish, ovate-oblong, inflated underneath, flat above. White flowers in corymbs. Habitat: Rocks and stony places in montane and sub-alpine zones. **7. Sedum dasyphyllum.** A smll plant, 3-8cm., pubescent-glandular. Leaves ovate or almost discoid, flat on upper surface. Pink-veined white flowers in lax corymbs. Habitat: Sub-montane and montane rocks. Flowers April-June. **8. Sedum magellense.** Glabrous with few, 6-15cm. - stems. Leaves often opposite, obovate-oblong, flat, rounded at tip. Inflorescence racemose with few white flowers. Habitat: Alpine and sub-alpine rocks, cool sites. **9. Sedum hierapetrae.** A tufted plant with flowering stems 3-7cm. Non-flowering stems shorter, with leaves in rosettes. Leaves oblong-spathulate, almost flat. Flowers in lax cymes. Very pointed purple petals. Endemic to Crete. Habitat: Lowland and littoral cliffs. Flowers April-May. **10. Sedum tristriatum.** Similar to 1 but pubescent-glandular. Pala pink petals. Endemic to Southern Greece and Crete. Habitat: Montane zone. Flowers May-June.

Group B. Annuals or biennials.

1. Sedum creticum. An annual or biennial with 5-8cm. long shoots, pubescent-glandular. Leaves alternate, oblong-spathulate, flat, glabrous, concentrated toward base. Flowers with pink, pointed petals. Endemic to Crete and Carpathos. Habitat: Sub-montane and lowland rocks. Flowers April-May. **2. Sedum cepaea.** Similar to 1 but taller, 15-30cm. Leaves opposite or whorled. Petals pink with a red midrib. Habitat: Shady rocks of montane zone. **3. Sedum annuum.** An often reddish annual or biennial. Stems branched from base, branchlets 4-12cm. Leaves linear-oblong with a pointed white tip. Flowers in lax corymbs. Petals yellow. Habitat: Alpine and sub-alpine zones. Flowers May-July. **4. Sedum litoreum.** A glabrous annual with upright branchlets, 4-15cm. Leaves 5-20mm., obovate-spathulate, flat. Small yellow flowers. Petals and sepals almost same length. Habitat: Rocks and ruins in lowland and littoral zones. Flowers March-May. **5. Sedum praesidis.** Very like 4 but sturdier; flowers slightly bigger, and petals about double the length of sepals. Habitat: Rocky places in montane, sub-montane and lowland zones. Flowers April-May. **6. Sedum rubens.** A 5-12cm. annual, pubescent-glandular towards

Sedum hispanicum

Saxifraga chrysooplonifolia

Ribes uva crispa

Platanus orientalis

top, glaucous or reddish. Leaves 10-20mm., linear, spreading. Flowers white or pink in one-sided racemes. Habitat: Sub-montane, montane, and sub-alpine zones. Flowers April-June. **7. Sedum caespitosum.** Similar to 6 but leaves broadly ovate, and flowers smaller, usually with 4 petals. Habitat: Sub-montane and montane zones. Flowers April-May. **8. Sedum hispanicum.** Annual or biennial, either glabrous or hairy, 7-15cm. Leaves linear, pointed, glaucous-green. Flowers with 6 to 9 segments, in one-sided cymes. Petals 5-7mm., white with a pink midrib. Habitat: Lowland and sub-montane rocks. Flowers April-May. **9. Sedum pallidum.** Similar to 8 but usually glabrous. Flowers 5-segmented, and almost upright pink petals. Habitat: Littoral, lowland, and sub-montane zones. Flowers March-April.

Saxifragaceae Family

Perennials, very seldom annuals. Flowers with 4 or 5 segments, in cymose inflorescences, rarely solitary. Ovary superior. Leaves usually fleshy.

Saxifraga (Saxifrage)

Annual, biennial, or perennial herbs, sometimes with a woody base. Leaves fleshy, simple or lobed. Flowers with 5-lobed calyx, 5 petals and 10 stamens.

1. Saxifraga chrysosplenifolia. Perennial basal leaves orbicular or reniform dentate, long-stalked, forming a rosette. Stem leaves very small, dentate, or palmately-lobed, sessile. Shoots 15-50cm. Flowers in sparse corymbs. Petals 6-11mm., white with red dots. Habitat: Shady montane rocks. Flowers April-May. **2. Saxifraga hederacea.** An annual or biennial plant with slender, spreading or ascending shoots. Leaves small, reniform to ovate, dentate, hairy-glandular. Solitary axillary flowers. White petals, 3mm. Habitat: Wet, shady rocks in montane and sub-montane zones. Flowers April-May. **3. Saxifraga tridactylitis.** Annual with small, trilobate, cuneate leaves. Shoots rarely over 3-8cm. in height. Small white flowers. Habitat: Montane and sub-montane rocks.

Grossulariaceae Family

Deciduous shrublike plants with alternate leaves. 5 segmented flowers in racemes or clusters. Petals free.

Ribes (Gooseberries)

Small shrubs; leaves palmately-lobed, with 3-5 lobes. Petals of flowers small, greenish. Fruit a small berry.

1. Ribes uva-crispa. A 1-1,50m. high shrub, with stout spines at the nodes. Leaves 2-5cm., glabrous or pubescent. Flowers small ones to three. Sepals 5-7mm., either light green or a reddish green. Petals tiny, white. Berry 10mm., green, yellow, or reddish, usually hairy. Habitat: Montane and sub-alpine zones. Flowers April-May.

Platanaceae Family

Trees with small flowers in dense globular inflorescences.

Platanus (Plane-trees)

Leaves large, alternate, palmately-lobed, long-stalked, with stalk wider at its base. Pendulous inflorescences, in ones up to fours along a common hanging pedicel.

1. Platanus orientalis. A large deciduous tree, with a thick trunk and spreading branches. Leaves 5 to 7-lobed, entire or dentate, narrow and deeply dissected, below middle. Habitat: River banks, ravines, and cool sites extending from the littoral to the montane zones. **2. Platanus orientalis - vag. cretica.** The same as the former but an evergreen. Sporadic occurrence in various places at a low altitude. This variety appears only in Crete.

Platanus orientalis

Rosaceae Family

Trees, shrubs or herbaceous plants. Leaves usually alternate, stipuled. Flowers usually 5-6 petalled; stamens usually numerous. Fruit very diversified, one or many-seeded.

Rubus (Blackberries and Brambles)

Perennial shrubs or, more rarely, herbs. Stems usually with prickles. Leaves usually either trifoliate or quintuple. 5-petalled flowers, and 5-lobed calyx. Fruit a head of many, tiny drupes, the well-known blackberries.

1. Rubus ulmifolius. Shrubs with arching, glabrous or pubescent stems which put out roots in autumn. Big prickles either straight or curved, broadly based. Leaves of 3-5 leaflets, dentate, dark green and smooth above; whitish and thickly downy beneath. The terminal leaflet ovate, obovate or nearly orbicular. Inflorescence long and narrow with spreading branchlets. Petals pink. Fruit black, hairy or pubescent. Flowers May-June, bears fruit in autumn. Habitat: Medium to low altitude. Hedges, ditches, gullies. **2. Rubus canescens.** Like 1, but leaves greyish-green and pubescent above, terminal leaflet rhomboid, very pointed; flower-petals whitish-yellow. Two kinds of prickles: small and large. The latter curved. Flowers May-June, and bears fruit in autumn. Habitat: Submontane and montane zones.

Rosa (Wild Roses)

Perennial shrubs, either evergreen or deciduous and usually prickly. Leaves pinnate. Petals and sepals 5, stamens numerous. Calyx urnshaped receptacle, enclosing numerous independent achenes. Fruit fleshy, usually red, which is simply the inflated receptacle.

1. Rosa sempervirens. Evergreen. Long stems with sparse, hooked prickles. Leaves are 5-7 leaflets, ovate-lanceolate, crenate, mucronate and smooth. Flowers 25-45mm. white. Sepals usually entire, ovate, mucronate and glandular. Fruit red 1cm. Habitat: Montane and sub-montane scrub Flowers April-May. **2. Rosa moschata.** Similar to 1, but stems reaching 12m., prickles bigger, leaves not mucronate, and usually downy. The 3 sepals have 2-4 lateral lobes; petals whitish-yellow. A native of the Himalayas and Persia, it has become naturalised in Crete. Flowers April-May. **3. Rosa Canina.** Deciduous. Stems reaching up to 3m. with stout, curved prickles. Leaves made up of 5-7 leaflets, 15-40mm., ovate, obovate or elliptic, crenate and glabrous. Petals pale pink, rarely white. The 3 sepals laterally lobed. Fruit scarlet, smooth, 12-20mm. Habitat: Montane and sub-montane zones. Flowers April-May. **4. Rosa pouzinii.** Similar to 3, but leaflets 15-25mm., with glandular teeth, rachis and stalk. Flower-stalk glandular. Fruit either glandular or glabrous. Habitat: Montane and sub-montane zones. Flowers April-May. **5. Rosa corymbifera (dumetorum).** Similar to 3, but with leaves pubescent underneath. Habitat: Montane and sub-montane zones. Flowers April-May. **6. Rosa heckeliana (orphanidis).** Deciduous, short-stemmed up to 1m. Sparse thorns of two kinds: straight and hooked. Leaves of 5-7 leaflets, disk-like or ovate, downy above, densely hairy beneath. Petals pink. Glandular sepals. Habitat: Montane and sub-alpine zones. Flowers May-June. **7. Rosa glutinosa.** Deciduous. Stems up to 60cm., very prickly, thorns two kinds: big and hooked, or small, fine and straight. Leaves glandular, with 5-7 leaflets. Sepals glandular too. Flowers pink, rarely white. Habitat: Montane and sub-alpine zones. Flowers May-June.

Sarcopoterium (Thorny Burnets)

Prickly shrubs, with two kinds of small flowers, male and female, 4 sepalled and petalled. Leaves very small.

1. Sarcopoterium spinosum. A dense, many-branched spiny shrub, up to 60cm. high. Leaves with 9-15 tiny leaflets. Flowers in a crowded head. The upper flowers female with no petals, the lower male with whitish-yellow petals. Habitat: Dry, stony places of middle and lower zones

Potentilla (Cinquefoils)

Usually perennials. Leaves trifoliate, palmate or pinnate. Flowers with 5 petals, 5 sepals, and 5 subtending bracts.

1. Potentilla reptans. Perennial, with creeping stems 30-100cm., and rooting at nodes.

Rubus ulmifolius

Rosa sempervirens

Rosa canina

Rosa corymbifera

Palmate leaves with 5(-7) obovate or oblong leaflets, dentate or crenate. Solitary, axillary flowers. Yellow petals 8-12mm. Habitat: Damp meadows and places in lowland and littoral zones. Flowers May-July. 2. Potentilla speciosa. Perennial. Trifoliate leaves, green and smooth above, silvery and densely hairy beneath. The rest of plant entirely covered with dense silvery hairs. Petals white or whitish-yellow. Habitat: Rocks of alpine and sub-alpine zones. Flowers May-July.

Pyrus (Pears)

Deciduous trees or shrubs. Simple leaves with caducous stipules. Flowers in corymbs.

93

Ovary inferior. 5 simle sepals. 5 petals, usually white. Fruit pear-shaped or nearly globular.

1. Pyrus amygdaliformis. Small tree up to 6m. Branches often spiny at tips. Leaves narrowly lanceolate or obovate, with sparse hairs when still tender, later almost glabrous. White petals. Fruit yellowish, 2-3cm., almost globular, edible when completely ripe. Habitat: Montane and sub-montane zones. Flowers March-April, bears fruit October-November.

Sorbus (Whitebeams)

Deciduous trees or shrubs. Pinnate, pinnately-lobed on entire leaves. White 5-petalled flowers in corymbose inflorescences. Ovary inferior. Fruit small, fleshy, usually scarlet.

1. Sorbus graeca. Shrub or small tree. Leaves 5-9cm., obovate or almost disk-like, dentate, dark green and smooth above, silvery and hairy beneath. Fruit dark red 10-20mm. Habitat: A rare plant, found in the montane zone. Flowers in May, and bears fruit from September to November.

Eriobotrya (Loquat)

Evergreen trees or shrubs. Leaves simple. Flowers with 5 petals and 5 sepals, and an inferior ovary. Fruit fleshy, big, with 1 or more big seeds.

1. Eriobotrya japonica. Tree reaching 10m. in height. Leaves 12-25cm., obovate or elliptic, dentate, glabrous, dark green above, woolly-haired beneath, hairs brown. Inflorescence hairy, densely clustered. Flowers white 1cm. across. Fruit edible, 3-6cm., yellow, elliptic or pear-shaped, the well-known loquat. Habitat: A Central China native, established in Crete, and often growing subspontaneously there. Flowers in winter.

Amelanchier (Snowy Mespilous)

Shrubs or small deciduous trees, without spines. Simple leaves with caducous stipules. Flowers in apical racemes. Rarely solitary. Narrow petals. 10-20 stamens. Small blackish fruit, with 4-10 seeds. Ovary inferior.

1. Amelanchier ovalis - var. cretica. Shrub up to 2m. Ovate or obovate leaves, 2,5-3,5cm., more or less round at tip, woolly-haired beneath. Racemes hairy, with 3-8 flowers. White petals. Habitat: Montane zone. Flowers in spring.

Cotoneaster (Cotoneasters)

Shrubs without spines. Leaves entire, stipules caducous. Flowers small, white or pink, with 20 stamens and 5 petals. Ovary inferior. Small fleshy fruit, usually red.

1. Cotoneaster nummularia. Deciduous shrub, growing to a height of 1,50m. Leaves either nearly disk-like or broadly elliptic, sparsely haired on top when they first come out, thickly haired and silvery beneath. 3-7 flowered inflorescences. Hairy calyx. Small pink petals. Round fruit, 8mm., red, pubescent at first and then smooth. It is an Asiatic and N. African species that grows in no other European country except in Crete. The Cretan plants have pink flowers while those of the other regions bear white ones. Habitat: Montane zone. Flowers in spring.

Rosa heckeliana

Rosa glutinosa

Potentilla speciosa

Pyrus amygdaliformis

Crataegus (Hawthorns)

Deciduous shrubs, usually thorny. Leaves stipuled, usually pinnately-lobed with dentate lobes. 5 obovate petals, usually white and small. Fruit a small red drupe, more rarely yellow or black.

1. Crataegus azarolus. Shrub up to 5m., with pubescent stems. Leaves 30-50mm., cuneate at base, with 3-5 lobes, almost entire, pubescent on both sides. Crenate, sickle-shaped (falcate) stipules. Flowers white in crowded corymbs. Fruit 20-25mm., orange-coloured, edible. Habitat: Montane and sub-montane zones. Flowers in spring. **2. Crataegus laciniata - subsp. laciniata.** Like 1, but densely hairy. Leaves 20-30mm., densely haired, with 3-7 lobes, dentate at tip. Fruit 15-20mm., reddish, at first covered with white down. Habitat: Montane zone. Flowers in spring. **3. Crataegus heldreichii.** Similar to 1 and 2, but fruit 7mm., red; hairy leaves 3-7 lobed, crenate at tip. Base of leaves not cuneate. Habitat: Montane zone. Flowers in spring. **4. Crataegus monogyna - subsp. azarella.** Similar to previous species, but leaves smaller, 12-30mm., pubescent at first, smooth with few hairs later, 3-5(-7) lobed. Hairy inflorescence. Fruit 7-10mm., deep red. Habitat: Rocky, mountainous places. Flowers in spring.

Prunus (Wild Cherries Wild Plums, and Almond Trees)

Trees or shrubs with simple leaves, dentate or crenate. Caducous stipules. 5-petalled flowers, singly or in inflorescences, of various shapes. Fruit drupe with large stone.

1. Prunus prostrata. A deciduous, creeping dwarf shrub. Leaves ovate-elliptic to linear-oblong, 9-12mm. long. Flowers small, pink, usually solitary. Fruit red, 8mm. Habitat: Montane and sub-montane zones. Flowers April-May. **2. Prunus webbii.** A shrub up to 1.50m. Flowers solitary or in twos, dark pink, 20mm. Fruit 20-25mm., greenish, thickly pubescent. Leaves very oblong. Habitat: Montane and sub-montane zones. Flowers March-April.

In Crete there are 3 more species of the Prunus genus which have been introduced from Asia for cultivation and have become so naturalised that they often grow subspontaneously. These are: the **Almond-tree (Prunus dulcis),** the **Peach-tree (Prunus persica),** and the **Apricot-tree (Prunus armeniaca).**

Leguminosae Family

Trees, shrubs or herbaceous plants. Leaves usually alternate, simple, trifoliate, pinnate or bipinnate, with stipules at their base. Quintuple flowers, usually zygomorphic, more rarely wheel-shaped. Fruit a pod with 1 or many seeds.

Cercis (Judas trees)

Small, deciduous trees or shrubs. Leaves entire. Calyx bell-shaped, with 5 teeth alike. Zygomorphic corolla. The 3 upper petals much smaller than the 2 lower ones. Stamens 10. Oblong pods, flat, many-seeded.

1. Cercis siliquastrum. Small tree with orbicular leaves, 7-12cm., cordate at base, glabrous. Flowers 18-25mm., rose-purple, appearing on previous year's branches, or even on older ones. Pods: reddish-brown, smooth, 6-10cm. Habitat: Montane and sub-montane zones. Flowers March-April.

Ceratonia (Carobs. or Locust-trees)

Evergreen trees, usually dioecious with pinnate leaves. Flowers in small racemes, and without petals. Large, fleshy, sweet pod.

1. Ceratonia siliqua. Tree reaching 10m. height. Leaves pinnate with 2-5 pairs of leaflets, usually without terminal leaflet. Leaflets elliptic or obovate, 30-50mm., smooth, light green beneath, dark green above. Small flowers, green, the male flowers with 5 stamens. Both self-growing and cultivated on the island. Habitat: Sub-montane and lowland zones. Flowers in autumn, and bears fruit at the end of following summer.

Sorbus graeca

Crataegus heldreichii

Crataegus monogyna - s. sp. azarella

Prunus prostrata

Anagyris

Shrubs with trifoliate leaves and fused stipules - opposite to leaves. Flowers zygomorphic, papilionaceous. The upper petal (standard) reflexed, the side petals (wings) straight towards the front, and the lower 2 straight, forming a keel. Pod slightly fleshy, large, constricted between the seeds.

1. Anagyris foetida. A shrub up to 4m., with an unpleasant small. Leaves with leaflets elliptic or lanceolate, 30-70mm. Corolla 18-25mm., yellowish or greenish, with standard smaller than the other petals, and with a black blotch. Pod 10-20cm. Habitat: Sub-montane and lowland zones. Flowers December-March.

Calicotome

Thorny shrubs. Leaves small, trifoliate. Flowers, 1 or many, in the axils of the leaves.

1. Calicotome villosa. Small, densely-branched shrub. The new branches, the calyx, and the underside of leaves densely hairy. Flowers small, yellow 2-15. Habitat: Bare stony sites at a low altitude. Flowers March-April.

Chamaecytisus

Shrubs without thorns or with thorny side branches. Leaves trifoliate. Flowers papilionaceous, usually yellow, in ones or many. Inflorescences racemose or head-shaped, surrounded at lower part by leaves. Calyx bilabiate. Pod slightly compressed, black.

1. Chamaecytisus creticus. Up to 30cm., many-branched, with smooth branches, the lateral ones being thorny. Leaflets obovate, 3-7mm., with dense adpressed hairs beneath. Flowers small, yellow, solitary. Pod black, covered with dense, white hairs. Endemic to Crete. Habitat: Dry, rocky sites at a low altitude. Flowers February-March. **2. Chamaecytisus subidaeus.** Similar to 1, but up to 150cm. Stems pubescent. Leaflets with grey down on the under side, up to 11mm. Calyx pubescent. Pod with adpressed down. Endemic to Crete. Habitat: Rocky sites in sub-montane zone. Flowers February-April.

Genista (Brooms or Needle Furzes)

Shrubs, either thorny or not. Leaves simple or trifoliate, often caducous. Stipules small or absent. Flowers papilionaceous, in heads or racemes, rarely solitary. Calyx bilabiate. Corolla yellow. Pods with one or more seeds.

1. Genista acanthoclada. A plant with crowded branches, prickly at tip. Lateral branches opposite. Leaves trifoliate, with narrow leaflets, 5-10mm. Flowers small, growing near the tip of the branches. Habitat: Dry, stony places at a low altitude. Flowers April-May.

Spartium

Shrubs with green branches, without leaves, or rarely with small, simple or trifoliate leaves. Flowers large, yellow, papilionaceous in many-flowered racemes. Pod small, oblong, with many seeds.

1. Spartium junceum. Shrub up to 3m. Leaves absent or when existing, very few and small. Flowers 20-25mm., scented. Habitat: Montane and submontane zones. Flowers May-June.

Lupinus (Lupins)

Herbaceous plants, usually annual. Leaves palmate, long-stalked. Stem simple, ending in a many-flowered raceme. Flowers papilionaceous with bilabiate calyx.

1. Lupinus albus - subsp. albus. A hairy annual, up to 100cm. Lower leaves with obovate leaflets, 25-35mm. Upper leaves with leaflets 40-50mm., obovate - cuneate, almost glabrous above and hairy on the beneath. Racemes 5-10cm. Flowers alternate, with corolla white, with keel blue at apex. Pods 80-100cm. with large light-coloured seeds.

Cercis siliquastrum

Ceratonia siliqua (male flowers)

Calycotome villosa

Lupinus albus - s. sp. albus

Cultivated of old for its seeds, and today naturalised on the island. Habitat: Lowland and sub-montane zones. Flowers March-April. **2. Lupinus albus - subsp. graecus.** Similar to 1, but with dark blue flowers, pods smaller, seeds dark and racemes larger. Habitat: Sub-montane and lowland zones. Flowers March-April. **3. Lupinus angustifolius. Similar** to 1 and 2, but smaller, 20-80cm., with leaves and flowers smaller. Flowers blue. Racemes 10-20cm , with alternate flowers. Habitat: Sub-montane and lowland zones. Flowers March-April. **4. Lupinus micranthus.** Similar to the previous plants, but smaller, 10-40cm. Flowers blue, the lower alternate, the others in whorls. Habitat: Sub-montane and lowland zones. Flowers March-April. **5. Lupinus varius - subsp. orientalis.** Similar to 4, but larger, up to

50cm. All the flowers whorled. Flowers larger, blue, with tip of wings creamish or pale purple. Habitat: Sub-montane and lowland zones. Flowers March-April.

Astragalus (Milk Vetches)

Annual or perennial herbs or small shrubs. Leaves pinnate, often ending in a terminal prickle. Stipules persistent. Flowers papilionaceous in racemes or axillary clusters. Pod very varied in size and shape, with 1 or more seeds. Calyx with 5, almost identical, teeth.

Group A. Annual plants, with leaves ending in a terminal leaflet and not in a prickle.**1. Astragalus boeticus.** Stems up to 60cm., erect. Leaves 5-20cm., with 10-15 pairs of lateral leaflets. Leaflets oblong-obovate, truncate or slightly bilobed at tip, sparsely hairy only on underside. Flowers yellow, about 8mm., in dense racemes. Pod 20-40cm., smooth. Habitat: Sandy tracts near the sea. Flowers March-April. **2. Astragalus peregrinus.** Similar to 1, but a sturdier, creeping plant with smaller leaves, 3-10cm., and with 8-10 pairs of lateral leaflets. Sparse racemes, with larger white flowers. Pod 40-60mm. A plant of N. Africa, it occurs only on Koufonisi Island. Flowers March-April. **3. Astragalus haarbachii.** Annual, but sometimes perennial with dense hairs. Stem 5-50cm., spreading or ascending. Leaves 4-10cm., with 8-12 pairs of lateral leaflets. Flowers yellowish, 25-30mm. long, in dense racemes of 7-18 flowers. Pods hairy. Habitat: Sub-montane and lowland zones. Flowers March-May. **4. Astragalus sinaicus.** Similar to 3, but smaller, up to 10cm. Leaves 3-8cm., with 7-10 pairs of lateral leaflets. Flowers 10mm. long, violet coloured. Racemes with 4-6 flowers. Habitat: Sub-montane and lowland zones. Flowers February-April. **5. Astragalus echinatus.** Stems up to 60cm., ascending. Leaves 4-8cm., with 6-9 pairs of lateral leaflets. Leaflets obovate, hairy only on the underside. Stems, inflorescence peduncles and stalks hairy. Flowers purple 10-12mm., in dense head-shaped racemes. Pod hairy. Habitat: Sub-montane and lowland zones. Flowers March-April. **6. Astragalus epiglotis - subsp. epiglotis.** Stems 5-25cm., ascending. Leaves 2-4cm. Leaflets small, in 5-7 pairs, hairy on both sides. Flowers yellow, small, in dense inflorescences with short peduncle. Pods 7-9mm., ovate-triangular, hairy. Habitat: Sub-montane and lowland zones. Flowers February-April. **7. Astragalus hamosus.** Stems up to 60cm. Leaves 5-10cm. with 9-11 pairs of lateral leaflets. Leaflets hairy beneath. Flowers 8mm., yellow. Crowded inflorescences. Pods smooth, falciformly upcurved. Habitat: Bare sites at a low altitude. Flowers March-April.

Group B. Perennial plants, with leaves ending in a terminal leaflet, not in a prickle.

1. Astragalus depressus. An almost glabrous plant, without stems or else with short ones, up to 10cm., spreading. Leaves 2-30cm., with 8-14 pairs of lateral leaflets. Leaflets obovate or obcordate, with adpressed hairs, only on underside. Racemes oblong with 6-14 flowers, 10-12mm., whitish or bluish-purple. Pod straight with adpressed hairs or almost smooth. Habitat: Montane zone. Flowers April-May. **2. Astragalis nummularius.** Similar to 1 but hairy. Leaflets ovate or almost orbicular densely hairy. Racemes almost sessile, with yellow flowers. Pods hairy. Habitat: Montane and sub-montane zones. Flowers May-June. **3. Astragalus angustifolius - subsp. angustifolius.** A dense, dwarf, cushion-like shrub. Stems numerous, woody at base. Leaves 2,5-4cm., with 6-10 pairs of lateral leaflets. Rachis of leaves hard, bending with difficulty, like a prickly needle, but with a terminal leaflet. Flowers white, 13-23mm., 3-8 in racemes with short peduncle. Habitat: Alpine and sub-alpine zones. Flowers May-June. **4. Astragalus idaeus.** A plant with almost no stem. Leaves 3-8cm. Leaflets in 3-5 pairs, densely hairy. Flowers yellow, in dense head-shaped racemes, with short pedicels. Habitat: Alpine and subalpine zones. Flowers May-June.

Lupinus albus - s. sp. graecus

Lupinus angustifolius

Lupinus micranthus

Astragalus angustifolius - s.sp. angustifolius

Group C. Perennial plants, woody at base. Leaves ending in a terminal prickle.

1. Astragalus creticus - subsp. creticus. A densely-branched, dwarf shrub, forming cushions. Leaves 2-5cm., with 6-7 pairs of leaflets. Leaflets linear-lanceolate, densely hairy. Flowers yellow, 10-12mm., in pairs, in the axils of leaves. Habitat: Alpine and subalpine zones. Flowers May-June.

Biserrula

Annual plants, similar to Astragalus. Leaves pinnate. Stipules small. Flowers in axillary racemes. Pod oblong, with many seeds, flattened, with an undulate-crenate margin.

1. Biserrula pelecinus. Stems 10-40cm., pubescent. Leaves with 7-15 pairs of oblong or obovate leaflets. Flowers small, blue or yellowish, in head-like racemes.

Glycyrrhiza (Liquorice)

Perennial herbaceous plants, more or less glandular and often viscid. Leaves pinnate, with terminal leaflet (imparipinnate). Stipules membranous caducous. Flowers papilionaceous. Pod oblong-flattened.

1. Glycyrrhiza glabra. Roots cylindrical, branched, fleshy, almost woody, 1-2m. long. Stems pubescent, 50-100cm. Leaves with 9-17 pairs of elliptic or oblong leaflets. Leaflets often viscid. Flowers lilac-coloured, 8-12mm. in multi-flowered oblong racemes. Habitat: Arid open spaces at a low altitude. Flowers in the spring. A self-seeding plant, also cultivated for its roots. The blackish extract known as liquorice is used for ailments of the respiratory system, and also for flavouring drinks, beer etc. For this purpose it is cultivated in many lands. **2. Clycyrrhiza echinata.** Similar to 1, but leaves with 5-13 leaflets. Flowers 4-6mm., blue. Racemes capitate. Root similar to 1 with the same uses, but of inferior quality. Habitat: Sub-montane and lowland zones. Flowers springtime.

Psoralea (Pitch Trefoil)

Perennial plants, with trifoliate long-stalked leaves, and small stipules. Flowers in axillary heads or racemes, with one pair of tripartite bracts at base. Calyx with 5 identical teeth. Corolla papilionaceous. Pod with one seed.

Psoralea bituminosa. Numerous pubescent stems, 20-100cm. Leaflets 10-60mm., lanceolate, ovate, or ovate-orbicular. Flowers in heads with long pedicels. Corolla bluish-violet, 15-20mm. Habitat: Montane and sub-montane zones. Flowers: April-May. This plant was used in the past as a treatment for epilepsy.

Cicer (Chick-peas)

Annual or perennial herbs with glandular hairs. Leaves pinnate, imparipinnate, or ending in a tendril. Solitary, papilionaceous flowers arising from the axils of the leaves. Saccate calyx usually bilabiate. Pod contains 1 to 4 seeds - the well-known chick-peas.

1. Cicer incisum. A creeping or climbing perennial plant, 10-30cm. high. Leaves imparipinnate, without tendrils, and with 1-3 pairs of lateral 3 or 5 - lobed leaflets. Stipules ovate, dentate. Flowers violet-coloured. Pod contains 1-2 seeds. Habitat: Dry and stony localities. Flowers April-May.

Vicia (Vetches)

Annual or perennial herbs, often climbers. Leaves pinnate without a terminal leaflet, with or without tendrils. Flowers papilionaceous, arising from the axils of the leaves, numerous or singly. Calyx bilabiate.

Group A. Flowers numerous in oblong axillary racemes, with long pedicels. Leaves with many leaflets, usually more than 5 pairs.

1. Vicia pinetorum. A 30-50cm. pubescent perennial. Leaves with 10-16 pairs of leaflets, terminating with a branched tendril at tip. Leaflets elliptic-lanceolate and pointed.

Vicia pinetorum

Vicia pubescens

Vicia sativa - s. sp. sativa

Vicia lutea - s. sp. lutea

Racemes bearing 8 to 20 yellowish flowers, 12-20mm. long. Dark brown pod 15-18mm. in length. Endemic to Southern Greece and Crete. Habitat: Montane zone. Flowers April-May. **2. Vicia dalmatica.** Similar to 1 but leaflets narrow, linear, in 5-13 pairs, and flowers pink or pinkish-violet. Habitat: Both fallow and cultivated fields in sub-montane and lowland zones. Flowers March-April. **3. Vicia sibthorpii.** Similar to 1 but densely hairy, and with 6-12 pairs of elliptic leaflets on each leaf. Flowers blue-violet. Habitat: Cultivated as well as uncultivated fields at a low altitude. Flowers March-April. **4. Vicia villosa - subspecies villosa.** Similar to 1, but annual, hairy, and up to 150cm. Leaves with 4-12 narrow leaflets, 10-35mm. long. Racemes have 10-30 flowers, violet, blue or variegated. Pod smooth. Habitat: Both cultivated and uncultivated ground in the sub-montane and montane zones. Flowers March-April. **5. Vicia villosa - subsp. eriocarpa.** Similar to 4 but glabrous. Leaves smaller with leaflets up to 15mm. Racemes with 5-20 smaller flowers, two-coloured with the upper petal (standard) purple and the lateral petals (wings) violet-coloured. Pod downy. Habitat: Sub-montane and lowland zones. Flowers February-April. **6. Vicia villosa - subsp. microphylla.** Resembles 4 but is smooth and has smaller leaves; leaflets up to 10mm., and racemes with 2-6 flowers only. Pod glabrous. Habitat: Sub-montane and lowland zones. Flowers February-April. **7. Vicia cretica - subsp. cretica.** Pubescent annual plant, 10-30cm. Leaves with 1 to 6 pairs of linear or elliptic leaflets, 4-10mm. long. Stipules entire. Racemes with 1-6 flowers. Corolla 9-16mm., white or yellowish, with purple at the edge of petals. Pod glabrous. Habitat: Sub-montne and lowland zones. Flowers February-March.

Group B. Plants similar to those of Group A, but with few-flowered racemes.

1. Vicia ervillia. An either glabrous or pubescent annual, 15-20cm. Leaves are without tendrils at tip and have 8-15 pairs of narrow leaflets. The stipules are entire or else palmately-lobed. Racemes with 1-4 small, white flowers flushed with pink. The 10-30mm. pod is yellow and smooth. Habitat: Sub-montane and lowland zones. Flowers February-April. **2. Vicia pubescens.** Similar to 1 but always pubescent. Leaves with simple tendril and only 3-5 pairs of leaflets. Racemes with more flowers - up to 6 - pink or pale blue. Pod pubescent. Habitat: Barren localities of lowland and sub-montane zones. Flowers February-April.

Group C. Flowers single or just a few, sessile or almost so, arising from the axils of the leaves. Leaves usually with more than 3 pairs of leaflets.

1. Vicia sativa - subsp. sativa. A pubescent annual reaching up to 80cm. in height. Leaves with 3-8 pairs of leaflets which are oblong, wedge-shaped at base, and with a tripartirte tendril at tip. Flowers 18-30mm. from 1 to 4, growing in the axils of the leaves. Corolla with violet-coloured standard and purple wings. Hairy pod. Habitat: Sub-montane and lowland zones. Flowers March-May. **2. Vicia sativa - subsp. amphicarpa.** Similar to 1 but with underground shoots bearing small apetalous flowers that develop into pods containing 1-2 seeds. Leaflets narrower. Flowers with a dark purple standard and much darker wings. Habitat: Sub-montane and lowlanc zones. Flowers February-April. **3. Vicia sativa - subsp. nigra.** Very like 1 but has smaller flowers, 10-18mm., and its standard is pale purple while the wings are only slightly darker. The smooth pod is black or dark brown. Habitat: Sub-montane and lowland zones. Flowers March-April. **4. Vicia lathyroides.** The pubescent leaves have simple tendrils and 2-4 pairs of elliptic or linear leaflets. Solitary purple flowers, 5-8mm. Pod smooth and black. Habitat: A common plant in the sub-montane and lowland zones. Flowers March-April. **5. Vicia peregrina.** Pubescent, annual, up to 100cm. Leaves with 3-7 pairs of leaflets terminating in 3 teeth at tip. Tendrils tripartite. Flowers single or in twos, 10-16mm., purple. Pod brown, pubescent. Habitat: Sub-montane and lowland zones. Flowers March-May. **6. Vicia lutea - subsp. lutea.** Like 5 and 6 but with entire leaflets pointed at tip, pale yellow flowers and hairy pods. Habitat: Sub-montane and lowland zones. Flowers March-May. **7. Vicia hybrida.** Resembling 5 and 6 but with obovate leaflets. Flowers pale yellow or purple. Standard pubescent at margins. Pod brown and pubescent. Habitat: Lowland and sub-montane zones. Flowers March-April.

Group D. Flowers 1-3, in axils of leaves. Leaves large with 1-3 pairs of leaflets.

1. Vicia bithynica. Glabrous or pubescent, annual, 20-60cm. high. Leaves with 2-3 pairs of leaflets, 20-50mm., and with tripartite tendrils. Stipules dentate. 1-3 flowers. Corolla 16-20mm. with purple standard and white wings. Brown or yellow, pubescent pod, 25-60mm. Habitat: Lowland and sub-montane zones. Flowers February-March. **2. Vicia faba.** Similar to 1 but taller, the leaves without tendrils, and the corolla with a white standard and black wings. Pods, 80-200mm., containing large seeds, the well-known "broad beans". It is both

Vicia bithynica

Vicia faba

Lathyrus laxiflorus

Lathyrus grandiflorus

a cultivated plant and a self-seeding established one. The natural sub-spontaneous plants are in general smaller, so are also the flowers and pods. The author has come across such plants in various localities on the island, in the sub-montane and lowland zones. Flowers February-March.

Lens (Lentils)

Plants similar to Vicia but the calyx of their flowers is not bilabiate, and the teeth are at least double the size of the tube. Seeds lentil-shaped.

1. Lens nigricans. Annual, 10-30cm. high, and pubescent. Leaves have 2-5 pairs of linear or oblong leaflets, with a small simple tendril at the tip. Flowers in racemes of 1-3 flowers. Corolla small, pale blue or lilac. Pod smooth. Habitat: Uncultivated ground and barren regions at a low altitude. Flowers March-April. **2. Lens ervoides.** Resembling 1 but leaflets linear-elliptic, corolla always blue, and pod pubescent. Habitat: Barren regions at a low altitude. Flowers March-April.

Lathyrus (Peas and vetchlings)

Annual or perennial herbaceous plants, often climbing. Leaves usually pinnate ending in a tendril or without one. Occasionally the leaves lack leaflets and have only the central vein and the tendril and large, leaf-like stipules, while at other times their central vein is broadened out into the form of a simple leaf (phyllode). The papilionaceous flowers are either in racemes or else solitary, but always axillary.

Group A. Flowers in long-stalked racemes. Leaves pinnate without tendrils or only with the upper ones having simple tendrils.

1. Lathyrus laxiflorus. A pubescent or glabrous perennial. Stem 30-80cm. Leaves with 1 pair of lanceolate or almost orbicular pointed leaflets, 20-40mm. Stipules large, almost the same as the leaflets. Racemes with 2-6 flowers. Corolla, 15-20mm., blue-violet. Pods pubescent, 30-40mm. Habitat: Montane zone. Flowers May-June. **2. Lathyrus neurolobus.** Resembles 1 but the stems are winged, the leaves is smaller, and the stipules much smaller than the leaflets. Upper leaves with simple tendrils. Racemes with 1-2 small blue flowers. Endemic to Western Crete. Habitat: Mountain gullies.

Group B. Flowers 1-5. The leaves are pinnate and have always simple or branched tendrils.

1. Lathyrus grandiflorus. Pubescent perennials with stems 30-150cm. high. Leaves with 1 pair (rarely 2-3 pairs) of ovate leaflets, 25-50mm long. Stipules linear, 2-10mm. Tendrils tripartite. Raceme with 1-4 large flowers, 25-30mm. Corolla with a pink standard and purple wings Pods 60-90mm. long, smooth. Habitat: Montane zone. Flowers May-June. **2. Lathyrus sphaericus.** A 20-50cm. tall annual. Leaves with a single pair of linear leaflets and a simple tendril. Flowers solitary, orange-red, 6-13mm. Pod hairless. Stipules like leaflets linear. Habitat: To be found in both cultivated and uncultivated fields of sub-montane and lowland zones. Flowers March-April. **3. Lathyrus angulatus.** Similar to 2 but corolla is purple or pale blue, and tendrils are tripartite. Habitat: In the lower zone. Flowers March-April. **4. Lathyrus setifolius.** Similar to 1 and 2 but the leaflets as well as the stipules are much narrower, almost thread-like. Leaf-stalks very small. Corolla orange-red. Tendrils tripartite. **5. Lathyrus cicera.** Similar to 2 but leaves have tripartite tendrils, and the corolla is a blackish-crimson. Habitat: Sub-montane and lowland zones. Flowers March-April. **6. Lathyrus sativus.** Similar to 2 but larger, and tendrils either tripartite or quinquepartite. Flowers 12-24mm., white, blue or pink. Habitat: It is both cultivated and self-seeding in the sub-montane and lowland zones. Flowers March-April. Lathyrus sativus is a well-known forage crop, commonly called 'chickling pea'. **7. Lathyrus annuus.** Similar to 2 but a sturdy plant, reaching from 40 to 150cm. in height. Linear leaflets 50-150mm. Leaves with tripartite or quinquepartite tendrils. Flowers 12-18mm., either single or in bunches of 2 or 3, yellow or golden-yellow in colour. Pod 30-80mm. Habitat: Occurs in cultivated fields. Flowers April-May. **8. Lathyrus hierosolimitanus.** Similar to 7 but pinkish-yellow flowers 7-12mm. The pod is smaller, too. Habitat: Sub-montane and lowland zones. Flowers March-April. **9. Lathyrus clymenum.** A hairless perennial. Leaves bear 2-4 pairs of leaflets; rachis broadened and winged. The lower leaves without leaflets. Tendrils tripartite. Flowers 154-20mm. single or in bunches up to 5 flowers standard blackish-crimson and violet wings. Habitat: Sandy ground at a low altitude. Flowers April-May. 10. Lathyrus articulatus. Similar to 9 but leaflets narrower, and corolla with white or pink wings. Habitat: Uncultivated tracts at a low altitude. Flowers April-May. **11. Lathyrus ochrus.** Similar to 9 but the rachis of the lower leaves, which have no leaflets, is greatly

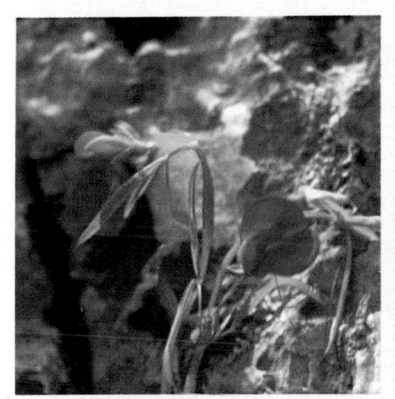

Lathyrus sphaericus

Ononis natrix - s. sp. natrix

Ononis reclinata

Ononis spinosa - s. sp. antiquorum

broadened and ovate-oblong so that it resembles a leaf. White and ovate. The pale yellow flowers are in ones or twos. Habitat: Found at a low altitude. Flowers April-May.

Group C. Flowers solitary. Leaves pinnate and lacking tendrils.

1. Lathyrus saxatilis. A pubescent annual plant with stem 10-30cm. Leaves are small with 1-3 pairs of leaflets which, on the lower leaves, are obcordate with 3 teeth at tip. Those of the other leaves are linear. Flowers, 6-9mm., pale blue or yellowish. Pod not hairy. Habitat: Dry locations at a low altitude. Flowers March-April.

Group D. Flowers solitary. Leaves consist of only one tendril. Stipules large and leaf-like.

1. Lathyrus aphaca. Glabrous, annual. Flowers small and yellow. Stipules ovate. Habitat: Fields at a low altitude. Flowers February-April.

107

Ononis (Restharrows)

Annual or perennial plants with papilionaceous flowers. Leaves trifoliate, sometimes trilobate or simple. Leaflets dentate. Stipules fused with stalk except at tips. Inflorescences racemose, spike-like, or cymose. Calyx 5-lobed.

1. Ononis natrix - subsp. natrix. Dwarf shrub with crowded, erect branches, 20-60cm. covered with dense glandular hairs. Leaves trifoliate with 12-20mm. long leaflets. Corolla 12-20mm., yellow and often with red or violet veins. Pod 12-25mm. Habitat: Seaboard and lowland areas. Flowers March-May. **2. Ononis reclinata.** A 2-15cm. creeping annual. Stem with glandular hairs. Leaves trifoliate, leaflets 5-8mm. Corolla 5-10mm., pink or purple. Habitat: Dry situations at a low altitude. Flowers March-April. **3. Ononis verae.** Similar to 2 but with stems ascending, rather erect, and simple, hairy-glandular leaves, the lower orbicular and the upper linear. Corolla 10-12mm. Endemic to Crete. Habitat: Submontane and lowland zones. Flowers April-May. **4. Ononis pubescens.** An annual hairy-glandular plant, 15-35cm. high. Upper and lower leaves simple, middle ones trifoliate. Dense inflorescence with yellow flowers, 15mm long. Pod 8-10mm. Habitat: Uncultivated ground at a low altitude. Flowers April-May. **5. Ononis viscosa - subsp. sieberi.** An erect annual with simple or trifoliate leaves. Single flowers arising from the axils of upper leaves on pedicels terminating in an arista. Yellow corolla up to 12mm. Frequently, the standard is pink. Pod a little longer than calyx. Habitat: Low altitude hills. Flowers March-April. **6. Ononis viscosa - subsp. breviflora.** Similar to 5 but flowers smaller and always yellow. Corolla smaller than calyx. Pod double the size of calyx. Habitat: Low altitude sites. Flowers March-April. **7. Ononis spinosa - subsp. antiquorum.** A perennial thorny shrub. Young stems hairy. Leaves trifoliate. Flowers pink. Corolla 6-10mm. Habitat: Uncultivated localities in sub-montane and montane zones. Flowers April-June. **8. Ononis variegata.** An annual with 10-30cm. long ascending stems. Simple leaves 5-10mm. Sparse flowers at apex of stems. Corolla yellow, 12-14mm. Calyx much smaller than corolla. Habitat: Sandy, coastal situations. Flowers March-April. **9. Ononis diffusa.** An annual with trifoliate leaves and hairy-glandular stems, spreading or ascending. Pink flowers in crowded racemes at apex of stems. Habitat: Sandy coasts. Flowers March-April. **10. Ononis mitissima.** Erect or ascending, pubescent or almost hairless, with stems 15-60cm. high. Leaves trifoliate, the upper ones are without leaflets but only with the membraneous middle vein. Flowers in dense apical racemes. Corolla pink, 10-12mm. Habitat: Uncultivated ground in montane and sub-montane zones. Flowers April-May.

Trigonella (Fenugreeks)

Annual plants with trifoliate leaves. Leaflets usually dentate. Flowers solitary in either axillary heads or racemes. Pods usually linear or oblong.

Group A. Flowers in crowded racemes.

1. Trigonella balansae. Stems 10-55cm., spreading or ascending. Leaflets 10-40mm., obovate, dentate. Flowers in axillary capitate racemes, long-stalked. Racemes bear from 8 to 16 golden-yellow flowers. Corolla 7-8mm. Pods up to 16mm., upcurved. Habitat: Hills and uncultivated fields at a low altitude. Flowers March-April. **2. Trigonella corniculata.** Very similar to 1 but stems are more slender, the flowers lemon-yellow, and racemes slightly elongated. Pods smaller and less upcurved. The existence of this species in Crete is cited but with reservations. Habitat: Montane and sub-montane zones. **3. Trigonella rechingeri.** Similar to 1 and 2 but smaller (3-20cm.), and with smaller leaflets (7-10mm.). Flowers lemon-yellow, in bunches of 6-10. Pods oblong, pendulous. Endemic to the South Aegean area. Habitat: To be found on sea-cliffs. Flowers March-April. **4. Trigonella cretica.** Resembles the previous plants but its leaflets are wedge-shaped at base, blunt at

Trigonella balansae

tip and slightly fleshy, while its pods are flattened, membraneous, and elliptic discoid. A plant of West Anatolia. Crete is the only spot in the whole of Europe where it occurs. Habitat: Calcareous rocky localities. Flowers April-May. **5. Trigonella monspeliaca.** Pubescent stems up to 35cm. Leaflets 4-10mm., almost entire, obovate-cuneate. Racemes sessile, bearing 4 to 14 flowers. Corolla 4mm., yellow. Pod linear, pendulous, slightly upcurved. Habitat: Stony places at a low altitude. Flowers March-April. **6. Trigonella spinosa.** Similar to 5 but sparsely hairy. Dentate leaflets 5-8mm. Racemes with 4-6 flowers. Pods upcurved and pendulous. Habitat: Stony localities on the islet of Gavdhos. However, in all probability it is to be found on Crete itself as well. Flowers February-April. **7. Trigonella procumbens.** Stems sparsely hairy. Leaves with linoar-lanceolate leaflets. Flowers blue, and in almost spherical racemes. Pods terminate in a

109

narrow, pointed tip. Habitat: Stony uncultivated ground at a low altitude. Flowers March-April.

Group B. Flowers, sessile, in ones or twos.

1. Trigonella foenum - graecum. Stems 10-50cm; sparsely pubescent. Leaflets 20-50mm., obovate or oblong, dentate. Flowers in ones or twos, cream-coloured, base flushed with violet. Pods 60-110mm., linear and somewhat erect. Habitat: Both cultivated and uncultivated ground at a low altitude. Flowers March-May. **2. Trigonella gladiata.** Similar to 1 but a smaller plant, leaflets 5-12mm, cream flowers, and pods ending in a long beak. Habitat: Stony sites at a low altitude. Flowers Februaary-April.

Medicago (Medicks)

Annual or perennial herbaceous plants or shrubs. Leaves trifoliate and stipules persistent. Flowers in axillary racemes, stalked. Calyx with 5 identical teeth. Corolla small. Pod usually coiled into a spiral and, frequently, spiny along outer margin of spiral.

1. Medicago lupulina. A more or less pubescent annual plant, 5-60cm. Leaflets orbicular, obovate or oblong, rounded at tip. Stipules lanceolate or ovate, either dentate or not. Racemes spherical, with 10 to 50 golden-yellow flowers, 2-3mm. Pods kidney-shaped. Habitat: Found on both cultivated and uncultivated land in the montane and submontane zones. Flowers April-October. **2. Medicago sativa - subsp. sativa.** Similar to 1 but leaflets always oblong; flowers violet-coloured; pods coiled into spirals of 1-3 turns. In addition, it is a perennial. Habitat: A cultivated plant but also a subspontaneous one of medium and low altitudes. Flowers June-October. **3. Medicago arborea.** A shrub up to 2m in height that sheds its leaves during the summer. Its leaflets are obovate, entire or dentate, and its racemes small, capitate, bearing 4 to 8 flowers. Corolla yellow, 12-15mm. The pod is coiled into a spiral of 1-1,5 turns. Habitat: Rocky sites at a low altitude. Flowers April-May. **4. Medicago strasseri.** Resembles 3 but is a smaller plant with flowers 9-13mm. Inflorescences with 6-12 flowers and pods in spirals of 1,5-2,5 turns. An endemic to the Rhethymnos region, it was first discovered only in 1981 by Dr. W. Strasser. Habitat: In sub-montane gorge. Flowers April-May. **5. Medicago orbicularis.** Annual, procumbent, 20-90cm. Dentate, obovate-cuneate leaflets. Racemes with 1-5 yellow flowers, 2-5mm. long. Pods with 4-6 turns. Habitat: On both uncultivated and cultivated ground. Flowers April-May. **6. Medicago scutelata.** Similar to 4 but densely pubescent-glandular. Stipules obovate-lanceolate. Racemes with 1-3 flowers, 6-7mm. Pods also, pubescent-glandular with 4-8 turns. Habitat: Arid, stony localities at a low altitude. Flowers April-May. **7. Medicago rugosa.** Similar to 4 but pubescent-glandular, and pods with 2-3 turns. Habitat: Sporadic occurrence on uncultivated ground. Flowers March-May. **8. Medicago marina.** A very leafy perennial densely covered with white hairs. Stems 20-50cm. The obovate leaflets are cuneate at base, and dentate are margin. Head-like racemes bear 5-12 pale yellow flowers, 6-8mm. Woolly pods with 2-3 turns, and with small spines. **9. Medicago truncatula.** Similar to 7 but a sparsely-haired annual. Racemes with 1-3 yellow flowers. Pubescent pods have more turns, and are much more prickly. Habitat: Uncultivated as well as cultivated ground at a low altitude. Flowers April-May. **10. Medicago rigidula.** Similar to 8 but with pod up to 7 turns while leaflets are obovate-obcordate. Habitat: Low altitude cultivated and uncultivated land. Flowers April-May. **11. Medicago litoralis.** A spreading, either hairy or pubescent annual or biennial plant, 10-30cm. high. Leaflets obovate-cuneate. Yellow flowers in bundles of 2-4. Pod hairless, discoid, either without spines or else with only a few sparse ones. Habitat: Sandy seaside localities. Flowers April-May.

Trigonella corniculata

Dorycnium hirsutum

Lotus corniculatus

Lotus stenodon

Dorycnium

Perennials with quinquefoliate leaves, with either a small stalk or else sessile. Stipules very small. Papilionaceous flowers in axillary heads.

1. Dorycnium hirsutum. A small hairy shrub let, 20-50cm. high. Leaves almost sessile. Flowers 10-20mm., white or pale pink; each head bearing 4-10 flowers. Habitat: Montane and sub-montane zones. Flowers April-May.

Lotus (Birdsfoot-trefoils)

Annual or perennial herbs. Leaves with 5 leaflets, the lower pair at the base of the stalk, in the place of stipules. Stipules either very small or absent. Flowers papilionaceous and either single or many in a cluster. Usually there is a trifoliate leaf at the bottom of the inflorescence.

Group A. Flowers yellow or whitish-yellow in clusters. Straight pods. **1. Lotus corniculatus.** A glabrous or pubescent, spreading perennial. Leaves with lanceolate or oblanceolate leaflets. Heads on long pedicels, and with 2-7 yellow flowers, often with red flowers on the same plant. Corolla 10-16mm. Pod straight and narrow, 15-30mm. Habitat: Montane and sub-alpine zones. Flowers April-June. **2. Lotus stenodon.** Similar to 1 but heads with 2-5 flowers, always yellow. Habitat: These plants are found at a low altitude, in damp localities near the sea. Flowers May-July. **3. Lotus uliginosus.** Similar to both former species but stems are from 30 to 100cm., erect or ascending. Leaflets up to 25mm. Heads with 5-15 yellow flowers. Habitat: Swamps and wet meadows at a low and medium altitude. Flowers June-August. **4. Lotus palustris.** Similar to 4 but thickly hairy. Flowers small (6-10mm), yellow or whitish, in few-flowered heads (2-4 flowers). Habitat: Wet meadows and swamps at a low altitude. Flowers May-July. **5. Lotus parviflorus.** A hairy annual up to 40cm. high. Leaflets obovate or oblong-lanceolate. Heads with 3-7 flowers, 5-10mm. yellow. Pod small, 4-6mm. Habitat: Sandy coastal places. Flowers April-May.

Group B. Yellow flowers in head-like inflorescences. Pods more or less curved.

1. Lotus cytisoides. A pubescent perennial up to 50cm. Flowers 2-6. Corolla 8-14mm. Pod slightly curved, 20-50mm. long. Obovate leaflets 4-14mm. Habitat: Rocky coasts. Flowers April-May. **2. Lotus halophilus.** Like 1 but an annual, 10-30cm. high, with small leaflets 3-7mm. Habitat: Sandy ground near the sea. Flowers March-May. **3. Lotus onrithopodiodes.** Similar to 1 but an annual. Leaflets 8-30mm., broader almost rhomboid, cuneate or cordate at base. Heads bear 2-5 flowers, 7-10mm. Pods 20-50mm., fairly curved. **4. Lotus peregrinus.** Like 3 but leaflets 5-15mm., and always cuneate at base. Pod very slightly curved.

Group C. Yellow flowers from 1 to 3.

1. Lotus angustissimus. An annual with shoots ascending or procumbent, up to 50cm. in length. Flowers 1-3, on heads. Corolla 5-12mm., yellow, often streaked with red. Leaves with leaflets oblong-lanceolate. Narrow, straight pod, 15-30mm. long. Habitat: Sandy-clayey ground of lowland and sub-montane zones. Flowers April-May. **2. Lotus edulis.** Similar to 1 but flowers only 1 or 2. Corolla 10-18mm. yellow, and pod 20-40mm., slightly curved upwards. Habitat: Sandy-clayey ground at low altitude. Flowers April-May.

Group D. Flowers white, pink, or purple.

1. Lotus conimbricensis. Annual, glabrous or pubescent, 5-30cm. Obovate or rhomboid leaflets, 4-10mm. long. Flowers single. Corolla 5-8mm., white or pale pink, with a violetcoloured keel. Habitat: Sandy fields near the sea. Flowers March.

Trifolium (Clovers)

Annual, biennial, or perennial herbs. Leaves trifoliate. Stipules persistent. Papilionaceous flowers in heads, racemes, or spikes, rarely solitary. Calyx with 5 identical teeth. Pods small and either the same length as calyx or just a little longer than it.

Group A. Flowers in heads or ovate racemes, with no leaves below inflorescence. Flowers violet, purple, pink, white or creamish but never yellow or orange-coloured.

1. Trifolium repens - subsp. orphanideum. A glabrous perennial with stems either creeping and rooting at nodes or else dense and non-rooting, 1-5cm. long. Leaflets of

Lotus angustissimus

leaves broad, obcordate or obovate, 5-7mm., stalk 10-20mm. Heads with 8-12 pale pink flowers, pedicels of heads 10-20mm. A Greek endemic. Habitat: Montane zone. Flowers May-June. **2. Trifolium hybridum - subsp. elegans.** A hairless perennial with shoots densely branched, spreading or ascending. Globular heads, 16-19mm. Flowers 7-10mm., purple or white, turning pink during maturation. Habitat: Meadows and uncultivated fields of the montane and sub-montane zones. Flowers April-May. **3. Trifolium nigrescens - subsp. nigrescens.** A glabrous spreading annual. Obovate or obcordate leaflets 8-15mm. Stipules triangular-lanceolate, mucronate. Globular heads 10-20mm, sparse, with pedicels longer than stalk of corresponding leaves. Corolla 6-9mm., white, yellowish-white, or pink, turning to brownish during maturation. Pods a little constricted between seeds. Habitat: Uncultivated, rather sandy places, at a low altitude. Flowers April-May. **4.**

Trifolium michelianum. Similar to 3 but sturdier and with erect shoots. Leaflets 10-30mm. oblong or obovate. Leaves with stalk about 70mm. long. Heads 20-25mm. with flowers 8-11mm., pink-coloured. It is mentioned as occurring in pastures of Kissamos region, but its existence has not been confirmed recently. Flowers April-June. **5. Trifolium glomeratum.** A glabrous annual, with many spreading stems, 10-20cm. Leaves with 5-10mm. obovate leaflets. Stipules ovate, mucronate. Heads 8-12mm., dense, globular, sessile or with a small stalk. Pink flowers, 4-5mm. Habitat: Low altitude pasture-lands. Flowers April-May. **6. Trifolium suffocatum.** A rather glabrous, tufted annual. Stems 1-3(-5)cm., spreading. Leaves with obovate-cuneate leaflets, 3-8mm. Leaf stalks 10-60mm. Numerous, 5-6mm., sessile heads. Flowers white, 3-4mm. long. Habitat: Dry sites at a low altitude. Flowers March-April. **7. Trifolium spunosum.** A glabrous annual with 10-30cm. long spreading shoots. 10-20mm., broadly obovate cuneate leaflets. Heads globular-ovate on 10-40mm. pedicules. Pink flowers; inflated calyx. **8. Trifolium vesiculosum.** A glabrous annual with rough stems, 15-50cm. long. Obovate leaflets on lower leaves, oblong-lanceolate on upper ones. Heads 20-60cm. long, globular or ovate. Flowers white in the beginning, pink when mature. Habitat: Dry sites, and montane and sub-montane pastures. Flowers April-May. **9. Trifolium physodes.** Perennial, glabrous, spreading stems 5-25mm. Narrow, mucronate stipules. Ovate or globular heads 15-20mm. Pedicule 10-80mm. Flowers 8-14mm., pink. Swollen calyx. Habitat: Pastures of low and medium altitudes. Flowers April-May. **10. Trifolium rechingeri.** Very similar to 9 but stems, stalks, and stipules hairy; calyx hairy; heads smaller. Habitat: Medium and low altitudes. Flowers April-May. **11. Trifolium sclerorrhizum.** Similar to 9 but hairy, and calices glabrous. Habitat: Middle and low altitudes. Flowers April-May. **12. Trifolium fragiferum - subsp. bonnanii.** A more or less hairy perennial. Stems 10-30cm., spreading, often rooting. Obovate leaflets. Heads of pale pink flowers 15-22mm. small, inflated calices which, when mature, form one solid, swollen head, like a strawberry. Habitat: Pastures in middle and low altitudes. Flowers April-May. **13. Trifolium resupinatum.** A glabrous annual, with ascending or spreading stems. Leaflets obovate-cuneate, 7-20mm. Globular heads, 8-20mm. Small pink flowers. Large calices, inflated, especially during maturation. Habitat: Fallow fields and barren places at a low altitude. Flowers March-April. **14. Trifolium speciosum.** An annual with erect stems, 10-30cm. adpreesed hairy. Leaflets 10-18mm. oblong-elliptic, glabrous or hairy. Heads ovate, lax, up to 30mm. on long peduncles. Habitat: Low altitude. Flowers violet, 8-10mm. Habitat: Lowland and submontane zones. Flowers April-May. **15. Trifolium boissieri.** Like 13 but stems with spreading hairs. head peduncles shorter than stalks of leaves, and flowers whitish-yellow. Habitat: Sub-montane and lowland zones. Flowers March-April. **16. Trifolium lagrangei.** Annual; stems erect or ascending, covered with adpressed hairs. Leaflets obovate or ovate, the middle one with a short stalk at base. Heads globular, dense, 8-15mm. Peduncles of equal length with (or shorter than) that of corresponding leaf. Flowers violet-carmine coloured, 4-6mm. Habitat: Rocky places at low and medium altitudes. Flowers April-May. **17. Trifolium striatum.** A hairy annual. Pink flowers 4-5mm. Flower heads 10-15mm. ovate leaflets obovate-cunate. Habitat: Mainly in sandy places at a low altitude. Flowers March-May. **18. Trifolium scabrum.** Annual. Numerous stems 5-25mm., spreading or ascending. Leaves. with obovate-cuneate leaflets, 5-10mm. Numerous heads, almost sessile, 5-12mm. Flowers white, rarely pink, 4-5mm. Habitat: Low altitude cultivated and uncultivated fields. **19. Trifolium stellatum.** Erect annual, 8-20cm. Leaves have obcordate leaflets, 8-12mm. Globular heads, 15-24mm. Flowers have a tiny pink corolla, and calices with long, spreading teeth, much longer than the corolla, giving the inflorescence the characteristic shape of a prickly ball. Habitat: Uncultivated fields at low and medium altitudes. Flowers March-May. **20. Trifolium dasyurum.** Similar to 18 but more robust, branched above middle, with the two topmost leaves almost opposite. Leaflets are larger, 20-25mm., oblong-elliptic, pointed. Heads 20-35mm., usually in twos. Habitat: Fallow fields at a low altitude. Flowers April-

Trifolium hybridum - s. sp. elegans   *Trifolium nigrescens - s. sp. nigrescens*

Trifolium glomeratum   *Trifolium uniflorum*

May. **21. Trifolium leucanthum.** An annual. Stems covered with thick adpressed hairs. Leaflets of leaves 10-20mm., oblong-cuneate. Inflorescences 10-15mm., globular, often in twos, with 30-120mm. peduncles, covered with adpressed hairs. Pubescent calices. Corolla 6-8mm., white or pink. Habitat: Dry places at a low altitude. Flowers March-April. **22. Trifolium squamosum.** Like 20 but is occasionally almost glabrous, flowers always pale pink, and inflorescence peduncles much shorter. Habitat: Meadows, usually near the sea. Flowers March-April. **23. Trifolium subterraneum.** An annual with numerous, hairy, creeping stems. Leaves with obcordate leaflets. Small inflorescences with few whitish flowers, 8-14mm. Habitat: Sandy sites at a low altitude. Flowers March-April.

Group B. Flowers on headlike or ovate racemes, leaflets below the inflorescence. Flowers always yellow or orange-coloured.

115

1. Trifolium aurantiacum. Annual; few hairy, 8-15cm. shoots; stipules ciliate; leaves with oblong leaflets, cuneate at base. The middle leaflet stalked. Spherical heads, 20-25mm. Flowers 8-9mm., orange-coloured. Endemic to Mainland Greece and Crete. Habitat: Montane, subalpine, and alpine zones. Flowers May-June. **2. Trifolium patens.** A sparsely - haired annual with narrowly elliptic leaflets, and 10-15mm. heads on long peduncles. Flowers golden-yellow. Habitat: Damp pastures of montane and sub-montane zones. Flowers April-May. **3. Trifolium dubium.** A slender-hairy-stemmed annual with obovate or obcordate leaflets up to 11mm. Heads small, 8-9mm. Flowers 3-3,5mm., yellow but turning a brownish-yellow during maturation. Habitat: Sandy pastures at medium altitude. Flowers April-May. **4. Trifolium micranthum.** Similar to 3 but smaller, with leaflets up to 8mm., and heads 4mm. with 1 to 6 flowers. Habitat: Sandy pastures at a low altitude. Flowers March-April.

Group C. Flowers on elongated spikes, leaflets below inflorescence. Flowers a variety of colours.

1. Trifolium arvense. An erect annual with pubescent stems 4-40cm. Leaves with a very small stalk, and leaflets narrow, linear-oblong. Inflorescence oblong up to 20mm. in length. Whitish or pink flowers. Hairy calices with relatively long teeth, giving the inflorescence a characteristically hairy look. Habitat: Sub-montane and lowland zones. Flowers March-April. **2. Trifolium bocconei.** A densely pubescent annual with few branchings. Leaves have oblong-cuneate leaflets. An elongated inflorescence, 9-15mm., crowded, with pink flowers, and a hairy calyx. Habitat: Low altitude pasture-lands, Flowers March-April. **3. Trifolium tenuifolium.** Similar to 2 but many-branched stems, and more spreading. Leaflets of upper leaves linear, flowers pink or a whitish-yellow. Habitat: Low altitude pastures. Flowers March-April. **4. Trifolium incarnatum.** An annual with 1 or more erect stems. Leaves with obovate-cuneate leaflets. Cylindrical inflorescences, 10-40mm. Corolla 10-12mm., red, pink, or whitish-yellow. A hairy calyx with long, pointed teeth that give inflorescence a strikingly spiny appearance. Habitat: Sub-montane, lowland, and maritime zones. Flowers March-May. **5. Trifolium angustifolium.** A flat-haired annual. Leaves with oblong leaflets. Conical-cylindrical inflorescences up to 8cm. Pink flowers, 10-12mm. Habitat: Dry places at a low altitude. Flowers April-May. **6. Trifolium smyrnaeum.** A grey-haired annual with stems 5-20cm. Leaves with 5-10mm. long, obovate-cuneate leaflets. Inflorescence ovate-cylindrical, densely hairy. Pale pink, 7-8mm. corolla. Habitat: Dry places at a low altitude. Flowers March-April.

Group D. Inflorescences clasped at base by 1 or 2 leaves.

1. Trifolium pallidum. Annual or biennial, hairy, with stems 15-40cm. long, usually branching. Leaves with obovate-cuneate or elliptic leaflets. Inflorescences spherical or ovate. Flowers 12mm., whitish or pale pink. Habitat: Cool spots in montane and sub-montane zones. Flowers April-June. **2. Trifolium hirtum.** Similar to 1 but always an annual, hairy with adpressed hairs, leaflets always obovate, and flowers purple and a little larger. Habitat: Barren areas of low altitude. **3. Trifolium cherleri.** Like 1 and 2 but smaller (5-15cm.). Leaflets obcordate-cuneate. Corolla whitish-pink, smaller than calyx. Habitat: Dry sites of lower zone. Flowers March-April.

Group E. Flowers 1 to 3 only.

1. Trifolium uniflorum. A creeping, tufted perennial. Leaflets of leaves rhomboid, discoid, or obovate. Flowers purple, pink, white, or cream, 15-20mm. Habitat: Bare, barren places and meadows in montane and sub-montane zones. Flowers March-May.

Tetragonolobus purpureus

Tetragonolobus (Winged Peas or Dragon's Teeth)

Plants similar to **Lotus** but with trifoliate leaes, and large stipules, almost as long as the leaflets. Flowers single or in twos. Pod with a quadrangular section.

1. Tetragonolobus purpureus. Annual, pubescent, 10-40cm. high. Leaflets obovate-rhomboid up to 40mm. Stipules ovate, pointed. Corolla crimson, 15-25mm. Habitat: Uncultivated fields, and meadows of lowland and sub-montane zones. Flowers: February-April.

Melilotus (Melilots)

Annuals, biennials, or perennials of short duration. Trifoliate leaves with free stipules.

Flowers small, papilionaceous, in axillary racemes. Corolla usually yellow or white. Legumes globular or ovate, seldom lanceolate-rhomboid, 1-2 seeds.

1. Melilotus italica. An erect, branched perennial, 20-60cm. Leaflets of leaves crenate, rounded at tip and cuneate at base. The upper leaves have narrower leaflets. Stipules entire. Racemes 1,5-3cm., with many yellow flowers, 6-9mm. long. Round legumes. Habitat: Bare, arid sites at a low altitude. Flowers April-May. **2. Melilotus neapolitana.** Similar 1 but racemes about 1cm., sparse, with 8-20 flowers Corolla 4-6mm. golden-yellow spherical legums with a conical tip. Habitat: Rocky places at a low altitude. Flowers April-May. **3. Melilotus indica.** Similar to 1 and 2 but leaflets oblong-lanceolate, and racemes many-flowered, flowers 2-3mm., pale yellow. Habitat: Coastal, damp places. Flowers May-June. **4. Melilotus sulcata.** Like the foregoing ones but with oblong leaflets, rounded at tip, dentate stipules, short racemes (1-1,5cm.), lengthening at fruit. Corolla yellow, 3-4mm. Habitat: Sandy places at a low altitude. Flowers April-May. **5. Melilotus segetalis.** Similar to the above species but the lower leaves have entire stipules while the upper ones have dentate stipules. Dentate obovate-cuneate leaflets. Racemes 3cm., dense, with 30-50 flowers. Corolla 4-8mm., yellow. Globular-oblong pod. Habitat: Damp places at a low altitude. Flowers May-June.

Securigera

Papilionaceous flowers on head-like inflorescences, with long pedicels. Pinnate leaves with small stipules. Pods long and slender, linear, ending in a long beak.

1. Securigera securidaca. A glabrous annual, 10-50cm. Leaves bearing 4-7 pairs of lateral leaflets. Leaflets oblong-obovate, blunt at tip. Heads of 4-8 yellow flowers, 8-12mm. long. Pods 5-10cm., slightly curved. Habitat: Low altitude uncultivated and cultivated fields. Flowers April-May.

Anthyllis (Kidney-vetches)

Herbaceous annual, or woody perennial plants. Flowers papilionaceous in crowded heads or, more rarely, in racemes. Calyx campanulate or inflated. Pods tiny, usually enclosed in the calyx.

1. Anthyllis vulneraria - subsp. praepropera. A perennial or annual plant with erect or ascending stems 10-35cm., hairy towards base. Lower leaves usually simple, the others pinnate with 7-13 leaflets. The apical leaflet is larger. All the leaflets are elliptic or ovate, glaucous-green, hairy. Flowers in big clusters with long pedicels, surrounded by leaflike bracts. Calyx hairy; corolla purple or reddish. Habitat: Stony places in montane and submontane zones. Flowers April-June. **2. Anthyllis tetraphylla.** A creeping annual with pubescent-hairy stems and leaves. Leaves pinnate with 5 leaflets or simple. The apical leaflet is largest, obovate. Flowers in sessile small, yellowish. Habitat: Sub-montane hills. Flowers April-May. **3. Anthyllis barba-jovis.** A shrub up to 90cm. with woody branches. Leaves pinnate with 13-19 narrowly elliptic or obovate leaflets, all the same size, green, and sparsely hairy on top, silvery and densely hairy beneath. Flowers in terminal heads of more than 10 flowers, surrounded by palmate bracts. Calyx hairy; corolla yellow. Habitat: Sea cliffs. Flowers May-JUne. **4. Anthyllis aegaea.** Like 3 but leaflets narrower, almost linear, heads with fewer flowers (5-9), and calyx 6,5-9mm. (4-6mm in 3). Habitat: Rocks near sea. Flowers April-May. An endemic of Crete, and the Aegean islands of Amorgos, and Folegandros. **5. Anthyllis hermanniae.** A woody shrub with dense branches inflexed, and covered with white pubescence. Leaves small, the lower ones simple, the others trifoliate, with the lateral leaflets much smaller. Flowers 1-3, in the axils of bracts at the

Securigera securidaca

Anthyllis vulneraria - s. sp. praepropera

Anthyllis tetraphylla

Anthyllis hermaniae

ends of branches, forming a sparse raceme. Habitat: Stony places in sub-montane and lowland zones. Flowers April-May.

Ornithopus (Birdsfoots)

Annuals with pinnate leaves and small linear stipules. Papilionaceous flowers in axillary heads. Linear pods, usually curved and constricted between seeds.

1. Ornithopus compressus. A pubescent plant with stems 10-50cm. long with 7-18 pairs of lateral leaflets which are oblong or elliptic. Heads with 3-5 yellow flowers, 5-8mm. long.

Pods 20-50mm., curved-falciform, very lightly constricted between the seeds. Habitat: Low altitude sandy and stony places.

Coronilla (Scorpion Senna and Scorpion Vetches)

Annual or perennial herbs or shrublets. Leaves pinnate, seldom simple or trifoliate. Flowers papilionaceous in axillary heads. Pods linear, articulated.

1. Coronilla emerus - subsp. emeroides. A shrub up to 1m., rarely bigger. Leaves with 2-4 pairs of lateral obovate leaves. Flowers 14-20mm., yellow, up to 8 on each head. Peduncles of heads longer than the leaves. Pods 50-110mm. Habitat: Rocks of montane and sub-montane zones. Flowers April-June. **2. Coronilla valentina - subsp. glauca.** Similar to 1 but leaves with 2-3 pairs of leaflets. Leaflets glaucous-green. Heads with 4-12 small, 7-12mm., flowers. Pods 10-50mm. Habitat: Montane zone, stony places at forest edges. Flowers April-May. **3. Coronilla varia:** A perennial herb, 20-120cm. Leaves with 7-12 pairs of 6-20mm., oblong or elliptic leaflets; heads with 10-20 pink, white, or purple flowers. Corolla 10-15mm. Pods 20-60mm. Habitat: Damp, montane sites. Flowers May-July. **4. Coronilla globosa.** Like 3 but leaflets 15-30mm., heads with 15-40 flowers, slightly smaller and usually white. A Cretan endemic. Habitat: Montane and sub-montane slopes and rocks. Flowers April-June. **5. Coronilla cretica.** An annual reaching up to 90cm. Leaves with 3-8 pairs of obovate-oblong leaflets. Heads with 3-6(-9) white or pink flowers, 4-7mm. Pods straight with a hooked beak. Habitat: Uncultivated ground and dry places at a low altitude. Flowers April-May. **6. Coronilla rostrata.** Similar to 5 but leaflets slightly bilobed at apex, flowers 7-10mm., pink, white, or pale yellow. Pods clearly curved and beak straight. Habitat: Low altitude pastures. Flowers March-April. **7. Coronilla scorpiodes.** A hairless annual up to 40cm. Leaves simple or trifoliate, with the middle leaflet much bigger, elliptic or almost discoid. Very small stipules. Heads with 2-5 yellow, 4-8mm. flowers. Habitat: Fallow fields and cornfields at a middle and low altitude. Flowers April-May.

Hippocrepis (Horseshoe Vetches)

Plants similar to Coronillas but flowers always yellow, and very conspicuous pods with deep cleavages or concavities between the seeds.

1. Hippocrepis ciliata. A slender, rather erect annual, up to 30cm. Leaves with 3-6 pairs of lateral, linear or oblong leaflets, 5-15mm. Heads with 2-6 flowers, 3-5mm. Habitat: Arid, barren localities in middle and lower zones. Flowers March-April. **2. Hippocrepis unisiliquosa.** Similar to 1 but flowers usually single ones, rarely 2-3, and somewhat larger. Habitat: Uncultivated ground in montane and submontane zones. Flowers April-May.

Scorpiurus

Annuals with simple leaves, having 3-5 parallel veins. Linear stipules. Small, papilionaceous flowers. Pods linear, strongly coiled into spirals.

1. Scorpiurus muricatus. Stems spreading, glabrous, pubescent, or hairy. Leaves lanceolate. From 2-5 flowers per head. Yellow corolla, 5-10mm. Pods covered with fine, spiny hairs. Habitat: Submontane and lowland zones. Flowers March-May.

Hedysarum (Sainfoins)

Plants similar to Coronillas but with pods conspicuously constricted between the seeds, glabrous or spiny. Pink, purple, or violet flowers.

Coronilla emerus - s. sp. emeroides

Coronilla varia

Onobrychis equidentata

Ebenus cretica

1. Hedysarum spinosissimum. A pubescent annual, 15-35cm. Leaves with 4-8 pairs of elliptic or oblong leaflets. Flowers in racemes with 2-10 pale pink or white flowers. Corolla 8-11mm. 2-4-segmented, spiny pods.

Onobrychis (Sainfoin)

Annual or perennial herbs. Pinnate leaves. Papilionaceous flowers in axillary, longstalked racemes, 1-3 seeded, small pods, round, flattened at sides, with conspicuous small pits and spines.

1. Onobrychis sphaciotica. A perennial with dense, silvery hairs. Lower leaves have 12-16 pairs of oblong-elliptic leaflets, up to 30mm. long. Calyx hairy and long-toothed. Purple corolla 11-12mm. Hairy-pubescent pods, with 8-10 spines. Endemic to the White

Mountains (Lefka Oree) in W. Crete. Habitat: Montane zone. Flowers May-June. **2. Onobrychis caput-galli.** An annual, either glabrous or pubescent. Leaves with 4-7 pairs of obovate or linear leaflets. Flowers 2-8 on stalk as long as that of leaves. Purple 7-8mm. corolla. Pod 6-10mm. long, with 4-9 teeth like spines. Habitat: Lowland and submontane hills. Flowers March-May. **3. Onobrychis aequidentata.** Like 1 but always pubescent. Inflorescence peduncles at least double the length of those of corresponding leaves. Corolla 10-14mm. Pods with 4-7 spines. Habitat: Lowland and sub-montane zones. Flowers March-May.

The North African and Asiatic species **Onobrychis crista-galli** has been mentioned as occurring in Crete, however, it is suspected that it is rather a case of confusing it with 3, above.

Ebenus

Small shrubs with leaves trifoliate or pinnate-quinquefoliate. Stipules fused with stalk, divided only at tip. Flowers in axillary racemes, pink or purple. Small pod, enclosed in calyx, with 1-2 seeds.

1. Ebenus cretica. Leaves trifoliate or quinquefoliate. Leaflets silvery-haired, elliptic oblong, 15-30mm. Deep pink flowers in dense hairy racemes. Corolla 10-15mm. Calyx hairy. A charactestic Cretan endemic. Habitat: Stony and rocky slopes of hills and gorges in the sub-montane and lowland zones. Flowers April-May.

Geraniales

Oxalidaceae Family

Herbaceous plants, seldom shrubs. Compound leaves. 5-petalled actinomorphic flowers. Ovary superior with 5 partitions. Fruit a capsule.

Oxalis (Wood-Sorrels or Oxalis)

Perennial herbs, frequently found with bulbs or bubils at root. Leaves trifoliate or, more rarely, palmate with 5-8 leaflets. Calyx with 5 free sepals.

1. Oxalis pes-caprae. An almost glabrous plant with perennial roots, buried deep in ground, and subterranean shoots that bear small perennial bulbils. Leaves trifoliate, green, with obcordate leaflets. Flowers yellow. Cuneate petals, 20-25mm. Umbellate inflorescences arising from the base on long bare stems. Sometimes the flowers are double (var. florae pleno). A South-African plant naturalised in Crete. Habitat: Fallow and cultivated fields of lowland and sub-montane zones. Flowers March-May. **2. Oxalis corymbosa.** Similar to 1 but with a perennial bulb 15-30mm. across, and flowers a pinkish-purple. A South-American plant naturalised comparatively recently along the coastal regions of W. Crete. Flowers March-May. **3. Oxalis corniculata.** A dwarf plant, with creeping and rooting stems. Leaves trifoliate, leaflets obcordate, 5-18mm., green, or often reddish. Small yellow flowers. Petals 4-7mm. Habitat: Both fallow and cultivated fields at a low altitude. Flowers From January to June, and from September to November.

Geraniaceae Family

Annual or perennial herbs. Leaves of various shapes, with stipules at their base. Flowers in cymes, spikes or umbels, 5-segmented, actinomorphic or, rarely, zygomorphic. 5 free petals, and 5 free sepals. Ovary superior with 5 fused carpels.

Oxalis pes - caprae

Oxalis corymbosa

Geranium tuberosum

Geranium mole

Geranium (Cranesbill)

Leaves more or less discoid, dentate, palmately-lobed or palmate. The lower and middle ones opposite and long-stalked. The upper leaves occasionally sessile alternate. Cymose inflorescences ending in terminal peduncles, each with 2 flowers. Fruit long-beaked, and with 5 carpels.

1. Geranium tuberosum. A pubescent plant with a perennial potato-like tuber. A 20-40cm., simple, erect, leaflets stem. Basal leaves 6-8cm. across, deeply dissected, almost to base, into 5-9 lobes. Pinnately-lobed lobes with 3-6 linear lobules on either side. Rosy-purple flowers with petals 8-13mm., obovate, bilobed at tip. Habitat: Montane and sub-alpine zones. Flowers April-May. **2. Geranium rotundifolium.** A sparsely-haired annual with 10-40cm. long stems, erect or ascending. Leaves 3-7,5cm. across, with 5-7 broad, obovate-cuneate lobes divided narrowly up to 40% of the leaf's surface. Lobes deeply serrated. Petals 5-7mm., entire or shallowly bilobed, pink. Habitat: Lowland and sub-montane zones. Flowers March-May. **3. Geranium mole.** Similar to 2 but thickly pubescent-hairy, greyish-green, spreading, basal leaves 1,5-4cm., more deeply cleft up to 70% of leaf surface. Leaf lobes trilobate at apex. Petals 3-7mm. bilobed at tip. Habitat: Lowland and sub-montane zones. Flowers February-April. **4. Geranium pusillium.** Like 3 but smaller. Flowers have 2-4mm. lilac petals. Habitat: Lowland and sub-montane zones. Flowers February-April. **5. Geranium columbinum.** A 10-60cm. annual with rather erect stems adpressedly-hairy. Leaves 2-5cm. with 5-7 lobes cleft almost to base, lobes deeply cleft into linear lobules. Flowers rosy-purple with petals 7-10mm. Habitat: Sub-montane and lowland zones. Flowers April-June. **6. Geranium dissectum.** Differs from 5 in having, usually, bigger basal leaves, and flowers short-stalked with petals about 5mm. Habitat: Montane and submomtane zones. Flowers April-June. **7. Geranium lucidum.** An annual with 10-20 (-40)cm. long stems; almost glabrous, 2-6cm., orbicular leaves with 5 obovate-cuneate lobes, 3-toothed at tip, green, often flushed with red. Pink flowers with obovate, 8-10mm. petals. Habitat: Cool parts of sub-montane and montane zones. Flowers April-June. **8. Geranium robertianum:** Biennial or annual, hairy, 10-50cm., ascending or spreading. Leaves 3-8cm., divided into 3 main lobes right down to base. Lobes bipinnate with oblong, pointed lobules. Flowers on hairy stalks. Sepals hairy, awned. Petal is pink, obovate-cuneate, 9-13mm. Habitat: Rocky places in montane and sub-alpine zones. Flowers April-June. **9. Geranium purpureum.** Similar to 8 but smaller with flowers also smaller. Petals 5-9mm. Sepals pointed without awns. Habitat: Cool, rocky places in montane and sub-montane zones. Flowers April-May.

Erodium (Storksbills)

Similar to **Geranium** but leaves longer than they are broad, pinnately lobed or pinnate, rarely entire, and flowers in few-flowered umbels. Fruit has 5 carpels with a long beak arista which at the time of maturation and the separation of the carpel coils like a spring.

1. Erodium chium - subsp. chium. An annual or biennial plant with hairy stems, 5-50cm. long. Ovate leaves, pinnately-lobed. Lobes broad and dentate. Umbels with 2-8 flowers. Purple, entire petals, 5-9mm. Habitat: Bare, dry places in sub-montane and lowland zones. Flowers March-April. **2. Erodium laciniatum.** A hairy annual or biennial plant up to 7-50cm. Oblong or broadly ovate leaves, greatly differing-they may be without lobes and crenate, or trilobate dentate to pinnate, or even bipinnate with linear lobules. Umbels with 4 to 9 flowers. Petals 7-10mm. purple. Habitat: Coastal sandy tracts. Flowers March-May. **3. Erodium malacoides.** An annual or biennial plant, 10-60cm. high, hairy-glandular. Leaves ovate or oblong, heart-shaped at base, dentated, occasionally trilobate or pinnately-lobed. Umbels have to 3 to 7 flowers. Petals purple, 5-9mm. Habitat: Arid, barren places at a low altitude. Flowers From February to April. **4. Erodium botrys.** An annual 10-40cm. with elongated spreading hairs. Leaves up to 5cm. with adpressed hairs; oblong or ovate and at least the upper deeply pinnately-lobed or pinnate. Umbels with 1-4 flowers. Petals about 15mm., violet-coloured. Habitat: Sandy ground in lowland and maritime zones. Flowers from March to May. **5. Erodium gruinum.** Annual or biennial, 15-50cm. high, with spreading hairs. Leaves up to 10cm., ovate or ovate-lanceolate, deeply pinnately-lobed or pinnate, occasionally with a pair of free leaflets at the base. Flowers 2-6. Petals 20-25mm. violet. Habitat: Arid places extending from the lowland zone down to the sea. Flowers March-April. **6. Erodium ciconium.** An annual or biennial plant with hairy-glandular stems, 10-70cm. high. Leaves pinnately-lobed, cleft almost to the base. Lobes also pinnately-lobed. Umbels with 3-10 flowers. Petals 8mm. blue or violet, with darker-coloured veins. Habitat: Sandy stretches and hills of lowland and littoral zones. Flowers March-May. **7. Erodium cicutarium - subsp. cicutarium.** An annual up to 60cm. in

Geranium columbinum

Geranium lucidum

Geranium robertianum

Geranium purpureum

height. Leaves pinnate with leaflets pinnate or pinnately-lobed. Petals rosy-purple, two of which are slightly larger and often with a black spot at their base. Habitat: Fallow and cultivated fields in the sub-montane zones. Flowers April-May. **8. Erodium moschatum.** A musk-smelling annual or biennial. Stems 10-50cm. high, hairy. Leaves up to 20cm., oblong-lanceolate, pinnately-lobed, cleft almost to the base; the lobes are ovate, dentate, crenate or pinnately-lobed, cleft almost to the base; the lobes are ovate, dentate, crenate or pinnately-lobed. The umbels have from 5 to 12 flowers. The petals which are about 15mm. are either violet or purple. Habitat: Fallow and cultivated arable land at a low altitude. This herb, under the names of "Myronia" and "Moscholachana", is gathered and cooked together with other wild herbs. **9. Erodium acaule.** A perennial, practically without a stem; Leaves pinnate. Leaflets pinnately-lobed with narrow lobes. Violet or purple petals 7-12mm. Umbels with 3-10 flowers. Habitat: Arid places, and hills of lowland and sub-montane zones. Flowers March–April. **10. Erodium hirtum.** A perennial with roots which produce spherical tubers up to 1,5cm. Stems 10-30cm., erect or ascending, with spreading, white hairs. Leaves up to 6cm., deeply pinnately-lobed, lobes being dentate or pinnately-lobed. Umbels with 3-5 flowers. Petals light pink, 8mm. Habitat: Seaboard dunes in South-East Crete (near Ierapetra). It is, perhaps, an introduced species brought from North Africa and West Asia.

Tropaeolaceae Family

These are plants with solitary flowers arising from the axils of the leaves. The flowers are zygomorphic, with 5 sepals, which are fused at their base, forming a spur and 5 petals.

Tropaeolum (Nasturtiums)

Usually sappy, climbing or creeping plants. Leaves alternate, usually without any stipules. Flowers with two upper petals and three lower ones.

1. Tropaeolum majus. A hairless annual or perennial. Leaves peltate-orbicular, almost entire or slightly angular. Flowers 3-6cm., yellow, orange, or a brownish-red, with 2-4cm. spur. It is widely cultivated and often established, growing subspontaneously. The author came across a very large number of these escaping plants amont the ruins of the old town of Chania. Flowers March to May, or even until later.

Zygophyllaceae Family

Herbs or shrubs with leaves usually pinnate, with stipules at their base. Flowers usually both actinomorphic and quinquepartite.

Tribulus (Maltese Cross)

Herbaceous plants. Flowers with 5 caducous sepals and 5 petals. Stamens 10. Ovary five-lobed. Fruit spiny.

1. Tribulus terrestris. An annual with creeping stems, and leaves opposite, pinnate, small, with 5-8 pairs of elliptic leaflets. Flowers yellow, 4-5mm. Fruit with tough spines. Habitat: Fallow and cultivated fields in lowland and sub-montane zones. Flowers May to September.

Zygophyllum

Herbs often with woody base. Leaves opposite. Flowers with 4-5 caducous sepals, and 4-5 petals. 8-10 stamens. Fruit a capsule.

1. Zygophyllum album. A small shrub, greyish-green, arachnoid lanate. Stems about 40cm. Leaves with a pair of elliptic or obovate, slightly fleshy leaflets, on a somewhat fleshy stalk. Stipules small and membraneous. Flowers small, white, solitary, growing in the axils of the leaves. It is a North African and West Asian species found in the islets around Crete, it also occurs in the Dodecanesian island of Cassos. Habitat: Seaboard regions. Flowers in springtime.

Fagonia

Herbaceous plants. The leaves often have spiny stipules. 5 caducous sepals. 5 petals. 10 stamens. Fruit a capsule.

Erodlum gruinum

Erodium cicutarium

Erodium acaule

Tribulus terrestris

1. Fagonia cretica. A glabrous, creeping perennial, 10-40cm. Stems branched, angular, and furrowed. Leaves opposite, trifoliate, stalked. Leaflets 5-15mm., lanceolate or linear-lanceolate, asymmetric. Spiny stipules. 10mm. flowers in the axils of the leaves. Petals purple. Habitat: Arid places at a low altitude.

Peganum

Herbs with quadripartite or quinquepartite flowers, and alternate, deeply pinnately-lobed leaves.

1. Peganum harmata. A glabrous, many-branched perennial, 30-60cm. high. Flowers 10-20mm., with 5 linear sepals and 5 lanceolate, whitish-green petals. Leaves slightly fleshy,

127

pinnately-lobed, almost pinnate, with linear lobes. Habitat: Dry places at a low altitude. Flowers in springtime. The occurrence of this species in Crete is noted with a question mark, for it has not been confirmed recently.

Linaceae Family

Herbaceous plants or small shrubs. Flowers quadripartite or quinquepartite. Both sepals and petals free. Ovary superior.

Linum (Flax)

Herbs or small shrubs. Leaves entire, sessile, narrow. Quinquepartite flowers. Wedge-shaped petals, with a claw at base. Fruit a capsule.

1. Linum arboreum. A shrub with glabrous stems reaching up to 1m. in height. Leaves 10-30mm., spathulate with a midrib, forming dense fascicules at the top of the stems. Inflorescences with few, rather dense, flowers. Yellow petals 12-18mm. Habitat: Rocks and stony places in the montane and sub-montane zones, especially in gorges. Flowers April-May. **2. Linum caespitosum.** Very similar to 1 but smaller, up to 20cm. Leaves up to 15mm. A Cretan endemic. Habitat: Montane and sub-alpine rocks. Flowers April-June. **3. Linum nodiflorum.** A glabrous annual with 1 or more erect stems, up to 40cm., slightly branched and winged. Leaves linear, the lower ones spathulate. Flowers in a sparse inflorescence, yellow, with petals 20mm. Habitat: Uncultivated arable land at a low altitude. Flowers March-April. **4. Linum bienne.** A biennial or perennial plant, 6-60cm., usually branched upwards, erect and slender. Leaves small linear or linear-lanceolate. Pale blue flowers. Petals 10-15mm. Habitat: Montane zone. Flowers June-July. **5. Linum usitatissimum.** Similar to 4 but more robust, and an annual, with flowers a deeper blue. It is a plant of unknown origin, introduced a very long time ago as a cultivated species; it is now naturalised. Habitat: Both uncultivated and cultivated arable land. Flowers May-July. **6. Linum pubescens.** A small annual, pubescent plant, 7-20cm. with pink flowers. Petals 15-20mm. Habitat: Barren stretches in the sub-montane, lowland, and littoral zones. Flowers February-April. **7. Linum trigynum.** A glabrous annual, 10-30cm. Linear leaves. Small, yellow flowers. Petals 4-6mm. Habitat: Hills of lowland and sub-montane zones. Flowers February-April.

Euphorbiaceae Family

Herbs, shrubs, or trees, dioecious or monoecious, frequently with a milky sap. Flowers either actinomorphic or zygomorphic, with or without petals. Male and female flowers often in a common, urn-shaped receptacle (cyathium).

Chrozophora (Turn-Soles)

Annual, monoecious herbs covered with star-shaped hairs. Male flowers on terminal racemes or in axillary clusters. Female flowers solitary at the base of the male ones. Male flowers with a five-lobed calyx, 5 petals, and 5-10 stamens. Female flowers with a ten-lobed calyx, without petals, otherwise with very small ones.

1. Chrozophora tinctoria. A green or greyish-green plant. Stems up to 50cm., more or less branched. Leaves ovate or rhomboid, entire or notched-dentate, wedge-shaped at base, and with a long petiole. Tiny flowers. Habitat: Bare, arid places by the sea. Flowers June-October. **2. Chrozophora obliqua.** Similar to 1 but whitish, densely hairy, and leaves

Linum caespitosum

Linum usitatissimum

Linum pubescens

Ricinus communis

truncated or slightly heart-shaped at base. Habitat: Bare, arid places in the lowland zone. Flowers June-October.

Ricinus (Castor Oil Plants)

Monoecious shrubs or big herbs. Leaves alternate, palmately-lobed. Flowers in panicles. The female flowers at the base of the inflorescence, the male ones at the tips.

1. Ricinus communis. Either a large annual herb or a perennial shrub. Leaves palmately-lobed, deeply cleft into 5-9 lanceolate or ovate-lanceolate lobes. Spherical, spiny fruit, 10-20mm., with large seeds that have the shape of a tick, dark-coloured with white streaks and dots. A tropical plant both cultivated and often self-seeding on the island. Its seeds produce castor-oil. Flowers April to September.

Mercurialis (Mercuries)

Usually dioecious plants. Leaves opposite with small stipules. Male flowers in spikes, terminal or axillary. Female flowers either solitary or only a few in the axils of the leaves. The male flowers have a trilobate calyx and 15 stamens, and the female flowers have a trilobate calyx, too, and 2 styles.

1. Merculiaris annua. A glabrous, 10-50cm. high, annual. Stem erect, branched. Leaves ovate or elliptic-lanceolate, serrate, 1,5-5cm. long, and with a small petiole. Flowers small and a greenish-yellow colour. Habitat: Cultivated fields and damp places.

Adrachne telephioides is, from a decorative point a view, an insignificant perennial plant, with small leaves and spreading stems. Habitat: Bare terrain at a low altitude.

Euphorbia (Spurges)

Herbs or small shrubs exuding a milky juice. Flowers usually yellowish, quite singular, having both female and male flowers together in a special receptacle called "cyathium". The female flowers are solitary, consisting of only the ovary. The male ones are numerous, encircling the female flowers, and consist of a single stamen. The cyathium with 4-5 horseshoe-shaped or semi-circular glands. Usually cyathia are surrounded by bracts. The whole inflorescence is frequently encircled by a whorl of leaves.

Group A. Perennial plants. Cyathia in umbels.

1. Euphorbia dendroides. A bushy shrub up to 1 (-2)m. Leaves oblong-lanceolate, 25-65mm. Inflorescence with 5-8 forked rays. The leaves surrounding the inflorescence are broader and shorter than the rest. Yellowish, rhomboid bracts. Habitat: Rocky positions of lowland and sub-montane zones. Flowers March-May. **2. Euphorbia oblongata.** A sturdy, thickly pubescent, caespitose plant reaching a height of 80cm. Flowers in a terminal umbel, frequently, however, they can be found in axillary rays as well. Leaves narrow, obovate, crenate. Leaves encircling umbel ovate. Umbel 5-rayed. Habitat: Shady positions in submontane and lowland zones. Flowers March-May. **3. Euphorbia apios.** A pubescent plant with either erect or spreading stems, 5-20cm. and an underground turnip-like tuber. Leaves linear-lanceolate or obovate-cuneate, slightly crenate. Leaves surrounding umbel like the cauline. Umbel with 3-5 rays. Habitat: Dry, rocky positions in sub-montane zone. Flowers April-June. **4. Euphorbia dimorphocaulon.** Very similar to 4 but flowers in autumn. In sub-montane and lowland zones. **5. Euphorbia acanthothamnos.** A dense prickly shrublet, 10-30cm. Leaves small, elliptic, or elliptic-obovate. The leaves surrounding the umbel yellow. Umbel with 3(-4) rays. Habitat: Lowland and sub-montane rocks. Flowers March-May. **6. Euphorbia pubescens.** Densely pubescent or almost glabrous, stem thick reaching up to 1m. 5-rayed umbels. Leaves oblong-lanceolate or linear. Habitat: Water-meadows and ravines in the sub-montane and lowland zones. Flowers May-June. **7. Euphorbia rigida.** Glabrous, glaucous-green, with woody base. Leaves lanceolate, pointed, tough and a little fleshy. Leaves encircling umbel obovate. Bracts nearly orbicular. Umbels with 6-12 short rays. Habitat: Arid, rocky positions. Flowers April-May. The existence of this species in Crete is not absolutely certain. **8. Euphorbia deflexa.** Glabrous, glaucous-green, caespitose, up to 35cm. Leaves 3-15mm., orbicular to oblong. Umbel leaves rhomboid or ovate. Bracts rhomboid or slightly reniform. Umbels with 3-9 rays, two or three times dichotomous. There are also lateral, axillary rays. Habitat: Montane zone. Flowers May-June. **9. Euphorbia herniariifolia.** A pubescent, glaucous perennial with numerous creeping or ascending

Euphorbia dendroides

stems, up to 20cm. Leaves 4-10cm., orbicular or obovate-elliptic. Umbel leaves and bracts similar to the other leaves. Umbel with 2-3 rays, simple or once dichotomous. Habitat: Alpine and sub-alpine zones. Flowers May-June. **10. Euphorbia paralias.** A glabrous, glaucous-green, fleshy, caespitose plant up to 70cm. high., branched from base. Leaves 3-30mm., the lower ones obovate-oblong, the middle elliptic-oblong, while the top ones are ovate. The bracts are either orbicular-rhomboid or nephroid. Umbels with 3-6 rays, up to three times dichotomous. Habitat: Sandy beaches. Flowers May-June. **11. Euphorbia terracina.** A glabrous perennial either with a simple stem or with a branched one, up to 70cm. high. Leaves 15-40mm., linear-lanceolate or elliptic-oblong. Leaves of umbel identical with the others. Bracts deltoid-rhomboid. Umbels with 4-5 rays up to 5 times dichotomous. Habitat: Coastal sandy places. Flowers May-June. **12. Euphorbia characias - subsp. wulfenii.** A glaucous-green, pubescent plant with robust stems reaching a height

131

of 180cm. Leaves 30-130mm., linear or oblanceolate; the same applies to the umbel leaves. Bracts almost discoid-deltoid. Umbels with 10-20 dichotomous rays, and lateral, simple rays to the upper leaves. Habitat: Montane and sub-montane zones. Flowers April-June. **13. Euphorbia rechingeri.** A dwarf perennial, glabrous and glaucous-green. Stems numerous, dense, and about 5cm. high. Leaves obovate-spathulate, pointed. Flowers in umbels with 5 very short rays. Endemic to the White Mountains. Habitat: Alpine and sub-alpine zones. Flowers June-July.

Group B. Annuals. Cyathia in umbels.

1. Euphorbia skenocarpa. Pubescent or glabrous, 15-45cm. Leaves elliptic or obovate, cuneate at base. Leaves surrounding umbel elliptic-ovate. Umbels with 2-5 rays, much longer than the encircling leaves. Habitat: Disturbed environment, rubble, etc. at a low altitude. Flowers March-April. **2. Euphorbia helioscopia.** Erect, glabrous, with one simple stem. Leaves obovate-spathulate, rounded at tip, and crenate at their upper end. The bracts resemble the leaves but are smaller. Umbels with 5 twice dichotomous rays. Habitat: Common in uncultivated as well as cultivated arable land in the lowland zone. Flowers March-April. **3. Euphorbia aleppica.** An almost glabrous, and rather glaucous-green plant with a simple stem up to 40cm. high, or quite often with many branches near its base. Leaves 10-25mm. linear or oblanceolate dense and overlapping. Bracts ovate-rhomboid or pointed-hooked. Umbels with 2-6 rays up to 5 times dichotomous. Its occurrence in Crete has not been confirmed. Habitat: Fallow and cultivated fields at a low altitude. Flowers in springtime. **4. Euphorbia exigua.** Glabrous up to 35cm. with either one or many stems. Leaves linear or oblong-cuneate. Bracts triangular-lanceolate. Umbels with 3-5 rays which may be dichotomous up to 7 times. Habitat: Cultivated fields of lowland and sub-montane zones. Flowers March-April. **5. Euphorbia falcata.** Glabrous, up to 40cm., with a simple stem or with a few branches arising from the base. Leaves 5-30mm., obovate-spathulate to linear-oblong, very pointed. Bracts elliptic-ovate or almost orbicular. Umbels with 3-6 simple dichotomous rays. Habitat: Gravelly and stony sites at a low altitude. Flowers March-April. **6. Euphorbia peplus.** A few-stemmed, glabrous plant, up to 40cm. high. Leaves 5-25mm., ovate or nearly orbicular. Bracts similar but smaller. Umbels with 3 rays, dichotomised up to 5 times. Habitat: Low altitude arable land. Flowers April-May. **7. Euphorbia peploides.** Very similar to 6 but a dwarf plant. Habitat: Uncultivated and arid positions at a low altitude. Flowers March-April. **8. Euphorbia taurinensis.** A glabrous plant up to 15cm. high, with 1-2 stems. Leaves 20-30mm., linear-oblanceolate. Bracts oblique, rhomboid. Umbels with 4 rays, frequently greatly branched. There are also rays in the axils of upper leaves. Habitat: Disturbed habitats, rubble, and roadsides, at a low altitude. Flowers March-May. **9. Euphorbia segetalis.** Glabrous with 1 or more stems up to 35cm. Leaves 10-30mm., linear or linear-lanceolate. Umbel leaves elliptic-oblong. Bracts deltoid-rhomboid, rounded at tip. Umbels with 5-6 rays, dichotomised up to 5 times. **Habitat:** Open sandy stretches near the sea. Flowers April-June.

Group C. Annuals. Cyathia single or more always in axils of leaves never in umbels. Leaves stipuled.

1. Euphorbia peplis. A slightly fleshy plant, glabroyus, usually with 4 creeping stems up to 40cm. Leaves 4-16mm., oblong, slanting, rounded at tip. Cyathia solitary. Habitat: Sandy beaches. Flowers March-May. **2. Euphorbia Chamaesyce.** Similar to 1 but stems more numerous, not fleshy, and leaves ovate, 3-7mm. Habitat: Sandy and gravelly expanses of lowland zone. Flowers March-May.

Euphorbia helioscopia

Rutales

Rutaceae Family

Herbs, shrubs, or trees. Leaves alternate or opposite, simple or compound, dotted with transparent glands. Flowers hermaphrodite, actinomorphic. Sepals and petals 4-5. Ovary superior.

Ruta (Rues)

Perennial herbs with alternate leaves, twice or thrice pinnately-lobed. Lobes linear to obovate. Cymose inflorescences. Flowers with 4 sepals, and petals, or frequently with 5, only on central flower. Petals curling, spoon-shaped (cochlear), yellow, crenate or ciliate. They are, usually, strong-smelling plants.

1. Ruta chalepensis. Stem 20-60cm., smooth. Lower leaves long-stalked. Lobes of leaves oblong-lanceolate or obovate, 1,5-6mm. broad. Inflorescence sparse. Flowers with long pedicels. Habitat: Montane and sub-montane zones. Flowers April-May. **2. Ruta fumariifolia.** Similar to 1 but a smaller size, and with leaf lobes rather ovate. It is, perhaps, a variant of 1. Habitat: Montane zone. Flowers April-May.

Haplophyllum

Perennial herbs. Leaves alternate, lanceolate, elliptic, linear or trilobate, with narrow lobes. Cymose inflorescences. Sepals 5, Petals 5, Petals yellow.

1. Haplophyllum buxbaumii. Stems 15-50cm. with crisped hairs. Leaves oblanceolate or linear-lanceolate, 25-50mm., entire or with 3 deeply dissected lobed, the centre one being larger than the other two. Inflorescence sparse and broad. It is a plant of South-West Asia. Habitat: Sub-montane zone. Flowers May-June.

Meliaceae Family

Shrubs or trees. Leaves pinnate, alternate. Actinomorphic, quinquepartite flowers.

Melia (Indian Bead Trees or Persian Lilacs)

Deciduous trees or shrubs with flowers in large axillary panicles. Petals and sepals 5-6. Stamens converging towards style. Ovary superior. Fruit a drupe.

1. Melia azedarach. A tree reaching up to 15m. Leaves bipinnate, up to 90cm. long. Flowers bluish-violet, sweet-scented. Narrow petals about 18mm. long. Fruit 6-18mm., yellow. This a South and East Asia plant which as well as being cultivated in Crete has become naturalised and self-seeding on the island. Habitat: Sub-montane and lowland zones. Flowers April-May.

Polygalaceae Family

Simple-leafed plants. Flowers zygomorphic, in spikes or racemes. Sepals 5. Petals 3-5. Stamens 8.

Polygala (Milkworts)

Small perennial herbs, seldom annual. Leaves usually alternate. Flowers in racemes at the end of stems, or in ones in the axils of the upper leaves. Sepals very dissimilar. The two inner ones much larger, are called "wings" 3 petals fused at their base into a tube. The bottom petal different from the others, with a fringed tip, called a "keel".

1. Polygala monspeliaca. An erect annual. Leaves lanceolate or linear. 10-25mm. pointed. Flowers in terminal racemes with wings 6-8mm., whitish-green, and a 4mm. white corolla. Habitat: Pasture-land in the montane and sub-montane zones. Flowers April-May. **2. Polygala venulosa.** Similar to 1 but a perennial with blue flowers, and a corolla longer than the wings. Habitat: Rocky positions in the montane zone. Flowers April-May.

Melia azedarach

Sapindales

Anacardiaceae Family

Trees or shrubs. Alternate leaves, pinnate or entire. Flowers small with 5 petals, or even without petals. Ovary superior. Fruit a one-seeded drupe.

Rhus (Sumachs)

Shrubs with pinnate leaves, usually exuding a resinous juice. Small flowers in compound racemes; female and male flowers on separate plants (dioecious). Fruit one small, hard drupe.

135

1. Rhus coriaria. A shrub reaching a height of 3m. An almost evergreen plant (shedding its leaves only at the end of winter), with leaves cleft into 7-21 ovate or oblong, serrate leaflets. Young shoots and rachis of leaves hairy. Inflorescence bears greenish-white flowers. Drupe maroon-coloured, hairy. Habitat: Montane and sub-montane zones. Flowers in springtime.

Cotinus (Wig-Trees or Smoke-trees)

Shrubs with entire leaves. Fruits on long stalks with long, spreading hairs.

1. Cotinus coggygria. A shrub up to 4m. Leaves ovate or obovate, glaucous-green, and in autumn golden-red. Inflorescence sparse, 15-20cm. across, with numerous hairy branches, most of which do not terminate in a flower. Drupes, 3-4mm. Habitat: Rocky places in sub-montane zone. Flowers springtime.

Pistacia (Terebinths and Lentiscs)

Dioecious resinous shrubs or trees. Leaves pinnate. Flowers without petals, on lateral inflorescences. Fruit a drupe.

1. Pistacia terebinthus. A deciduous shrub or small tree. Leaves with 3-9 ovate, obovate, or oblong leaflets. Flowers a brownish colour. Drupes hard, 5-7mm., reddish or light brown. Habitat: Sub-montane zone. Flowers springtime. **2. Pistacis lentiscus.** Similar to 1 but smaller, shrubby, evergreen, with leaves usually without apical leaflet. Flowers yellowish or purple. Drupes reddish, and when fully mature blackish. Habitat: Stony places in sub-montane, lowland, and littoral zones. Flowers in the spring.

Aceraceae Family

Trees or shrubs with opposite leaves. Flowers actinomorphic, in racemes or panicles. Petals and sepals 5.

Acer (Maples)

Trees or big shrubs, evergreen or deciduous, with small greenish or yellowish flowers, and fruit samaras, that is, two fused winged fruit on a common stalk.

1. Acer sempervirens. A large, 5m., evergreen shrub, seldom taller. Leaves obovate-cuneate, entire or with three shallow lobes, 2-5cm. long. Flowers few, in erect corymbs. Samara with about parallel wings. The only species of this genus in Crete. Habitat: Montane and sub-montane zones.

Rhamnales

Rhamnaceae Family

Trees or shrubs with simple leaves, usually with small stipules at their base. Inflorescences cymose. Flowers with a 4-lobed or 5-lobed calyx. Petals 4-5, usually small or, occasionally, absent. Ovary superior.

Zizyphus (Jujubes)

Leaves with spine like stipules and parallel veins. Flowers five-segmented. Fruit a fleshy drupe.

Cotinus ooggygria

Pistacia terebinthus

Pistacia lentiscus

Acer sempervirens

1. Zizyphus jujuba. A small tree; leaves 2-5,5cm. alternate, oblong, rounded at tip, dentate. Flowers in small, axillary cymes. Drupe brownish-red, ovate or oblong, 1,5-3cm. long, edible. An Asian species, cultivated for its fruit, and frequently growing subspontaneously in sub-montane and lowland zones. Flowers springtime.

Rhamnus (Buckthorns)

Leaves with caducous stipules, and a feathery nervature. Fruit a small drupe containing 2-4 seeds. Flowers quadripartite, usually monoecious, that is male and female on the same plant

1. Rhamnus lycioides - subsp. oleoides. A small up to 1m., evergreen shrub. Leaves often opposite, obovate, 1-4cm. Drupe 4-6mm., yellowish to begin with then turning black.

Branches prickly at tip. Habitat: Rocky sub-montane sites. Flowers in the springtime. **2. Rhammus lycioides - subsp. graecus.** Similar to 1 but deciduous, with leaves 6-18mm. Habitat: Rocky and stony places in the sub-montane zone. Flowers springtime. **3. Rhamnus prunifolius.** A small, deciduous, creeping, very prickly shrub. Leaves oblong or ovate, crenate and glabrous, 5-12mm. long. Drupe small and black. Habitat: Montane zone. Flowers May-June.

Malvales

Malvaceae Family

Shrubs, small trees, or herbs, with leaves alternate, dentate, palmately-lobed or palmate, with stipules at their base. Flowers with 5 petals and 5 sepals, and epicalyx bracts. Ovary superior, composed of numerous carpels in a circular arrangement around the style. Stamens fused at lower end thus forming a tube round the styles and ovary, free at upper end.

Malope

Herbs with flowers on a long pedicel, solitary, in the axils of the leaves. Epicalyx bracts 3, ovate or orbicular heart-shaped at base, broader than the sepals. Petals roundish at the tip.

1. Malope malacoides. Perennial, only rarely annual, hairy, at least on the upper part. Stems 20-50cm. Leaves oblong-lanceolate or ovate, or the upper leaves trilobate, all crenate, with a quite long stalk. Petals a deep pink or purple, oblong, not overlapping, 20-40mm. long. Habitat: Sub-montane and lowland zones, and cultivated fields. Flowers April-June.

Malva (Mallows)

Herbaceous plants. 2-3 free epicalyx bracts. Petals more or less bilobed at tip or, at least, shallowly notched. Sepals fused at base.

1. Malva sylvestris. A biennial or perennial plant, hairy, up to 150cm. high. Leaves palmately-lobed with 3-7 crenate lobes, slightly heart-shaped at base. Flowers in axils of leaves, pink or purple with darker-coloured veins. Petals wedge-shaped, bilobed at tip, not overlapping, and 12-30 mm. long. Habitat: Sub-montane and lowland zones, in fallow and cultivated fields. Flowers April-June. **2. Malva nicaeensis.** Similar to 1 but either an annual or a biennial; the flowers, too, are smaller, and the lilac-coloured petals are 10-12mm. long. Habitat: Sub-montane and lowland zones. Flowers March-May. **3. Malva parviflora.** Similar to 1 but smaller, leaves less lobular, flowers very small, lilac petals 4-5mm. Habitat: Lowland and sub-montane zones. Flowers February-May. **4. Malva cretica - subsp. cretica.** A hairy, erect annual, 40cm. with adpressed hairs. Flowers in the axils of the leaves on long pedicels. Sepals narrow, 7-10mm. Petals, either the same length as the sepals or longer, are pink or lilac-coloured. Leaves deeply cleft into three or five crenate lobes. Habitat: Montane zone. Flowers May-July. **5. Malva aegyptiaca.** Similar to 4 but smaller. Lobes of leaves deeply dissected into linear lobules. Lilac flowers. Habitat: Lowland zone. Flowers March-May.

Lavatera (Tree Mallows)

Similar plants to **Malva** but epicalyx bracts always 3 in number, more or less fused at their base.

Rhamnus lycioides s. sp. graecus

Rhamnus prunifolius

Malva silvestris

Malva nicaeensis

1. Lavatera cretica. In general appearance resembles **Malva sylvestris** greatly. Flowers 2-8. Petals pale violet, 10-20mm. It is an annual or biennial plant. Habitat: Uncultivated land, and barren, waste ground in the lowlands and the sub-montane zone. Flowers March-April. **2. Lavatera arborea.** A sturdy biennial plant, thick at its base, with erect stems up to 3m. Leaves with 5-7 shallow lobes. Flowers in 2-7. Petals 15-20mm., pink or pale violet with dark-coloured veins near their base. Habitat: In rocky spots, usually near the sea, or frequently in lowland gardens. Flowers February-May. **3. Lavatera bryonifolia.** A perennial plant completely woody at its base. Leaves with 3-5 lobes, deeply cleft. Solitary flowers in axils of leaves. Petals pink, 1,5-2,5cm. Habitat: Uncultivated arid places in the sub-montane and lowland zones. Flowers March-May. **4. Lavatera punctata.** A branched annual with an upright stem, 20-90cm., purple with sparse stellate hairs. Lower leaves discoid-nephroid with 5 shallow lobes. The rest of the leaves deeply trilobate or 5-lobed, the central lobe larger, and the lateral ones divergent. Flowers singles on elongated pedicels. Pale pink 1,5-3cm. petals. Habitat: Lowlands. Flowers springtime.

Althaea (Althaeas)

Annual or perennial herbs, usually with erect stems. 6-9 epicalyx bracts, fused at their base. Petals obovoid, entire or slightly concave at tip.

1. Althaea hirsuta. An annual up to 60cm., covered with thick star-shaped hairs. Leaves practically orbicular, cordate at base, crenate or dentate, and concentrated largely at the base of the plant. The few leaves of the stem have 3-5 linear, dentate lobes. Single flowers in axils of leaves. Petals about 15mm., pale violet. Habitat: Found in arid, barren localities at a low altitude. Flowers May-June.

Alcea (Hollyhocks)

Plants similar to **Althaea** but always perennial, and with stems always erect and robust. Large flowers, almost sessile, in terminal racemes. Epicalyx bracts usually 6, fused at base, and either equally long as, or longer than the sepals. Petals slightly concave at tip.

1. Alcea setosa. Stem simple, often with purple dots, hairy and with groups of star-shaped hairs on its surface. Leaves cordate orbicular or deltoid, the superior ones divided into 3-5 oblong or deltoid lobes. Broad, overlapping petals, 35-50mm. long violet, and usually, with yellow at their base. It is a plant of South-West Asia. Crete is the only place in Europe where it has become naturalised; it has been, however, introduced into Italy and Yugoslavia, too. Besides growing spontaneously in Crete it is also cultivated for decorative purposes. Habitat: In sub-montane and lowland zones by roadsides, and in hedges as well as on arable land. Flowers May-July. **2. Alcea pallida - subsp. cretica.** Resembles 1 but its petals are 30-45mm. long, deep pink or purple. A densely haired plant. Habitat: Sub-montane and lowland zones in hedges and at waysides. Flowers May-July.

Abutilon

Trees, shrubs, or herbs. Flowers with no epicalyx bracts. Petals cuneate-obovate. Calyx deeply cleft into five lobes. Fruit with 12-15 capsules around central axis.

1. Abutilon theophrastii. A tall, erect annual, 50-100cm., hairy or pubescent. Leaves long-stalked, cordate, very long-pointed, and shallowly crenate. Flowers in few-flowered cymes in the axils of superior leaves. Petals yellow, 7-13mm. Habitat: Cultivated ground, and disturbed habitats at a low altitude. Flowers July-October.

Cossypium (Cottons)

Shrubs, or else annuals woody at their base. Leaves palmately-lobed. Solitary flowers in axils of leaves. Calyx small, campanulate, five-lobed. Petals large, wedge-shaped, and clawed. Epicalyx bracts 3. Fruit a large capsule, with dense hairs (cotton) inside among the seeds.

1. Gossypium herbaceum. A 1-1,5m. annual, smooth or sparsely-haired plant. Leaves about 11X14cm., cordate at base, cleft into five, ovoid lobes, cleavage not very deep. Epicalyx bracts 2-2,5cm., deltoid-ovoid, with 6-8 large teeth. Petals yellow with a purple claw. Capsule 2-3,5cm., nearly globose. The species was introduced into Crete and has since become established. It is rather of W. Pakistan origin. Habitat: Cultivated fields, ditches, and other damp localities in the sub-montane and lowland zones. Flowers August-September. **2. Gossypium hirsutum.** Similar to 1 but hairy. Lobes of leaves

Lavatera arborea

Althaea hirsuta

Alcea pallida - s. sp. cretica

Daphne oleoides

triangular or lanceolate. Epicalyx bracts about 4,5cm., with aristate teeth. Aristas very elongated. Capsule 4-6cm., ovate. Flowers yellow but without a purple claw. A native of Peru naturalised in Crete. Habitat: Cultivated ground, ditches, damp localities. Flowers August-September.

Hibiscus (Hibiscus)

Herbs or shrubs. Large solitary flowers in axils of leaves. Epicalyx bracts linear, 6-13. Petals rounded at tip, covering each other. Fruit ovate, conical, or almost spherical.

1. Hibiscus cannabinus. An annual, with erect simple stems reaching up to a height of 2m. Glabrous, except for the calyx and the spherical capsule which are pubescent. Petals

141

cream-coloured, sometimes purple at the base. Introduced from tropical Asia and Africa and naturalised in Crete. Habitat: Cultivated ground, ditches, and damp localities, at a low altitude. Flowers August-October.

Thymelaeales

Thymelaeaceae Family

Small shrubs. Leaves simple, entire, usually alternate. Flowers with a four-lobed calyx, and corolla practically tubular at base, and four-lobed at the opening or else absent. Ovary superior.

Daphne

Dense, many-branched small shrubs. Flowers usually sweet-smelling, small, in terminal heads, or axillary spikes, or panicles. Corolla absent. Calyx, coloured, in the form of a corolla, encircled at its base by a hypanthium of the same colour.

1. Daphne oleoides. An evergreen up to 50cm. Leaves 10-45mm., obovoid, oblong, or elliptic and at first hairy. Scented flowers, white or cream, in heads of 3 to 6. Habitat: Montane and sub-alpine zones. Flowers May-July. **2. Daphne sericea.** Similar to 1, but flowers pink, and 5-15 per head. Leaves densely covered with hairs underneath. Habitat: Montane and sub-montane zones. Flowers April-May.

Thymelaea

Plants resembling **Daphne** but which are, however usually, dioecious. Flowers solitary, or only few, in axils of leaves. Hypanthium funnel-shaped or crateriform. Calyx four-lobed.

1. Thymelaea tartonraira - subsp. argentea. A dense small shrub with silvery leaves, linear, 1,5-3mm. broad, and 10-18mm. long, covered with silvery hairs. Flowers small, yellow, 2-5. Habitat: Stony localities in montane and sub-montane zones. Flowers March-May. **2. Thymelaea hirsuta.** A 40-100cm. high, dense leaves ovoid or lanceolate 3-8mm. long, dense and alternate, greenish and fleshy. Stems dense and hairy. Flowers small and yellow in bunches of 2-5. Habitat: Stony localities in the sub-montane zone.

Eleagnaceae

Trees or shrubs. Leaves entire. Flowers with a 2 to 4 lobed hypanthium and without either calyx or corolla.

Eleagnus (Oleaster)

Hypanthium campanulate or tubular, 4-lobed, similar to a corolla.

1. Eleagnus angustifolia. A small deciduous tree or a big shrub, spiny or not. Sweet-scented yellowish flowers, 8-10mm. Fruit an elliptic brown drupe, 10-25mm long, with farinaceous flesh, edible. Leaves oblong or linear-lanceolate, green on upper surface and silvery beneath. Believed to be a native of Asia; established in Crete since olden times. Habitat: Sandy beaches. Flowers May-June. Fruit September-October.

Daphne sericea

Thymelaea tartonraira - s. sp. argentea

Thymelaea hirsuta

Eleagnus angustifolia

Guttiferales

Guttiferae Family

Shrubs or herbs with pellucid glands on the leaves, and frequently with black glands on leaves, sepals, and petals. Leaves simple, opposite or, rarely, in whorls. Flowers actinomorphic. Petals free. Stamens usually numerous, arranged in bunches. Ovary superior.

Hypericum (St. John's Worts)

Plants having, usually, 5 sepals and petals, seldom 4. Petals always yellow, occasionally

143

flushed with red on the outside. Stamens in bundles of 3-5. Leaves opposite or in whorls.

Group A. Perennials, shrub-like, without black glands. Leaves opposite.

1. Hypericum hircinum. Shoots quadrangular or with 2 lines lengthwise 30-100cm. Leaves ovoid or lanceolate, practically sessile, 2-6,5cm. long. Flowers in sparse, cymose inflorescences. Sepals entire. Petals 11-18mm. oblanceolate or obovoid. Stamens longer than petals. Habitat: Swamps and banks of small rivers. Flowers May-July. **2. Hypericum aciferum.** A low, creeping shrub, with spathulate-linear leaves, glaucous-coloured, 5-12mm. Flowers usually in threes, with a conspicuous pedicel. Petals about 9mm., caducous. Stamens remain after petals have fallen off. An endemic of South-West Crete. Habitat: Calcareous rocks close to sea. Flowers April-May. **3. Hypericum aegypticum.** A low, dense, spreading shrub similar to 2 but with elliptic or narrowly oblong leaves; flowers solitary, almost sessile, petals just a little larger and persistent. Habitat: Cliffs near the sea. Flowers April-May.

Group B. Perennial plants with black glands on sepals. Leaves in whorls.

1. Hypericum empetrifolium. A many-branched shrub up to 50cm. high. Glabrous leaves in whorls of 3, 2-12mm. long. Flowers in either compound or simple cymes. Sepals with sessile glands around margin. Narrow petals, 3 to 4 times longer than sepals. Habitat: Stony localities in sub-montane and lowland zones. Flowers May-July. **2. Hypericum amplycalyx.** Similar to 1 but the sepals are without glands, and the leaves in whorls of 4. Habitat: Stony places in sub-montane and lowland zones of East Crete.

Group C. Perennials. Black glands on the sepals, the leaves, the anthers and the petals or, at least, on certain of these parts of the plant. Leaves opposite.

1. Hypericum perfoliatum. Erect or ascending stems, 25-75cm. high. Leaves ovate, triangular-lanceolate, or linear-lanceolate, usually amplexicaul, and from 13 to 60mm. long. Quite large flowers in corymbs. Habitat: Wet meadows and sandy stretches among rocks near the sea. Flowers May-July. **2. Hypericum trichocaulon.** Stems either procumbent or ascending, 5-25cm., rooting at nodes. Leaves ovate-oblong or linear, 5-14mm. Inflorescences with few quite large flowers. It is a West and Central Cretan endemic. Habitat: Montane zone. Flowers May-July. **3. Hypericum kelleri.** Similar to 2 but stems 1-5(-20)cm. long, and leaves 2-4mm. Habitat: Montane and sub-montane zones. Flowers April-June. **4. Hypericum perforatum.** Erect stems arising from a procumbent base. The stems have lines lengthwise. Leaves ovate to linear, Practically sessile, and bearing numerous transparent glands. The flowers are in large panicles. The petals are twice the size of the sepals. Habitat: Lowland and sub-montane zones. Flowers May-September. **5. Hypericum triquetrifolium.** Similar but smaller than 4 with smaller amplexicaul leaves, and with either a few or without any transparent glands. Habitat: Arid localities or sandy situations at a low altitude. Flowers May to September.

Violales

Violaceae Family

Small plants with alternate leaves, with stipules at the base. Flowers usually zygomorphic. Sepals and petals 5. Ovary superior. Fruit a capsule, dehiscing with 3 valves.

Hypericum aogypticum

Hypericum perforatum

Viola suavis

Viola cretica

Viola (Violets and Pansies)

Leaves petiolate. Sepals recurved to form bract-like appendages. Petals arranged zygomorphically, the bottom ones are spurred.

Group A. Stemless plants. Leaves large, more or less heart-shaped with long petioles arising directly from rootstock to form a rosette.

1. Viola odorata. A perennial herb with long rooting stolons, 5-15cm. Leaves cordate orbicular or reniform with heart-shaped base, obtuse at tip with long stalks and small ovate stipules that are either smooth or with a slight ciliate fringe at margin. Sweet-scented violet-coloured flowers, 1.5cm. across. Lateral petals bearded at base. Habitat: Montane zone. Flowers March-April. **2. Viola hirta.** Similar to 1 but without stolons, pubescent-hairy with ovate-cordate leaves, on the whole pointed. Scentless violet flowers. Habitat: Montane and sub-alpine zones. Flowers March-May. **3. Viola alba - subsp. dehnhardtii.** Similar to 1 but leaves are cordate or ovate-cordate, rather pointed at tip. Sweet-smelling violet flowers. Stipules linear-lanceolate with ciliate fringe. Habitat: Found in wet meadows of the montane zone. Flowers March-May. **4. Viola suavis.** Resembles 1 but leaves ovate-cordate and rather pointed, stolons short and thick and flowers pale violet with throat and spur white. Flowers March-May. Its occurrence in Crete, however, is uncertain. **5. Viola cretica.** Similar to 1 but leaves ovate-triangular, cordate at base, and hairy. Flowers violet-coloured, lateral petals not bearded. A Cretan endemic. Habitat: Montane zone. Flowers March-May.

Group B. Plants with one or more stems. The leaves are small, discoid to linear in shape, not cordate at base, and with short petioles.

1. Viola fragrans. This is a perennial pubescent or hairy herb with numerous dense stems reaching 5-10(-15)cm. in length. Oblong or oblong-linear leaves, about 1,5cm. long. Stipules resemble the leaves but are smaller. The flowers are yellow, only rarely pale violet, about 1cm. across. Endemic to Crete and Peloponnese. Habitat: Among rocks in the montane and sub-alpine zones. Flowers May-June. **2. Viola kitalbeliana.** A hairy annual herb, 2-10cm. Crenate leaves 1-3cm. The lower ones discoid, the others oblong-spathulate. The stipules are divided into narrow lobes, the middle one longer than the others, similar to corresponding leaf. Flowers pale yellow, 4-8mm. Habitat: Montane zone. Flowers April-May. **3. Viola rauliniana.** Similar to 2 but either hairless or only slightly haired. It is also a more dwarf-like plant (usually no higher than 3cm.), and bears cream-coloured flowers. Habitat: Stony places in montane, sub-alpine and alpine zones. **4. Viola scorpiuroides.** A perennial plant with a woody rootstock, greyish-green leaves that are pubescent, broadly obovate, and small linear stipules. Yellow flowers about 1cm. across. Habitat: Among rocks near the sea. Flowers March-April. This plant is of North African origin, and in Europe grows only on the islands of Kythera and Crete.

Cistaceae Family

These plants can be found either as shrubs or as herbs. Leaves simple and mostly opposite and, usually, covered with stellate hairs. Flowers with 5 petals and 3 or 5 sepals. Stamens numerous.

Cistus (Cistus)

Small shrubs with big white, pink or purple flowers. They are aromatic and resinous plants, producing the substance known as laudanum.

1. Cistus incanus - subsp. creticus. A bushy shrub up to 100cm. high. Leaves ovate, obovate or elliptic, 15-25mm. long, thickly pubescent and with an undulating margin. Flowers rosy-purple in colour with 5 sepals and 4-6cm. across. Habitat: On hillsides in the lowland, sub-montane and montane zones. Flowers April-May. **2. Cistus parviflorus.** Similar to 1 but leaves more greyish-green in colour, and flowers pink and smaller (2-3cm.). Habitat: Lowland and sub-montane zones. Flowers March-May. **3. Cistus salvifolius.** Similar to 1 but its flowers are white and 3-5cm. across. Habitat: Sub-montane and montane zones. Flowers April-May. **4. Cistus monspeliensis.** Similar to the 3 foregoing species, but usually a taller plant with stems more erect. Flowers white, 2-3cm. across. Leaves linear or linear-lanceolate. Habitat: Lowland and sub-montane zones. Flowers April-May.

Cistus Incanus - s. sp. creticus   *Cistus parviflorus*

Cistus salvifolius   *Cistus monspeliensis*

Tuberaria

Annual or perennial plants with leaves in a basal rosette and erect stems. Leaves with 3 parallel veins. Flowers yellow in apical cymes. 5 sepals, 2 of which are smaller.

1. Tuberaria guttata. A 30cm. high pubescent annual. Leaves either elliptic or obovate with stipules. Flowers 10-20mm., yellow and mostly with purple blotches at the base of the petals. Habitat: Uncultivated ground of the sub-montane zone. Flowers March-May.

Helianthemum (Rockrose)

Small shrubs or annual herbs. Leaves opposite and mostly stipuled. Flowers usually yellow, seldom white, in apical cymose or racemose inflorescences. 5 sepals, two of them smaller than the other three.

1. Helianthemum lavandulifolium. A 10-50cm. tall shrub covered with thick grey pubescence. The leaves are 10-50mm., lanceolate or linear-lanceolate with upcurved lips, greyish-green above and whitish beneath. Stipules conspicuous, frequently caducous. Numerous flowers in dense cymes. Yellow petals, 5-10mm. Habitat: Sandy localities in the lowlands. Flowers April-May. **2. Helianthemum nummalarium - subsp. nummularium.** A perennial with a few spreading or ascending stems, 5-20(-50)cm. Ovate to lanceolate-oblong hairy leaves, greenish above and grey or whitish beneath. Yellow flowers in one-sided cymes. Petals 6-12mm. long. Habitat: Montane and sub-montane zones. Flowers April-June. **3. Helianthemum ledifolium.** A pubescent annual, 10-60cm. high. Elliptic, lanceolate, or obovate leaves 10-15mm. long, green above and grey beneath. Linear stipules half the length of leaves. Inflorescences with bunches of 3-13 flowers. Sepals 6-10mm. The yellow petals are slightly smaller than the sepals. Habitat: Arid places at a low altitude. Flowers April-May. **4. Helianthemum salicifolium.** Usually a many-branched annual up to 30cm. Leaves either ovate-lanceolate or elliptic-oblong, 5-30mm. Inflorescences bearing 5-20 flowers. The 5-14mm. petals yellow. Habitat: Dry hilly situations at a low altitude. Flowers April-May. **5. Helianthemum sanguinem.** Similar to 4 but stems shorter, up to 10cm., usually reddish. A hairy, glandular plant. Inflorescences have only 3-6 yellow flowers. Petals 6-8mm. Habitat: Sandy localities in lowland and littoral zones. Flowers March-April. **6. Helianthemum aegyptiacum.** An erect annual with a few pubescent stems up to 30cm. high. Leaves linear-lanceolate or oblong, frequently with curled edges. Dark green on upper surface and grey below. Linear stipules. Inflorescences with 3 to 9 flowers. Petals yellow, 5-9mm., smaller than the sepals. Habitat: Dry, sandy spots in the lowlands. Flowers April-May. **7. Helianthemum hymettium.** A dwarf perennial shrublet, with slender patent branches up to 10cm. Leaves 7-15mm., flat, oblong-lanceolate or elliptic with white down on either surface, rarely greenish above. Lower leaves lack stipules. Inflorescences of 7-9 flowers. Yellow petals, 3-4mm. Endemic to South Greece and Crete. Habitat: Dry, barren hills of the sub-montane zone. Flowers April-May. **8. Helianthemum apenninum.** A shrublet up to 50cm. Leaves linear or oblong, greenish or whitish above and silvery beneath. Flowers quite large, white with only a yellow centre. Habitat: Stony sites in the sub-montane and lowland zones. Flowers March-May.

Fumana

Shrublets with alternate (very seldom opposite), small narrow leaves with or without stipules. Two of its 5 sepals are much smaller than the other three. Petals yellow.

1. Fumana arabica: A densely branched plant reaching 25cm. in height. Leaves ovate or oblong-lanceolate, flat and pointed, pubescent-glandular or almost glabrous. Flowers, from 1 to 7 on lax terminal inflorescences, 10-12mm. across. Habitat: Sub-montane and lowland zones. Flowers March-April. **2. Fumana procumbens:** A many - branched plant with patent stems up to 40cm. Leaves are linear, ciliate, and without stipules. Flowers solitary in the axils of the upper leaves. Habitat: Stony sites in the sub-montane and lowland zones. Flowers April-May. **3. Fumana thymifolia:** A shrublet up to 20cm. with erect branches. Leaves opposite, at least the lower ones, linear, glabrous or pubescent with stipules. Inflorescence with 3-9 long-stalked flowers which are about 10mm. across. Habitat: Stony localities in lowland and sub-montane zones. Flowers March-May.

Two more species: **Fumana ericoides** and **Fumana scoparia** are mentioned tentatively as occurring in Crete. The former has ascending stems, while the latter's are on the whole erect. Their leaves are generally narrow, alternate, and without stipules. In the case of **Fumana scoparia** the lower leaves are compact.

Helianthemum nummularium
s. sp. nummularium

Helianthemum hymettium

Fumana procumbens

Fumana thymifolia

Tamaricaceae Family

Shrubs or small trees. Flowers tiny, solitary or in racemes. Both petals and sepals 4-5 free.
Stamens from 4 upwards. Minute alternate simple leaves.

Tamarix (Tamarisks)

Small bract-like and amplexicaul leaves. The white or pink flowers in racemes. Sepals and
petals either 4 or 6. Stamens 4-15.

1. Tamarix parviflora: A shrub or small tree with brown or purple branches. Leaves 3-
5mm., pointed with membraneous margins. Racemes 20-40mm. long, and 3-5mm. broad.
Flowers white and usually quadripartite. Petals 2mm. long. Habitat: River and stream

banks, as well as hedges in the lowland and littoral zones. Flowers in springtime. **2. Tamarix dalmatica:** A small tree with brownish-black branches, and leaves 2,5-4mm. long. Racemes 20-60 X 8-10mm. The white flowers are usually quadripartite. Petals 2,5-5mm. Habitat: Maritime marshes and banks of rivers or streams near the sea. Flowers in the spring. **3. Tamarix smyrnensis:** Similar to 1 but leaf margins non-membraneous, while racemes are both longer and narrower 15-60 X 3-4mm. Habitat: Damp seaboard localities, and river banks in the lowland and sub-montane zones. Flowers in the autumn.

Frankeniaceae Family

Dwarf shrubs or herbs with entire, opposite minute leaves. Flowers with 4-6 sepals which are fused at base, and 4-6 free petals. Six stamens.

Frankenia (Sea Heaths)

Annual or perennial plants. 5-sepalled, and 5-petalled flowers. Calyx lunate.

1. Frankeria pulverulenta: An annual with up to 30cm. long, prostrate stems. Leaves obovate or oblong-spathulate, 1-5mm. long. Flowers on one side only of small terminal, or axillary, spikes. Petals 3,5-5mm. violet-coloured. Habitat: Sandy tracts and salt-marshes by the sea. Flowers May to August. **2. Frankenia hirsuta:** Similar to 1 but a perennial, thickly pubescent, with dense branches and both wider and longer leaves. The flowers which are on terminal racemes are white or pale purple. Habitat: Seaside stretches of sand and in salt-marshes. Flowers May-August.

Only one species of the **Elatinaceae** family occurs in Crete, namely **Elatinae alsinastrum.** From a decorative point of view it is an insignificant plant which grows on marshy ground. The leaves are in whorls, and the tiny flowers are white and quadripartite.

Datiscaceae

These are mostly dioecious plants with alternate leaves. The male flowers lack petals, have a 4-9 segmented calyx, and 4-25 stamens. The calyx of the female flowers is 3-8 segmented.

Datisca

Herbs with trifoliate or pinnate leaves. Stamens with large anthers.

1. Datisca cannabina: A plant with a perennial root, an erect stem reaching a height or 1m., and pinnate leaves whose leaflets are lanceolate and very pointed. Its general appearance reminds one of hemp. Small flowers on long racemes arise from the axils of the upper leaves. A native of South-West Asia and the Himalayas, the only place in Europe where it occurs is Crete.

Cucurbitales

Cucurbitaceae Family

Procumbent or climbing, tendril-bearing herbs. Stamens 5, in rare cases 3. Ovary inferior usually with 1 style and 3 stigmas, mostly cleft.

I amarix parviflora

Tamarix dalmatica

Tamarix smyrnensis

Ecbalium elaterium

Ecbalium (Squirting Cucumbers)

Monoecious perennials, with bristle-like hairs and a tuber-like root. Stems procumbent and with no tendrils. Calyx campanulate and 5-lobed. Corolla rotate and 5-lobed. Male flowers with 3 stamens in axillary racemes. Female flowers, single, in the axils of the leaves.

1. Ecbalium elaterium: Stems 15-60cm. Leaves long-stalked with lamina 4-10cm., cordate-triangular, dentate or undulate at margins. Male flowers yellow, 18-20mm. Female flowers smaller. Fruit fleshy, very hairy-prickly capsule, 4-5cm , that splits open explosively to eject seeds far afield. Habitat: Bare, dry places of the sub-montane and lowland zones. Flowers May-September.

Bryonia (Bryonies)

Monoecious or dioecious perennial plants with tubular roots. Stems climbing by means of simple tendrils. Greenish-white flowers in axillary inflorescences, with both calyx and corolla 5-lobed. Male flowers with 3 stamens. Leaves alternate, palmately lobed, five-lobed, cordate at base.

1. Bryonia cretica - subspecies cretica. Dioecious plant. Stems up to 4m. Leaves with white spots, 5-10cm. long, cordate-pentangular or palmately-lobed, with lobes entire or slightly dentate. Flowers small. Male inflorescences smooth. Fruit a red berry, with white spots before ripening. Habitat: Hedges, ditches and scrub of the sub-montane and lowland zones. Flowers February-May. Bears fruit from August to October. **2. Bryonia cretica - subsp. dioica:** Very similar to 1 but male inflorescences are glandular, both leaves and unripe berries without white spots. Habitat: Hedges and ditches of sub-montane and lowland zones. Flowers February-March. Bears fruit from August to October.

Among the **Castales** only 2 species of the **Castaceae** family occur in Crete as sub-spontaneous plants, originating from introduced plants. These species are **Opuntia vulgaris** from N. America and **Opuntia ficusindica** from tropical America, known by the common name of "Frangosykies" or in English Prickly Pears.

Myrtales

Lythraceae Family

Herbaceous plants with simple, entire leaves, stipules small or absent, and flowers quadripartite to sixpartite. Under the flowers there is a continuation of the capsule, the hypanthium. Calyx 5- lobed. Petals free, growing on the lips of the calyx. Ovary superior.

Lythrum (Purple Loosestrifes)

Annual or perennial plants. Leaves alternate, opposite or in whorls. Flowers usually six-partite, usually single in the axils of the leaves. Stamens 2-12.

1. Lythrum junceum: Glabrous, perennial, with stems branching from the base. Branches spreading or ascending, 20-70cm. Leaves alternate 8-22 X 2-11mm., elliptic-elongate or linear-elongate. Flowers solitary. Hypanthium 5-6mm. Petals 5-6mm., purple, seldom white. Habitat: Wet places at a low altitude. Flowers March-May. **2. Lythrum hyssopifolium:** Similar to 1 but annual, with spreading, reddish stems. Leaves slightly smaller. Petals 2-3mm. pink. Habitat: Wet or seasonally flooded areas at a low altitude. Flowers May- June. **3. Lythrum borysthenicum:** Similar to the two previous plants but a dwarf annual, with a single stem 3-10(-18)cm. Flowers with very small purple petals, often absent. Habitat: In seasonally flooded areas at a low altitude. Flowers April-June.

Myrtaceae Family

Evergreen trees or bushes. Leaves simple, usually opposite, with scented oleiferous glands. Flowers with 4 or 5 petals and calyx 4-lobed or 5-lobed. Numerous stamens. Ovary semi-inferior.

Myrtus (Myrtles)

Shrubs with opposite leaves. Flowers solitary in the axils of the leaves. Fruit a fleshy berry.

1. Myrtus communis - subsp. communis. Shrub up to 5m. Leaves ovate-lanceolate,

Bryonia cretica - s. sp. cretica

Bryonia cretica - s. sp. dioica

Lythrum junceum

Myrtus communis - s. sp. communis

pointed, 2-5cm. Flowers white, about 2cm. across with 5 petals. Fruit an elliptic berry, black, seldom white, about 12mm. long. Habitat: Forests, gullies and cool localities of the sub-montane and lowland zones. Flowers April-May. **2. Myrtus communis - subsp. tarentina:** Similar to 1 but not higher than 2m. Dense leaves up to 2cm. long. Berry almost spherical. Habitat: Mainly in sea-side places. Flowers March-May.

Punicaceae Family

The leaves of these plants do not have oleiferous glands. Flowers with 5-7 sepals and petals. Ovary semi-inferior with many seeds covered by pulpy seed-coats.

Punica (Pomegranates)

Prickly shrubs or trees. Leaves opposite or occasionally ternary. Flowers with bell-shaped calyx, 5-lobed and 5 free petals.

1. Punica granatum: Deciduous shrub, prickly, with leaves oblong lanceolate or obovate. Flowers with red petals and red calyx, large 30-40mm. across. Fruit 5-8cm. greenish-red, with numerous seeds in pink or purple pulpy seed-coats. Habitat: A native of South-West Asia it has been cultivated in Crete since antiquity becoming established in gullies, ditches and gorges of the montane and sub-montane zones. Flowers May-June.

Onagraceae Family

Herbs or shrubs with flowers usually actinomorphic, hardly ever zygomorphic. There is usually a hypanthium tube, like an extension of the calyx. Sepals 2, 4 or 5. Petals free, 2, 4, 5, or none. Stamens 2, 4, 8, or 10.

Epilobium (Willow herbs)

Perennial herbs with leaves alternate, opposite or in whorls. Flowers quadripartite, white, pink or purple with a long hypanthium tube. Stamens 8.

1. Epilobium hirsutum: A plant with underground stolons and stems up to 100(-200) cm. robust, pubescent-hairy. Leaves pubescent, oblong or lanceolate, sessile, slightly crenate. Petals purple, 10-16mm. Habitat: Banks of streams, roadside ditches in the montane and sub-montane zones. Flowers June-September. **2. Epilobium parviflorum:** A plant producing rosettes of leaves at base that persist during the winter also. Stem up to 75cm., sturdy, usually hairy. Leaves pubescent, oblong or linear-lanceolate, slightly serrate, almost sessile. Petals pinkish-purple, 4-9mm. Habitat: Damp places of the montane zone. Flowers May-July. **3. Epilobium tetragonum - subsp. tetragonum:** Similar to 2 but many-branched, almost glabrous, with a quadrangular stem and flowers with smaller petals 2,5-7mm. Habitat: Damp places of the montane zone. Flowers May-July.

The genus **Myriophylium** of the **Haloragaceae** family which includes aquatic plants is represented in Crete only by **M. spicatum.** Leaves pinnate in whorls with hairlike segments and in fours. Unimportant pink flowers in spikes. Of the **Theligonum** genus of the **Theligonaceae** family, only **T. cynocrambe** occurs in Crete. It is an insignificant small annual plant with small, long-petioled leaves and tiny inconspicuous flowers. Of the **Hippuris** genus, belonging to the aquatic **Hippuridaceae** family, only 1 species is to be found in Crete, namely **H. vulgaris.** A plant of no importance, with lanceolate-linear leaves in whorls, and tiny, barely discernible flowers in bundles of 6 to 12.

Umbeliflorae

Araliaceae Family

Shrubs or dense climbers. Leaves alternate and small actinomorphic flowers. Calyx small. 5 free petals. 5 stamens. Fruit a berry.

Hedera (Ivy)

Woody stems, climbing or procumbent, clinging to rocks and trees, with numerous small roots. Leaves simple, angular, elliptic or cordate. Flowers small, greenish.

Myrtus communis - s. sp. tarentina

Punica granatum

Epilobium hirsutum

Hedera helix - s. sp. helix

1. Hedera helix - subsp. helix. A plant with dark green smooth leaves 5-lobed or pentangular, and those of the flower-bearing stems elliptic. Flowers in spherical umbels with few rays. Berries black, 8-10mm.

Umbeliferae Family

Herbaceous plants seldom shrubs. Leaves alternate, with laminae usually long and deeply divided into many segments. Inflorescence usually a compound umbel. Flowers small with 5 sepals or without any, and 5 free petals. Ovary inferior, with two carpels fused lengthwise. Fruit hard, consisting of two carpels called schizocarps. The shape of the schizocarps plays an important role in determining the genus of the plant, since they often greatly resemble each other as to the rest of the characteristics, and are therefore easily confused.

Eryngium (Sea Hollies)

Annual or perennial herbs, glabrous, with leaves prickly, hard, pinnate or at least dentate. Flowers white or blue, in dense headlike umbels, surrounded by prickly leaves.

1. Eryngium maritimum: Perennial, 15-60cm. high. Leaves glaucous and have large prickly teeth or 3-5 prickly lobes. Flowers pale blue. Crowded inflorescences with many heads, surrounded by 4-7 bracts. Habitat: Sandy shores. Flowers June-September. **2. Eryngium creticum:** Perennial 25-100cm. high, with stems and leaves glaucous, tinged with violet. Leaves deeply dissected into narrow spiny lobes. Basal leaves entire or trilobate. Inflorescence blue, surrounded by linear-lanceolate, bluish-violet bracts. Habitat: Low altitude bare hills or plains. Flowers June-August. **3. Eryngium ternatum:** A perennial glaucous plant, 20-50cm. high. Lower leaves tripartite, with linear lobes. Bracts barely tinged with blue. Flowers white. Endemic to Crete. Habitat: Dry places at a low altitude. Flowers June-August. **4. Eryngium amethystinum:** Perennial 20-45cm. high. Basal leaves bipinnate, with prickly lanceolate segments. The leaves of the stem are similar. Inflorescence with blue flowers, and bluish-violet bracts. Habitat: Dry places, hilly sites. Flowers June-August. **5. Eryngium campestre:** Perennial 20-70cm. high, glaucous-green with a thick turnip-like root. Flowers white, in ovate dense inflorescences surrounded by 4-6 narrow, entire or dentate bracts. Basal leaves tripartite, with the middle lobe bipinnate, very prickly. Habitat: Uncultivated, barren fields and hills. Flowers May-July.

Lagoecia

Annual aromatic plants with pinnately-lobed or pinnate leaves. Umbels globular. Petals white. Fruit a single carpel, the second one having atrophied.

1. Lagoecia cuminoides: Stem 10-30cm. Basal leaves have ovate, dentate segments. Upper leaves have small, lanceolate lobes barbate at tips. The umbels arising from the axils of the leaves are small, dense, globular, surrounded by pinnate involucre leaves, the same as the flowers are. Habitat: Fallow fields and meadows at a low altitude. Flowers April-May.

Echinophora

Leaves bi- or tripinnately lobed. Sepals persistent, petals white or yellow. Fruit ovate or oblong. Schizocarps with long persistent stolons.

1. Echinophora tenuifolia - subsp. sibthorpiana: A perennial plant, greyish-green, with many dense branches. Basal leaves pubescent, twice or thrice pinnately lobed, with slightly fleshy and dentate lobes. Many small umbels, with 3-5 rays and 5-10 small, yellow flowers on each ray, of which only the middle one is fertile, developing into a fruit that is surrounded by thick spiny bracts. Habitat: Dry places of the lowland zone. Flowers July-September.

Smyrnium (Alexanders)

Basal leaves usually twice or thrice tripartite, the upper ones usually simple. Flowers with

Smyrnium apifolium

yellow petals and without sepals. Umbels without bracts at base of rays. Fruit ovoid or almost spherical with almost globular schizocarps.

1. Smyrnium olusatrum: A glabrous perennial plant with a thick hollow stem, 50-150cm. high. Leaves smooth, dark green, the basal long-stalked, up to 30cm., twice of thrice tripartite, with large lobes ovate-rhomboid, dentate, the upper leaves tripartite. Umbels with 5-15 rays. Habitat: Stony and rocky places of the sub-montane and lowland zones. Flowers May-June. **2. Smyrnium apifolium:** Biennial. Stem up to 60cm. Lower leaves long-stalked, thrice-tripartite, with lobes oblong-cuneate, dentate. Middle leaves tripartite or trilobate. Upper leaves entire, oblong-ovate, dentate, amplexicaul, greenish-yellow. Umbels with 15-18 rays. Habitat: Cool places of the montane zone. Flowers April-May. **3. Smyrnium perfoliatum.** Similar to 2 but taller (up to 150cm.). Stem angular and with narrow wings. Basal leaves tripartite or twice tripartite. Upper leaves ovate-cordate, dentate. Umbels with 5-12 rays. Habitat: Olive groves and bushy localities of the sub-montane zone. Flowers April-May. **4. Smyrnium rotundifolium:** Very similar to 3 but stem with wings and upper leaves with entire margins. Habitat: Scrub and olive groves of the sub-montane and lowland zones. Flowers March-April.

Chaerophylium (Rough Chervils)

Leaves pinnate, up to thrice pinnate. Petals white, pink or yellow. Fruit narrowly oblong or narrowly ovate, slightly flattened at sides.

1. Chaerophylium creticum: Annual, with smooth stem, up to 80cm. Leaves thrice pinnate, with lobes linear - lanceolate, up to 2mm. wide. Flowers yellow, with bracts and bracteoles linear or often divided. Endemic to Crete. Habitat: Montane zone, in the vicinity of the Omalos Plateau. Flowers May-June.

Anthriscus (Cow Parsleys)

Leaves twice or thrice pinnate. Sepals small or absent. Petals white. Fruit narrowly oblong or ovoid.

1. Anthriscus nemorosa: A perennial plant with stem up to 1m., and leaves thrice pinnate, with lobes pinnately lobed, smooth above, hairy at the veins beneath. Umbels with 7-12 rays of almost equal length. Fruit greenish or blackish-green, 8-10mm. Habitat: Forests of the montane zone. Flowers July-August.

Scandix (Shepherd's Needles)

Comparatively small plants, with leaves twice or thrice pinnate, with narrow lobes. Umbels with few rays or with only one. Sepals absent. Petals white, often large on the outer flowers. Fruit linear-cylindrical, with very long beak.

1. Scandix australis - subsp. australis: An annual plant, 10-30cm., with most of the leaves at the base. Flowers very small, in umbels with 1-3 rays. Fruit with a beak of the same length as the fruit itself. Habitat: Sub-montane and lowland zones, in dry places. Flowers February-April. **2. Scandix pecten-veneris - subsp. pecten-veneris:** Very similar to 1, but the beak is 3-4 times longer than the main part of the fruit, and the bracteoles are large and permanent at the base of the fruit. **3. Scandix pecten-venenis - subsp. macroryncha:** Similar to the two previous species, but the beak is 2-3 times longer than the fruit itself and with small caducous bracteoles. Habitat: Hills and barren expanses at a low altitude. Flowers February-April.

Coriandrum (Corianders)

The lower leaves lobed, the others pinnate to thrice pinnate. Sepals persistent. Petals white, the outer larger and deeply bilobed. Fruit ovoid or spherical.

1. Coriandrum sativum: Glabrous, annual, foetid plant 30-60cm. high. Lobes of lower leaves ovate-cuneate, dentate. On the other leaves the lobes are linear. Umbels with 3-5 (-10) rays, and with 1 or no bracts, and 3 bracteoles on each secondary ray. Fruit 2-6mm., aromatic and medicinal. A plant of Asia and Africa, long established in Crete. Habitat: Fallow and cultivated fields. Flowers May-June.

Lagoecia cuminoldes

Smyrnium olusatrum

Lecokia cretica

Scandix australis s. sp. australis

Bifora

Leaves pinnate or twice pinnate, with linear or filiform lobes. Sepals small or absent. Petals white. Fruit with globular schizocarps.

1. Bifora testiculata: A 20-40cm. high glabrous annual plant. Stems usually sparsely branched. Leaves pinnate or twice pinnate, with linear lobes. Umbel rays 1-3. Bracts 1 or none. Fruit with globular wrinkled schizocarps. Habitat: Uncultivated fields at a low altitude. Flowers April-May.

Scaligeria

Leaves bipinnate or tripinnate, the lower with rhomboid or ovate lobes, the others with linear lobes. The uppermost usually entire. Flowers white. Fruit ovoid.

159

1. Scaligeria napiformis: Biennial, glabrous plant, 10-50cm. high. with a tuber at its root. Basal leaves with triangular margin and rhomboid-triangular, crenate lobes. The upper leaves simple, linear or consisting of only the sheath. Umbels with 5-20 rays, without bracts. Fruit 1,5-2mm. Habitat: Arid, rocky localities of the sub-montane and lowland zones. Flowers May-July. **2. Scaligeria halophila:** Very similar to 1 but leaves are fleshy and fruit larger. Habitat: Littoral zone, but only on the islets of S. and E. Crete.

Tordylium (Hartworts)

Aromatic, annual, hairy plants, with pinnate leaves. Leaflets oblong to orbicular, never linear. Petals usually white, the outer ones larger. Sepals present. Fruit orbicular, ovoid or elliptic, strongly compressed from the back, with a thick moniliform margin.

1. Tordylium officinale: A slender annual, 20-50cm. in height. Lower leaves have leaflets which are ovate or almost orbicular, deeply cordate at their base, dentate at the margin. Upper leaves simple or pinnate lanceolate or oblong, dentate. Umbels with 8-14 rays. Bracts and bracteoles narrow, linear, long, of about the same length as the rays. Habitat: Lowland and sub-montane zones, in both uncultivated and cultivated fields in W. Crete. Flowers April-May. **2. Tordylium apulum:** Similar to 1 but the basal leaves have leaflets more apart, and umbels with small bracts and bracteoles. Habitat: Fallow and cultivated fields in the lowland and sub-montane zones. Flowers April-May. **3. Tordylium byzantinum:** Similar to the two previous plants, but basal leaves entire, ovate, crenate or with 3-5 ovate-crenate leaflets. Umbels with 20-40 rays. Numerous filiform bracts and bracteoles. In Europe, it occurs only in Crete and in E. Thrace. Habitat: Lowland and sub-montane zones.

Thapsia

Leaves twice or thrice pinnate. Flowers with yellow petals and small sepals. Fruit large, oblong or ovoid, compressed at the back.

1. Thapsia garganica: A glabrous or slightly hairy, glaucous-green, perennial plant, 30-250cm. high. The root consists of many tough fibres. The stem is hollow, striate. Lower leaves glaucous beneath, with lobes (leaflets) usually linear-oblong 10-50mm. Umbels with 5-20 rays, without bracts or bracteoles. Fruit 12-25mm., oblong or elliptic, with marginal wings 3-6mm. broad, deeply bilobed at tip and at base. Habitat: Waste and stony ground, at a low altitude. Flowers May-June.

Torilis (Hedge-parsleys)

Usually annual plants. Leaves pinnate, bipinnate or tripinnate, with dentate or pinnately-lobed leaflets. Petals white or pink. Sepals small. Fruit ovoid or linear, covered with hard spiny hairs.

1. Torilis nodosa: Annual, up to 50cm. usually procumbent. Leaves pinnate or bipinnate, with deeply pinnately-lobed leaflets. Umbels almost sessile, opposite to leaves and with few, short rays. Flowers pale pink. Fruit ovoid 2-3mm. Habitat: Uncultivated ground of sub-montane and lowland zones. Flowers April-May. **2. Torilis arvensis:** Similar to 1 but usually erect, with very varied leaves, from trifoliate to twice pinnate and lobes ovate or lanceolate. Umbels not sessile, with 2-12 rays; with either 1 bract or none, and with many bracteoles. Fruit 3-6mm. A very varied species, divided into a series of subspecies whose exact distribution has not been studied. Habitat: Fallow and cultivated fields in the sub-montane and lowland zones. Flowers April-May. **3. Torilis leptophylla.** Similar to 1 but erect, often branching. Bipinnate leaves, with linear leaflets. Umbels opposite to leaves,

Tordylium apulum

but with distinct peduncles and rays. Fruit oblong-linear. Habitat: Cultivated and fallow ground of the montane and sub-montane zones. Flowers April-June.

Orlaya (Orlayas)

Leaves twice or thrice pinnate. Petals white, rarely pink, the outer much bigger and bilobed. Spiny ovoid, prickly fruit.

1. Orlaya grandiflora: Annual, 20-40cm., almost glabrous. Leaves thrice pinnate, with tiny, oblong or linear leaflets. Umbels with 5-12 rays and bracts lanceolate. Flowers white. Outer petals up to 8 times larger than the remainder. Spines of fruit, short. Habitat: Fields

161

and roadsides in montane zone. Flowers May-July. **2. Orlaya kochii:** Similar to 1 but the umbels have 2-4 rays, the outer petals are only 2-3 times larger than the others, the fruit, too, is larger with longer spines. Habitat: Fields and waste ground of the sub-montane and lowland zones. Flowers April-May.

Daucus (Carrots)

Leaves twice or thrice pinnate. Umbel bracts numerous, usually pinnate. Petals white, yellow or purple, the outer often larger. Fruit elliptic or ovoid, slightly or not at all compressed at the back, spiny.

1. Daucus carota: Annual or biennial, very varied. Stem sturdy, up to 100cm. high, glabrous or hairy. Leaves twice or thrice pinnate, with segments, (leaflets) linear or narrowly lanceolate glabrous or pubescent, occasionally slightly fleshy. Umbels large, with many rays. Large, pinnate or twice pinnate bracts and bracteoles linear or tripartite. Petals white, seldom pink. The middle flower of umbel often dark purple. Fruit 2-4mm. The taproot is thick and edible in the cultivated varieties, slender when wild. Both cultivated and established in the lowland and sub-montane zones. Flowers May-July. It is divided into a series of subspecies. The subspecies **sativus** is the familiar cultivated carrot which often sprouts spontaneously. The supbspecies **carota** is similar to the cultivated kind, but its root is slender and white. As regards the other 6 subspecies that grow in S. Europe and in the Mediterranean area, it is difficult to specify which exist in Crete, because no relevant work has been carried out. **2. Daucus broteri:** Annual, with stem 15-50cm., erect or ascending, many-branched from the base; glabrous or slightly hairy at base. Leaves bipinnate. Flowers white or pink. Umbels with 8-14 rays. Bracts pinnate of equal length with or shorter than, the rays. Bracteoles linear, entire or tripartite. Fruit 4-6mm. Habitat: Fallow fields at a low altitude. Flowers August-September. **3. Daucus guttatus -subsp. guttatus:** Similar to 2, but umbels with 8-25 rays, bracts usually longer than the rays, and bracteoles always simple, linear. Habitat: Uncultivated ground and bare stretches in the lowland zone. Flowers July-September. **4. Daucus involucratus:** Similar to 2 and 3 but smaller, up to 20cm. high, glabrous or sparsely hairy. Leaves small, often once-pinnate. Umbels smaller with 2-4 rays. Habitat: Bare, arid sites at a low altitude. Flowers In the Summer.

Pseudorlaya

Leaves twice or thrice pinnate. Numerous linear bracts. Petals white or purple. Elliptic, prickly fruit.

1. Pseudorlaya pumila: A densely hairy annual up to 20cm., branched at base. Segments of leaves ovate. Umbel rays 2-5. Bracts 2-5, linear or tripartite. Petals white or purple, the outer only a little bigger than the others. Fruit 7-10mm. Habitat: Sandy shores. Flowers July-September.

Turgenia

Hairy plants. Umbels with white, pink or purple flowers whose outer petals are larger and bilobed. Ovate burred fruit.

1. Turgenia latifolia: An annual aromatic plant up to 60cm. Leaves pinnate, with lanceolate or oblong crenate leaflets. Umbels with 2-5 rays and 3-5 bracts. Bracteoles ovate to oblong. Flowers white or pink. Habitat: Cultivated places and waste ground of the submontane and lowland zones. Flowers April-May.

Orlaya grandiflora

Bunium

Plants with tuberous roots, almost globular. Leaves twice or thrice pinnate, with narrow lobes. Flowers with white petals, and with small sepals or without any. Fruit oblong or oblong-obovate, compressed on sides.

1. Bunium ferulaceum: Erect or ascending, 20-60cm. Basal leaves few and small. Umbels with 6-15 rays, with 1-2 bracts at base, or without any. Secondary umbels with 3-6 bracteoles. Habitat: Rocks of the montane zone. Flowers May-July.

Huetia

Plants similar to **Bunium** but with fruit linear-oblong.

1. Huetica cretica: A perennial, procumbent dwarf plant up to 5cm. Basal leaves have broad elliptic or oblong lobes, the remainder narrow ones. Umbels without bracts with 2-5 rays. Fruit 4,5mm. Endemic to Crete. Habitat: Montane zone. Flowers May-June.

Pimpinella (Burnet Saxifrages)

Basal leaves usually entire, trilobate or tripartite, more rarely pinnate to tripinnate. Middle leaves usually bipinnate, with narrow lobes. Sepals small. Petals white or yellow, seldom pink. Fruit ovate-oblong or almost globular.

1. Pimpinella anisum: An annual, slightly pubescent, aromatic plant. Stem hollow, branching upwards. Basal leaves tripartite or quinquepartite, with dentate, obovate leaves. The bottom leaves are kidney-shaped or lobose. The stem leaves are twice or thrice pinnate, with linear-lanceolate lobes. Flowers white. Umbels with 7-15 rays. Fruit ovate, 3-5mm., known as anise. An Asiatic plant, cultivated since antiquity, and today subspontaneous. **2. Pimpinella cretica:** Similar to 1 but smaller. Lower leaves almost orbicular, the immediately superior ones are trifoliate, while those of the stem are pinnate or bipinnate with few, linear lobes. Fruit 1,5mm. Habitat: Arid sites at a low altitude. Flowers March-April. **3. Pimpinella peregrina:** Similar to 1, but basal leaves have 5-9, almost orbicular and dentate lealets. The topmost leaves are cordate, dentate. Umbels with 8-50 rays. **4. Pimpinella tragium - subsp. depressa:** Similar to 1 but perennial, pubescent, grey, with stems 5-10cm., and basal leaves pinnate, with small about 5mm., ovate, deeply dentate leaflets. Habitat: Stony localities at a low altitude. Flowers April-June.

Crithmum (Rock Samphires)

Leaves pinnate or twice pinnate, with fleshy segments. Umbels with broad bracts and bracteoles. Flowers yellowish-green, with very small sepals. Fruit ovoid-oblong.

1. Crithmum maritimum: Glabrous perennial, 15-50cm. woody at base, glaucous-green. Leaves have linear-oblanceolate lobes. Umbels with 8-36 rather thick rays. Fruit 5-6mm., yellowish or purple. Habitat: Maritime rocks. Flowers July-October.

Seseli

Biennial or perennial herbaceous plants, with roots as a rule fibrous. Leaves decurrent, twice, thrice or more times divided, ending in narrow lobes. Umbels with or without bracts. Petals usually white. Sepals small or absent. Fruit oblong, elliptic or ovoid, slightly compressed.

1. Seseli gummiferum - subsp. aegaum: A velutinus perennial. Basal leaves twice or thrice pinnate, with lobes 10-25mm., elliptic or obovate. Umbels dense, with 30-60 rays. Bracts 8-16. Flowers white. Fruit 3-4mm., oblong, pubescent. Endemic to E. Crete and the Aegean islands Folegandros and Sikinos. Habitat: Stony slopes of the sub-montane, lowland and littoral zones. Flowers August-October.

Oenanthe (Dropworts)

Leaves pinnately lobed, pinnate or twice, thrice or 4 times pinnate. Petals white or pale

Daucus carota

pink. Sepals pointed. Fruit ovoid, cylindrical or obconical, with the two styles of the ovary persisting, erect and long.

1. Oenanthe pimpineloides. An erect plant, with simple stem up to 100cm. high. Perennial root, with many, small tubers. Basal leaves bipinnate, with leaflets cuneate or ovate, divided into lobules. Stem leaves pinnate or bipinnate, with linear or linear-lanceolate leaflets. Flowers creamy-coloured. Umbels with 6-15 rays, without bracts, Fruit cylindrical, 3mm. Habitat: Damp localities of montane and sub-montane zones. Flowers May-June. **2. Oenanthe prolifera:** Similar to 1 but with many stems. Lobes of basal leaves broader; umbels have only the middle flower of each ray fertile. Habitat: Damp sites at a low altitude. Flowers May-June.

Foeniculum (Fennels)

Leaves thrice or 4 times pinnate, with long, filiform lobes. Flowers yellow, without sepals. Fruit ovoid-oblong, slightly compressed. Aromatic plants.

1. Foeniculum vulgare: Glabrous, perennial or biennial, up to 150cm. Lobes of leaves filiform, 5-50mm. Umbels with 4-30 rays and bractless. Fruit 4-10mm. Habitat: Lowland and littoral zones. Flowers June-September. This plant is usually divided into two subspecies: a) into the genuinely sub-spontaneous one that grows in stony places **(subspecies pipertitum);** its leaves are slightly fleshy, the terminal umbel is surrounded by other lateral umbels and it has.4-10 rays, b) into **subspecies vulgare** that is cultivated and is also established in lowland regions; its leaves are not fleshy, the umbels are 12-25 rayed, and with no lateral umbels.

Anethum (Dills or False Fennels)

Plants similar to Foeniculum but fruit elliptic, strongly compressed at the back.

1. Anethum graveolens: A very similar to **Foeniculum vulgare,** aromatic annual plant, 20-70cm. Umbels with 15-30 rays. Fruit 5-6mm., brown with a light-coloured narrow wing. It is an Asian plant, established since long ago in Crete. Habitat: Both cultivated and subspontaneous in the sub-montane and lowland zones. Flowers June-July.

Kundmania

Leaves pinnate or twice pinnate, with ovate segments. Petals yellow and sepals small. Fruit cylindrical.

1. Kundmania sicula. Glabrous, perennial 30-70cm. Lower leaves usually twice pinnate, with one pair of additional leaflets, at the base of every main branching. Upper leaves pinnate with crenate leaflets. Umbels with 5-30 rays. Numerous linear bracts and bracteoles. Habitat: Dry, uncultivated sites at a low altitude. Flowers May-June.

Conium (Hemlock)

Leaves twice to 4 times pinnate. Flowers without sepals, with white petals. Fruit almost globular, compressed at sides.

1. Conium maculatum: Biennial plant with a stinking smell. Stem hollow glaucous-green, streaked, many-branched, with reddish spots, as a rule at the base. Lower leaves twice to four times pinnate, smooth with lobes 10-20mm., oblong-lanceolate or deltate, deeply pinnately-lobed or crenate. Umbels with white flowers, 5-6 small bracts, 10-12 rays and 3-6 bracteoles. This is the well-known hemlock which Socrates had to drink. Habitat: Hedges, rubble, rubbish, waysides in the montane and sub-montane zones. Flowers May-June.

Lecokia

Leaves pinnate or twice pinnate. Flowers white, sepals small. Fruit short-beaked, ovate-oblong and somewhat compressed at the sides.

1. Lecokia cretica: Glabrous, perennial 60-100cm. Lower leaves broadly triangular at margin, with oblong lobes, deeply dentate or lobose. Umbels with 6-10 rays and with a single bract or none. Rays with few bracteoles. Fruit 10-20mm. An Asian plant that does not occur in any other part of Europe. Habitat: Sub-montane scrub. Flowers May-July.

Oenanthe pimpineloides

Cachrys

Leaves 2-4 times pinnate with linear segments. Petals yellow. Fruit obovoid, a little compressed at the sides.

1. Cachrys crista: An erect plant, glabrous, perennial, with an angular stem and branching opposite or in whorls. Leaves 2-4 times pinnate, with very narrow lobes, linear trilobate at tip. Umbels with 10-12 rays. Bracts and bracteoles linear and small. Fruit 7-10mm. Habitat: Scrub of the sub-montane zone. Flowers May-June.

Bupleurum (Thorow-waxes)

Plants with simple, entire leaves. Flowers tiny, without sepals. Petals yellow. Fruit ovoid or oblong.

1. Bupleurum lancifolium: Annual, with many branchings, height 20-50cm. Leaves yellowish-green, the lower lanceolate-oblong, narrowing at base, the upper lanceolate-ovate, perfoliate. Umbels, small with 2-3 rays. Secondary umbels with large ovate bracteoles at their base. Fruit 3-5mm., ovoid-globular. Habitat: Sub-montane and lowland zones. Flowers May-June. **2. Bupleurum gracile:** Erect, annual 10-40cm. high, glaucous-green, leaves linear-lanceolate-linear, yellowish. Habitat: Sandy and salty soils in the lowland and littoral zones. Flowers May-June. **3. Bupleurum trichopodum:** Similar to 2 but basal leaves long-stalked, narrow, oblanceolate or spathulate, the upper leaves have a stem-clasping base. Umbels with long, slender rays. Habitat: Sub-montane zone. Flowers May-June. **4. Bupleurum semicompositum:** Similar to 2 but densely branched. Lower leaves linear or spathulate, converging. The upper leaves slightly amplexicaul. Bracts linear, with 3 veins. Habitat: Sandy sites in lowland zone. Flowers April-May.

Apium (Celeries)

Leaves pinnate or bipinnate. Flowers small, creamy in umbels with short peduncles. Fruit ovoid or elliptic-oblong.

1. Apium graveolens: A sturdy biennial, up to 1m. high, with a characteristic smell, the well-known celery. Leaves pinnate or twice pinnate. Lobes 5-50mm., deltoid, rhomboid or lanceolate, crenate or lobose. Umbels with 4-12 rays. Habitat: Damp localities of the lowland zone, mainly near the sea. Also widely cultivated. Flowers May-July.

Apium nodiflorum and **Apium repens** are two species of the genus **Apium** which are tentatively mentioned as occurring in Crete. They are plants of damp areas, marshes and streams, similar to Celery, but their leaves are once pinnate, and they are known as Fool's Watercress.

Petroselinum crispum; the well-known Parsley, which is widely cultivated on the island, is also often found growing subspontaneously. It is a smaller plant than Celery, with smaller leaves and yellowish flowers.

Ammi (False Bishop's Weeds)

Leaves pinnate up to tripinnate. Petals white or cream. Sepals small or absent. The outer petals larger. Fruit ovoid or ovoid-oblong, slightly compressed at sides.

1. Ammi majus: Annual 30-100cm. high, very varied. Leaves twice or thrice pinnate. The lower have elliptic or ovate crenate leaflets. The middle leaves have lanceolate lobes while the upper ones have linear lobes. Umbels with 15-20 rays. Bracts tripartite or pinnate with filiform lobes. Bracteoles linear. Habitat: Fields of the sub-montane and lowland zones. Flowers June-August.

Carum (Caraway)

Leaves 2 to 4 times pinnate. Sepals small or absent. Petals usually white. Fruit obovoid-oblong, compressed at sides.

1. Carum multiflorum - subsp. multiflorum: Biennial or perennial with rather thick stem and numerous branches. Basal leaves twice or thrice pinnate, with lobes up to 10mm.

Ferula communis - s. sp. communis

ovate or obovate, dentate or pinnately-lobed. Stem leaves similar, but smaller. Umbels with 15-25 rays and white flowers. Bracts and bracteoles oblong or lanceolate. Habitat: Alpine and sub-alpine zones. Flowers June-August.

Cnidium

Leaves 2 to 4 times pinnate. Sepals small. Petals white. Fruit ovoid or almost globular, slightly compressed at sides.

1. Cnidium silaifolium - subsp. silaifolium: Glabrous perennial, 60-120cm., with simple stem. Leaves 2 to 4 times pinnate, with lobes (leaflets) linear-lanceolate or obovate pointed. Fruit ovoid, about 4mm. Habitat: Stony places in the sub-montane zone. Flowers June-September.

Bonania graeca, a perennial with almost all the leaves close to root, twice pinnate, with oblong-lanceolate lobes and yellow flowered umbels, with linear bracts and bracteoles. It is a matter of conjecture if it grows in Crete.

Ferula (Giant Fennels)

Plants with perennial roots and big strong stems. Leaves 3 to 4 times pinnate, with linear lobes (leaflets). Large umbels with yellow flowers. Bracts, bracteoles and sepals absent. Fruit elliptic or oblong-elliptic strongly compressed at the back.

1. Ferula communis - subsp. communis: Very thick stem up to 2m. high. Leaves with sheath at base, divided into very narrow (1mm.) linear lobes. Large umbels, the terminal umbel surrounded by other lateral ones. Fruit about 15mm. Habitat: Sub-montane and lowland zones. Flowers April-May.

Ferulago

Leaves twice or thrice pinnate, with filiform or linear-lanceolate lobes. Bracts and bracteoles present. Flowers yellow. Sepals very small. Fruit strongly compressed at the back, with conspicuous lateral and vertical wings.

1. Ferulago nodosa: Erect, glabrous perennial, about 60cm. high. Stems decidedly swollen at nodes. Leaf lobes linear and short. Bracts and bracteoles of umbels ovate-lanceolate. Fruit 8-10mm. Habitat: Sub-montane and lowland zones. Flowers May-June.
2. Ferulago thyrsifolia: Similar to 1 but sturdier, without swollen nodes, and leaves with long lobes. Many umbels forming a large compound inflorescence. Bracts and bracteoles linear. Endemic to Crete. Habitat: Rocks of the Montane zone. Flowers June-July.

Opopanax

Leaves pinnate or twice pinnate, with broad lobes and stellate hairs. Large umbels with yellow apetalous flowers. Fruit obovoid, strongly compressed at the back.

1. Opopanax hispidus: Plant with perennial root and stem up to 3m. Lower leaves twice pinnate, with ovate-lanceolate lobes. Umbels with 3-13 rays and with few bracts and bracteoles. Fruit 7-9mm. Habitat: A rare plant found only in the lowland and sub-montane zones. Flowers May-June.

Peucedanum (Hog's Fennels, Milk Parsleys, Master Worts)

Leaves usually many times pinnate, rarely trifoliate. Umbels with yellow or white flowers, as a rule without sepals. Fruit strongly compressed at the back, with narrow wings.

1. Peucedanum creticum: Glabrous perennial with stem simple or double, up to 15cm. All the leaves at base, trifoliate or 3-lobed, with orbicular-cuneate, dentate lobes. Umbels with 3-5 rays, without bracts and bracteoles. Petals greenish-white. Fruit 6-7mm. Habitat: Alpine and sub-alpine zones. Flowers June-July.

Erica arborea

Ericales

Ericaceae Family

Shrubs or small trees usually evergreen with simple leaves. Flowers with corollas of various shapes, 4-partite or 5-partite. Stamens 2 or more on each lobe of corolla. Ovary usually superior.

171

Erica (Heathers)

Medium or small shrubs, with small leaves, usually linear, arranged in whorls. Small flowers in dense, terminal or axillary inflorescences. Calyx with divided sepals. Corolla cylindrical, campanulate or almost globular, usually with 4 lobes at opening.

1. Erica arborea: Shrub 1-4m. high. Leaves linear, in fours. Flowers white, 2,5-4mm. across. Habitat: Forests or scrub of a low or medium altitude. Flowers in spring. **2. Erica maniculiflora:** Similar to 1 but smaller reaching no higher than 1m. Flowers pink or purple. Habitat: Scrub and phrygana at a medium and low altitude. Flowers in autumn (September-November)

Arbutus (Strawberry-Trees or Arbutus)

Evergreen shrubs with alternate, entire leaves. Flowers almost globular, with 5 lobes at orifice. Fruit a succulent edible red drupe.

1. Arbutus unedo: Height 1,5-2m. Leaves oblong-lanceolate, dentate. Flowers white or pale pink. Fruit about 20mm. across. Habitat: Scrub at a medium and low altitude. Flowers in autumn. At the same time the flowers of the previous year fructify. **2. Arbutus adrachne:** Similar to 1 but taller, up to 4m. Leaves more or less ovate, with margins rather entire. Fruit smaller, 8-12mm. Habitat: Scrub at a medium and low altitude. Flowers in autumn, rarely in spring. Bears fruit in autumn.

Hybrids between the two species have occasionally been noted, and have been described as a separate species under the name **A. adrachnoides.**

Primulaceae Family

Plants with perennial rhizome. Flowers with a 5-lobed corolla and campanulate or cylindrical calyx, with 5 teeth. Fruit a capsule, with numerous seeds.

Primula (Primroses, Cowslips)

Leaves all gathered round base, in a rosette. Flower-bearing stem bare, with flowers clustered in a terminal umbel or flowers arising straight from the base. Flowers with a more or less cylindrical calyx and a long-tubed corolla ending in 5 broad, spreading lobes.

1. Primula vulgaris - subsp. vulgaris: Leaves light green, oblanceolate or ovate, with conspicuous veins. Flowers cream-coloured with a dark yellow centre 2-3cm. across, arising from the rootstock. A rare plant occurring in W. Crete. Habitat: Montane zone. Flowers March-April.

Cyclamen (Cyclamens or Sowbreads)

Plants with a tuber at their roots and long-petioled leaves, more or less cordate at base. Numerous solitary flowers on leafless stems appearing direct from the base. Calyx campanulate. Corolla with short tube and 5 long lobes, conspicuously reflexed and rolled inwards. Spherical many-seeded capsule.

1. Cyclamen graecum: Large tuber (3-10cm.), spherical or slightly flattened with roots on the underside. Leaves cordate, reddish beneath and dark green with silvery patterns above. Flowers pink or almost white with a purple blotch at the base of each lobe, of the corolla, where there are also 2 characteristic projections (auricles). Habitat: Stony places

Arbutus unedo (fruits)

Arbutus unedo (flowers)

Arbutus adrachne

Primula vulgaris - s. sp. vulgaris

of the montane and sub-montane zones. Flowers September-December. **2. Cyclamen hederifolium:** Similar to 1, but tuber up to 15cm. more flattened, without roots beneath, and leaves angular, shaped like ivy leaves. Rarely met with in Crete. Habitat: Cool localities of the montane zone. Flowers October-December. **3. Cyclamen persicum:** Similar to 1, but leaves green beneath and flowers without auricles. Rare in Crete and probably a disappearing species today. Habitat: Hills, scrub and forests of sub-montane zone. Flowers February-March. **4. Cyclamen repandum:** Leaves ivy-shaped as in 2, but flowers without auricles. Corolla lobes pink with purple blotch at base. Tubers small,

173

flattened. Habitat: W. Crete. Flowers March-April. **5. Cyclamen creticum:** Similar to 4 but flowers pure white, very rarely pale pink. Endemic to Crete. Although it is described as a separate species, it should rather be considered a subsp. of **C. repandum. Habitat:** Montane and sub-montane zones in shady places. Flowers March-April.

Lysimachia

Perennial plants. Leaves usually opposite, seldom in whorls, entire or dentate. Flowers with rotate 5-lobed corolla.

1. Lysimachia serpyllifolia: Plants with perennial roots and many stems, 10-40cm. high, simple prostrate, rooting at nodes. Leaves opposite, sessile, broadly ovate, cordate at base. Flowers yellow, about 10mm. arising singly from the axils of the leaves, on long pedicels. Endemic to S. Greece and Crete. Habitat: Montane zone. Flowers May-June.

Asterolinon

Annual plants with opposite leaves. Flowers quinquepartite. Corolla smaller than calyx.

1. Asterolinon linum-stellatum: Glabrous, with erect stems, up to 12cm. Leaves opposite, small, lanceolate and sessile. Flowers small. Calyx 3-6mm. Corolla white, up to 2mm. Habitat: Arid places at a low altitude. Flowers in spring.

Anagallis (Pimpernel)

Glabrous plants, with opposite leaves. Corolla rotate or campanulate, 5-segmented. Flowers solitary arising from the axils of the leaves.

1. Anagallis arvenis: Annual or biennial, with numerous quadrangular stems. Leaves sessile, the lower ovate, the upper ovate-lanceolate. Flowers in the axils of the upper leaves. Corolla 5-10mm., rotate, red or blue. Corolla lobes entire or dentate with marginal hairs. Flower pedicels longer than the corresponding leaf. Habitat: Cultivated ground and seaside, sandy stretches. Flowers March-May. **2. Anagallis femina:** Similar to 1, but flower pedicels usually shorter than the corresponding leaf. Upper leaves narrow, lanceolate. Corolla lobes cuneate, with few or no hairs. Habitat: Cultivated ground and seaside sites. Flowers March-May. **3. Anagallis tenella:** Perennial with rooting procumbent stems. Leaves small, orbicular or broadly elliptic. Flowers pink or, very occasionally white. Corolla campanulate with lanceolate lobes. Habitat: Marshes, dikes, and banks of lakes. Flowers April-June.

Plumbaginales

Plumbaginaceae Family

Herbaceous plants or shrubs, with leaves alternate or forming a rosette at root base. Inflorescences either cymose or in dense heads seldom in spikes. Flowers 5-segmented, with rotate corolla, and tubular calyx, more or less membraneous and persisting after flowering.

Cyclamen graecum

Cyclamen hederifolium

Cyclamen persicum

Cyclamen repandum

Plumbago (Plumbagos or Leadworts)

Shrub-like plants with simple alternate leaves. Flowers in terminal spikes or in racemes.

1. Plumbago europaea: Stems 30-100cm., dense and branching. Lower leaves oblong-ovate, with long petiole. Upper leaves lanceolate or linear, sessile, with auricles at base. Calyx covered with dense glands. Corolla with violet or pinkish-violet lobes. Habitat: Roadsides, ditches, seaside beaches. Flowers June-October.

Acantholimon

Prickly, dense cushion-shaped shrubs. Flower-bearing stems short. Inflorescences with few flowers. Calyx tubular, membraneous.

1. Acantholimon androsaceum: Leaves dense, needle-like, 10-20mm. long and 1mm. wide. Flowers purple or pink. Habitat: Rocks in alpine and sub-alpine zones. Flowers May-June.

Limonium (Sea Lavenders)

Perennial plants, or on rare occasions, annual, with leaves clustered at the base on crowded leaf-bearing stems, round the base. Flower-bearing stems few or many, leafless. Inflorescences in many-branched panicles. Flowers with bell-shaped calyx, membraneous, coloured, and corolla more or less campanulate, with 5 lobes.

1. Limonium sinuatum: A perennial plant. Leaves pinnately-lobed, hairy, up to 10cm. Stems winged, hairy. Inflorescence dense. Calyx smooth, 10-12mm., white or lilac. Corolla yellow or pink. Habitat: Maritime localities. Flowers May-September. **2. Limonium vulgare - subsp. serotinum:** Basal leaves entire, oblanceolate-spathulate, 10-15 cm., with bearded awn at tip, and featherlike veins. Cylindrical stems 30-70cm. Corolla reddish, 6-8mm., and calyx blue-purple. Habitat: Maritime swamps. Flowers in summer. **3. Limonium frederici:** Leaves cuneate, grooved, up to 18mm. wide, on crowded leaf-bearing stems, concentrated at base. Flower-bearing stems branched towards top. Corolla violet and calyx white. Habitat: Calcareous rocks at a low altitude. Flowers May-July. **4. Limonium graecum - subsp. graecum:** Perennial. Leaves linear-lanceolate or oblong-spathulate, 20-40cm. long with a mid-rib only, clustered on stems round the base. Inflorescence with numerous, non-flower-bearing branchlets. Corolla small, violet-coloured. Habitat: Littoral sites, rocks and sandy shores. Flowers May-August. **5. Limonium oleifolium - subsp. oleifolium:** Perennial. Leaves linear-spathulate, 30-35cm., with a midrib only. Stems long, non-flower-bearing, round the base. Inflorescence with many non-flower-bearing branchlets. Small violet-coloured flowers. Habitat: Maritime localities. Flowers June-September. **6. Limonium echioides:** Annual, 5-30cm. Leaves obovate or spathulate, 20-40mm. long with featherlike veins. Flowers small, with pink corolla. Habitat: Salt-rich soil, littoral swamps. Flowers in summer.

Limoniastrum

Small shrubs, with flowers similar to those of the **Limonium** genus. Stems with leaves.

1. Limoniastrum monopetalum: Many branching stems, with oblanceolate or linear-spathulate leaves, up to 3cm. long, fleshy and glaucous-green, stem-clasping at their base. Inflorescences without flowers, 1-2cm. across. Corolla pink that turns to violet when it withers. Habitat: Littoral sandy shores and salty swamps. Flowers in summer.

Cyclamen creticum

Anagallis arvensis

Acantholimon androsaceum

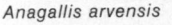

Limonium sinuatum

Ebenales

Styracaceae Family

Trees or shrubs with actinomorphic flowers. Corolla with small tube at base or with completely free lobes. Calyx fused on to the superior ovary. Fruit a capsule or a drupe.

Styrax (Storaxes)

Flowers in sparse axillary inflorescences. Calyx campanulate. Corolla with short tube at base, and large free lobes.

1. Styrax officinalis. A deciduous shrub with leaves ovate or oblong, entire, rounded at tip, pubescent - more so underneath. Inflorescence with 3-6 white, bell-shaped flowers, with 5-7 lanceolate lobes, 2cm long. Habitat: Scrub, forests, ravines, of medium and low altitude. Flowers April-May.

Oleales

Oleaceae Family

Trees or shrubs with hairless leaves, opposite, on rare occasions alternate. The actinomorphic flowers are 4 to 6-lobed. Only 2 stamens.

Olea (Olives)

Evergreen shrubs or trees. Entire leaves opposite. Flowers small in many-flowered axillary inflorescences. Corolla with 4 lobes.

1. Olea Europaea - subsp. oleaster. This is the wild form of the cultivated olive-tree; it is also known as **varietas silvestris.** It is a shrub or small tree with leaves dark green above and silvery beneath, smaller than those of the cultivated species. The small flowers have a white corolla. The fruit is a fleshy drupe that is smaller than that of the cultivated variety. The branches are more or less spiny. Habitat: Common in the sub-montane and lowland zones. Flowers April-May.

Phyllirea

Evergreen shrubs or small trees with their leaves opposite. Flowers tiny in axillary inflorescences. Corolla 4-lobed. Fruit a small blackish drupe.

1. Phyllirea latifolia. A shrub which is seldom bigger than 1-2m. Leaves ovate or ovate-lanceolate, more or less dentate or crenate, 10-70mm long. Flowers greenish-white. Drupe black, 7-10mm. Habitat: Moors of medium and low altitudes. Flowers March-April.

Gentianales

Gentianaceae Family

Glabrous plants with leaves opposite, entire, usually stalkless. Corolla inflexed when a bud. Ovary superior.

Centaurium (Centauries)

Flowers in dichasia or corymb-like, head-shaped or spikelike cymes. Calyx, as a rule, deeply divided into 5 lobes. Corolla pink or, occasionally, white or yellow, with 5 (4) lobes.

1. Centaurium erythraea. Biennial, 10-50cm. Stem simple, occasionally branched at the upper part. Basal leaves obovate or elliptic, 1-5cm. long, with blunt tip and from 3 to 7 parallel veins. Stem leaves much smaller, 3-veined and pointed. Flowers pink, in closely packed multiflowered inflorescences. Habitat: Montane and sub-montane zones. Flowers April-May. This species is divided into several sub-species of which three, at least, grow in the Aegean area, viz.: 1) **subsp. erythraea;** 2) **subsp. rumelicum,** and 3) **subsp. rhodense.** It

Styrax officinalis

Olea europaea - s. sp. oleaster

Phyllyrea latifolia

Centaurium erythraea

is difficult to specify which of the three occurs, or occur, in Crete. It is possible, however, that all three do so. **2. Centaurium pulchellum.** An annual 2-20cm., no rosette of leaves at base. Stem branches, as a rule, below the middle. Leaves ovate or ovate-lanceolate, acute, up to 1,5cm. Flowers pink. Corolla with 5 lobes, or 4 in the very small plants. Habitat: Meadows near the sea. Flowers April-May. **3. Centaurium tenuiflorum.** Annual, 15-25 (-40)cm., with no rosette of leaves at base. Stem branching occurs above middle. Leaves ovate to elliptic, rounded at tips or somewhat pointed. Flowers 12-14mm. Habitat: Damp meadows, mainly near the sea. Flowers April-June. There are two subspecies: the **subsp. tenuiflorum** with 2-90 flowers on each plant, and with a rosy purple corolla; and the **subsp. acutiflorum** with 20 to 180 flowers to a plant, and with a pale pink corolla. It is not certain whether both occur on Crete or only one of them. **4. Centaurium spicatum.** An annual or biennial, 10–55cm. high, with a rosette of leaves at base. The stem usually branches from the base, otherwise from the middle. Leaves of rosette broadly ovate. Stem leaves elliptic-oblong or lanceolate, with 3 or 5 veins. Flowers 12-14mm. Corolla pink. Habitat: Watery meadows near the sea. Flowers April-June. **5. Centaurium maritimum.** An annual or biennial, 10-20cm., with stem either simple or branched, and yellow flowers, 20-25mm. Habitat: Sandy expanses and seaboard meadows. Flowers May-June.

Blackstonia (Yellow-wort)

Annual plants with calyx divided into 6-12 lobes. Yellow corolla rotate, also with 6-12 lobes.

1. Blackstonia perfoliata - subsp. serotina. Stem slender. Glaucous-green leaves opposite, entire, more or less ovate. Flowers in sparse inflorescences at the top of the stem. Corolla with 6-8 lobes, and 8-10mm across. Habitat: Medium and low altitudes. Flowers May-September.

Apocynaceae Family

Trees, shrubs, or herbacious plants, with poisonous sap. Leaves simple. Flowers with 5-lobed corolla, lobes oblique, incurved when a bud.

Nerium (Oleanders)

Shrubs with leaves opposite or else in whorls, inflorescences corymb-like. Corolla with cylindrical tube and spreading lobes, and 5 large scales at base round the throat.

1. Nerium oleander. Stems up to 4m. Leaves lanceolate-linear, up to 12cm. long. Small, 5-lobed calyx. Corolla 3-5cm. across, usually pink. Habitat: Gullies and damp localities in lowland, sub-montane, and montane zones. Flowers June-August. Varieties of different colours, ranging from white, and yellow to magenta, with single or double flowers, are cultivated all over the island.

Asclepiadaceae Family

Shrubs or perennial herbaceous plants, frequently climbers. Leaves usually opposite and simple. Flowers in cymose inflorescences. Corolla with 5 lobes which are inrolled when a bud.

Periploca

Shrubs that have either erect or climbing stems. Leaves opposite. Flowers in axillary cymes. Lobes of corolla more or less erect. Corona with 5 free lobes.

1. Periploca laevigata - subsp. angustifolia. Stems 1,5-3m. Leaves linear, almost sessile, hairless, 1-3,5cm. long. Inflorescences with few flowers. Corolla 1cm. across, purplish-brown, and white. Habitat: Arid and rocky localities at medium and low altitudes. Flowers in summer.

Periploca graeca, with 2cm. flowers in dense inflorescences, is mentioned in **Flora Europaea** as occurring in Crete but with a question mark.

Centaurium pulchellum

Nerium oleander

Gomphocarpus fruticosus

Cionura erecta

Gomphocarpus

Shrubs with leaves opposite or, occasionally, in bunches of three. Corolla and corona 5-lobed. Fruit oblong and spiny. Seeds with long, soft silky hairs.

1. Gomphocarpus fruticosus. Stems 1-2m. high, erect. Leaves linear-lanceolate, hairless, 2-10cm. long. White flowers, 1,5cm. across, in dense inflorescences. Habitat: Uncultivated as well as cultivated land. Flowers end of summer or in autumn. This is a South African plant which has become naturalised in the Mediterranean area.

Cynanchum (Strangleworts)

Woody climbers with opposite leaves. Flowers in axillary or terminal umbels. Corolla with spreading lobes. Corona with 10 lobes.

1. Cynanchum acutum. Slender and climbing stems rising to a height of 3m. Leaves 2-15cm., arrow-shaped, and with 1-5cm. long petioles. Flowers 8-12mm., white or pink, with narrow linear lobes. Habitat: Dry locations, frequently near the sea. Flowers in summertime.

Vincetoxicum

Plants with perennial rhizomes and slender, herbaceous stems. Opposite, short-stalked. Corolla small with spreading lobes. Corona with 5 small fleshy lobes.

1. Vincetoxicum canescens. Stems 40-70cm. high. Leaves greyish-green, pubescent, ovate, 6-8cm. Inflorescences with 8-15 yellow flowers, hairy on the outer side. A plant of S.W. Asia not occurring in any other part of Europe except Crete. Habitat: Stony and rocky sites, at medium and low altitudes. Flowers May-June. **2. Vincetoxicum creticum.** Similar to 1 but a smaller, dwarflike plant. Endemic to Mt. Dhikti. Habitat: Montane and sub-montane zones. Flowers May-July.

Cionura

Plants similar to Vincetoxicum but the lobes of the corolla are not fleshy and the leaves are long-stalked and glabrous.

1. Cionura erecta. Stems 50-100cm. Leaves ovate with cordate base, and a 5cm. long petiole. Flowers white, 1cm. across. Habitat: Rocks and seaboard sandy stretches. Flowers May-June.

Tubiflorae

Convovulaceae Family

Shrubs or herbaceous plants, frequently climbers. Leaves alternate. Flowers actinomorphic with 5 sepals. Corolla funnel-shaped, on rare occasions 5-lobed.

Convolvulus (Bindweeds, Cornbines)

Annual or perennial shrubs or climbers. Flowers arising singly from the axils of leaves, or else in terminal or axillary inflorescences. Flower pedicels with two bracts at their base.

Group A. Not climber plants

1. Convolvulus libanoticus. A small woody shrublet with crowded branches, and slender linear or oblanceolate leaves. Corolla 10-15mm., reddish. Habitat: Slopes and meadows of montane zone. Flowers May-June. **2. Convolvulus dorycnium.** Pubescent shrub, 50-100cm., with numerous densely branched greenish stems. Leaves small, linear-spatulate or oblanceolate. Flowers pink, 10-20mm. with long pedicels. Habitat: Low altitude arid, barren localities. Flowers May-June. **3. Convolvulus lanatus.** Similar to 2 but smaller and with densely pubescent stems, spiny at tip. Flowers in closely-packed axillary inflorescences. It is a South-West Asia and North-East Africa plant discovered in Crete, too, a long time ago, but its existence there, today, is doubtful. **4. Convolvulus oleifolius.** A many-branched shrub, covered with dense, silvery hairs. Linear leaves also silvery. Flowers pink or, more seldom, white in dense terminal inflorescences. Corolla 15-25mm. Habitat: Calcareous rocks near or by the sea. Flowers April-May. **5. Convolvulus argyrothamnos.** Similar to 4 but stems longer, arcuate, branching mainly towards tips. Habitat: Montane gorges. Known to have been growing in only one gorge in East Crete,

Convolvulus dorycnium

Convolvulus oleifolius
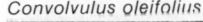

Convolvulus cantabrica

Convolvulus arvensis

however in our time it seems rather not to exist. In all probability it is now an extinct species. Flowers May-June. **6. Convolvulus lineatus.** A small perennial plant 3-25cm. high, with linear, elliptic or oblanceolate, hairy leaves. Its flowers are pink, 12-25mm across. Its existence in Crete is doubtful. **7. Convolvulus cantabrica.** A pubescent-hairy perennial with sparse stems, 10-50mm. Its existence in Crete has been noted with certain reservations in **Flora Europaea.** However, its occurrence on the island has been ascertained by the writer who came across it in the village Pefki of Seteia (East Crete), on April 19 1985. **8. Convolvulus siculus.** An annual or, more rarely, a perennial with slender stems, 10-60cm. Leaves lanceolate or ovate, sparsely pubescent, as a rule cordate at base. Flowers 7-12mm. blue, arising singly or in twos from the axils of the leaves. Habitat: Dry, bare localities. Flowers April-May.

Group B. Climber plants

1. Convolvulus arvensis. A glabrous or pubescent plant with stems up to 2m. Leaves ovate, triangular or oblong, with base more or less arrow-shaped. Flowers white or pink, arising singly or in pairs from the axils of the leaves. Habitat: Both in fallow and in cultivated fields. Flowers April-July. **2. Convolvulus althaeoides - subsp. althaeoides.** Plant with perennial root and stems up to 1m high. Leaves palmately lobed with broad lobes not very deeply notched. Flowers large up to 4,5cm. pink with the centre darker. Leaves and stems pubescent-hairy and with spreading hairs. Habitat: Fallow and cultivated fields at low and medium altitudes. Flowers April-June. **3. Convolvulus althaeoides - subsp. tenuissimus.** Resembling 2 but leaves, flowers, and stems more slender, flowers pink but with a light-coloured centre; also, leaves with narrower lobes. All the plant is covered with dense, silvery hairs. Habitat: Fallow and cultivated fields at a low altitude. Flowers April-June.

Ipomaea (Morning Glory)

Perennial or annual plants with long procumbent or climbing stems. Flowers large, funnel-shaped, growing singly or many together in the axils of the leaves, with two very small bracts at their base.

1. Ipomaea stolonifera. Stem procumbent and frequently rooting. Leaves fleshy, 1-5cm., oblong-entire, or deeply cleft into 3-5 lobes. Flowers white, 35-40mm. across. Habitat: Sandy shores. Flowers August-October.

Calystegia (Bindweeds)

Plants similar to convolvulus and ipomaea but always perennials, exuding a milky sap, while flowers are surrounded at their base by large bracts that cover the calyx.

1. Calystegia soldanella. Plant similar to **Ipomaea stolonifera** but with flowers pink and leaves always entire and kidney-shaped. Habitat: Sandy shores. Flowers April-May. **2. Calystegia sepium - subsp. sepium.** A climber with cordate-sagittal leaves. Big white flowers, 30-70mm. Habitat: Maritime marshes and river banks. Flowers June-September.

The very similar **Calystegia silvatica,** which is a mountain plant, is mentioned in **Flora Europaea** as existing in Crete but with a question mark.
The genera **Cuscuta** and **Cressa** belong to the Convolvulaceae family. The former is represented in Crete by 5 species, the latter by one. Insignificant plants of no decorative interest or value.

Boraginaceae Family

Herbaceous plants or shrubs, usually hairy. Leaves simple, alternate. Flowers with 5-lobed calyx and corolla of various shapes. Inflorescences as a rule in curls.

Heliotropium (Heliotrope)

Annual or perennial plants with small white flowers. Corolla with short tube and spreading lobes.

1. Heliotropium europaeum. A hairy, branching annual up to 40cm. Leaves greyish-green, ovate or elliptic, up to 5,5cm. Corolla 2-4mm across. Fruit pubescent, and usually with swellings. Flowers scentless. Habitat: Uncultivated land and waysides. Flowers May-July. **2. Heliotropium dolosum.** Very similar to 1 but flowers scented and fruit smooth. Habitat:

Convolvulus althaeoides
- s. sp. althaeoides

Convolvulus althaeoides
- s. sp. tenuissimus

Ipomoea stolonifera

Calystegia soldanella

Uncultivated ground and roadsides. Flowers May-July. **3. Heliotropium suaveolens - subsp. suaveolens.** Similar to 1 and 2 but flowers bigger, 4-6,5mm. across, scented. Its occurrence in Crete is mentioned with a certain reservation. **4. Heliotropium hirsutissimum.** Similar to the aforementioned plants but with very dense grey or yellowish hairs. Corolla 5-8mm. Flowers scented. Habitat: Uncultivate land and waysides. Flower May-July. **5. Heliotropium supinum.** Annual branching from rootstock with the central stem erect and the lateral ones spreading. Leaves up to 3,5cm., elliptic or almost orbicular, covered with white down, at least on the under surface. Flowers small 2,5-3mm. Habitat: Uncultivated ground and waysides. Flowers May-July.

Neatostema

Annual plants. Bearing yellow flowers. The yellow corolla has spreading lobes and a regular tube.

1. Neatostema apulum. Stems 3-30cm, erect hairy, and branching at their upper section. Leaves linear or oblong, the lower rather spathulate, all of them hairy especially at their margins. Corolla 6-6,5mm. Habitat: Arid locations and barren stretches. Flowers April-May.

Buglossoides

Plants similar to **Neatostema** but often perennial or shrub-like, while flowers are never yellow.

1. Buglossoides arvensis. Annual, 5-50cm. high, with adpressed hairs. Lower leaves oblong-spathulate or obovate, the remainder oblong or linear. Inflorescences cymose, solitary or in pairs. Corolla white, purple, or blue, 6-9mm. Habitat: Montane and sub-montane cultivated and uncultivated ground, and in meadows. Flowers March-May.

Lithodora

Dwarflike shrubs with flowers in terminal inflorescences surrounded by leaves. Corolla tubular at base, 5-lobed at mouth, blue, purple or white.

1. Lithodora hispidula. A much-branched shrublet, 10-35cm. with whitish-hairy branches and oblong-obovate or oblanceolate leaves, dark green, hairy on the upper surface, whitish-green and densely hairy underneath, up to 15mm. long. Inflorescences bearing 1 to 4 flowers. Corolla blue-violet, hairless, 10mm. across. Habitat: Dry, stony sites. Flowers April-May.

Onosma

Biennial or perennial hairy, plants. Hairs as a rule stellate. Flowers yellow or yellowish, tubular, in terminal inflorescences.

1. Onosma erecta. A caespitose perennial plant with numerous simple flowers bearing stems, 15-25cm. long. Basal leaves oblong or linear-lanceolate, 30-60mm. long with thick star-shaped hairs. Corolla yellow, 20-24mm. long. Habitat: Among rocks of montane zone. Flowers April-May. **2. Onosma graeca.** A caespitose biennial with stems 10-30cm. long, multi-branched and with patent hairs. Lower leaves linear or linear-lanceolate up to 10mm. Corolla 14-15mm., pubescent, pale yellow, tinged with red. Habitat: Montane and sub-montane zones. Flowers April-May.

Onosma frutescen, which is similar to **Onosma graeca** but has bigger hairless flowers and its leaves are shorter is mentioned as occurring on Crete but with a certain amount of doubt.

Cerinthe (Honeyworts)

Hairless annual plants, more rarely biennial or perennial. Leaves often have white blotches. Flowers more or less tubular with 5 small teeth at tip.

Calystegia sepium

Heliotropium ouropaeum

Heliotropium suaveolens - s. sp. suaveolens Onosma erecta.

1. Cerinthe major. Annual with stems 15-60cm. Lower leaves obovate-spathulate with white blotches. The upper leaves ovate-lanceolate, cordate at base. Corolla tubular, 15-30mm. long, yellow but brownish-purple at base, very seldom brownish-purple all over. Habitat: Wastelands as well as on cultivated ground at low and medium altitudes. Flowers February-April. **2. Cerinthe retorta.** Similar to 1 but flowers are smaller, yellow or two-coloured, and surrounded by violet bracts.

One other species **Cerinthe minor** is, with some doubts, mentioned as occurring in Crete.

Alkanna (Alkannas or Dyer's Alkannas)

Hairy plants, usually perennial. Corolla tubular at base and with 5 spreading lobes. Flowers with conspicuous bracts are arranged in terminal inflorescences.

1. Alkanna tinctoria. Perennial with spreading stems on the ground, 10-20(-30)cm. long. The smooth blue corolla is 6-8mm. across. Terminal inflorescences crisped. Habitat: Sunny sites at a low altitude. Flowers April-May.

Echium (Bugloss)

Hairy perennial, biennial or annual plants, shrubs, or shrublets with bristly hairs. Flowers in inflorescences more or less forked. Tubular-campanulate corolla has oblique mouth and 5 small lobes.

1. Echium angustifolium. A perennial 25-40cm. high, with numerous flower-bearing stems that are covered with white hairs. 16-26mm. corolla is purplish-red or violet. Leaves narrow, lanceolate or oblanceolate. Habitat: Waste ground and bare localities of medium or low altitudes. Flowers April-May. **2. Echium italicum.** Biennial with one or more erect stems. Basal leaves large - 200-350mm., lanceolate, with adpressed hairs. Large, branched inflorescences often pyramnidal in shape. Flowers with yellowish, pink, or blue corolla, 10-12mm. long. Habitat: Medium and low altitudes. Flowers April-May. **3. Echium vulgare.** Usually biennial, 20-90cm., with 1 or more stems. Lower leaves stalked, 50-150mm. long, elliptic or lanceolate. The upper ones sessile, lanceolate. Inflorescences spike-shaped. Corolla 10-19mm. blue or violet. Habitat: Sunny situations at medium and low altitudes. Flowers April-May. **4. Echium plantagineum.** Annual or biennial, erect, 20-60cm. with 1 or more flower-bearing stems. Basal leaves oblong or lanceolate, 50-140mm., with conspicuous lateral veins. Forked inflorescences. Corolla 18-30mm., initially blue and later turning purple. Habitat: Roadsides and meadows in the neighbourhood of the sea. Flowers March-April. **5. Echium parviflorum.** Annual, 10-40cm., with numerous stems. Leaves ovate or lanceolate, 20-80mm. long. Inflorescences forked, sparse. Corolla pinkish-violet, 11-25mm. long. Habitat: Dry localities at a low altitude. Flowers March-April. **6. Echium arenarium.** Biennial, 10-25cm. with ascending stems. Leaves with white hairs, the lower 30-60mm., spathulate with long petioles. Corolla 6-11mm., dark blue. Habitat: Sand dunes and sandy meadows near the sea. Flowers March-April.

Procopiana

Perennial hairy plants. Corolla with short tube and long lobes, narrow and reflexed, or spirally coiled inwards.

1. Procopiana cretica. A branching plant 10-50cm. high. Leaves ovate, frequently almost cordate at base. Multiflorous inflorescences. Lobes of calyx acute. Corolla blue-violet, on rare occasions white, lobes spreading and reflexed, but not incurved. Habitat: Montane and sub-montane zones. Flowers April-May. **2. Procopiana insularis.** Similar to 1 but corolla lobes are shorter, and calyx lobes rounded at tip. Habitat: Medium and low altitudes. Flowers April-May.

Anchusa (Alkanets)

Perennial, biennial, or annual herbaceous plants. Flowers in terminal and axillary inflorescences. Corolla with cylindrical, straight or curved tube, and spreading lobes with one scale at their base.

1. Anchusa caespitosa. A caespitose, hairy, dwarflike perennial plant with stems 1-10cm. long. Leaves oblong, strap-shaped, 20-50mm., forming rosettes. Flowers blue, 10-12mm. across, in bunches of 3-5. A Cretan endemic. Habitat: Montane and sub-alpine zones. Flowers May-June. **2. Anchusa undulata - subsp. hybrida.** A pubescent and hairy biennial

Cerinthe major

Alkanna tinctoria

Echium angustifolium

Echium vulgare

or perennial plant with erect or ascending stems, 10-50cm. and leaves oblong, frequently undulate at margin, 50-150mm. long. Corolla bluish-violet or violet, 5-8mm. across. Flowers in dense inflorescences. Habitat: Montane and sub-montane zones. Flowers April- May. **3. Anchusa azurea.** A perennial hairy plant with erect stems 20-150cm. and oblong leaves 100-300mm. long. Sparse, cymose inflorescences with large dark blue flowers, 12-15mm. across. Habitat: It grows in both cultivated and uncultivated ground in medium and lower zones. Flowers April-May. **4. Anchusa aegyptiaca.** A hairy annual with procumbent or ascending stems, 5-30cm. Leaves oblong, ovate or lanceolate, dentate or shallowly notched. Inflorescences very sparse. Pale yellow flowers 4mm. across. Habitat: From low altitude down to sea-level. Flowers March-April. **5. Anchusa variegata.** Similar to 4 but leaves almost entire, and purple flowers turn to blue with white streaks as they approach full bloom. Habitat: Montane and sub-montane zones. Flowers April-May.

Borago (Borages)

Perennial or annual herbs. Flowers in sparse branching inflorescences. Corolla large, as a rule, rotate in shape with a very short tube.

1. Borago officinalis. A hairy annual that smells like a cucumber. Stems 15-70cm., thick and erect. Basal leaves ovate or lanceolate, stalked. Corolla rotate, bright blue, rarely white, with lanceolate acute lobes, 8-15mm. Habitat: Both uncultivated and cultivated ground at medium and low altitudes. Flowers March-May.

Myosotis (Forget-me-nots, Scorpion Grasses)

Perennial or annual herbs. Flowers in curllike cymose. Inflorescences usually in pairs. Corolla wheel-shaped with very small tube and broad lobes which are as a rule blue.

1. Myosotis incrassata. An annual covered with staight hairs. Stem 5-20cm. frequently branching from the base. Basal leaves ovate-lanceolate up to 4cm. long, and 1cm. wide. The others smaller. Corolla blue, up to 3mm. Habitat: Dry sites in montane and sub-montane zones. Flowers April-May. **2. Myosotis ramosissima - subsp. ramosissima.** An annual with stems up to 40cm. Basal leaves lanceolate, not pointed, covered with straight patent hairs. Inflorescences sparsely-flowered with bright blue flowers 3mm. across. Habitat: Sub-montane and montane zones. Flowers April-May. **3. Myosotis congesta.** A slender annual plant with stems at most up to 25cm. usually shorter. Flowers blue up to 2mm. across. Habitat: Sub-montane zones. Flowers in Spring. **4. Myosotis refracta - subsp. refracta.** An annual up to 25cm. Stem with leaves reaching up to the base of the inflorescence. Inflorescence sparse at lower end and crowded at tip. Leaves narrowly lanceolate with crisped hairs beneath. Calyx with crispate hairs. Blue flowers 1-1,5mm. across. Habitat: Montane zone. Flowers April-May. **5. Myosotis refracta - subsp. pauciflora.** Resembling 4 but calyx without crispate hairs and stem always erect. Habitat: Montane zone. **6. Myosotis refracta subsp. aegagrophila.** Similar to 4 but leaves broadly lanceolate or ovate. A Cretan endemic. Habitat: Montane zone. **7. Myosotis solange.** A creeping and sparsely caespitose perennial. Leaves 6-20mm. lanceolate-spathulate. Stems 4-6(-10cm.) Flowers blue, 3mm. across, in sparse inflorescences. Endemic to W. Crete with restricted distribution in the White Mountains. First published about in 1981 by W. Greuter and Zaffran. Habitat: Sub-alpine zone. Flowers June-October.

Cynoglossum (Hound's-Tongues)

Usually perennial or biennial plants, more rarely annual. Flowers with corolla that is cylindrical or campanulate at base, and with 5 lobes at tip.

1. Cynglossum creticum. Biennial with pubescent stems 30-60cm. long. Leaves densely hairy, oblong or lanceolate and with a short petiole, or else slightly amplexicaul. Inflorence flowers blue with darker veins. Corolla tube campanulate. Length of Corolla 7-9mm. Habitat: Dry localities in montane and sub-montane zones. Flowers April-May. **2. Cynoglossum sphacioticum.** A perennial, 10-18cm. high. Leaves linear-lanceolate, sessile and hairy. Corolla 4mm. long, dark blue or violet-coloured. Tube bell-shaped. Endemic to Crete. Habitat: Stony situations of montane zone. Flowers May-June. **3. Cynoglossum columnae.** An annual 25-45(-60)cm. Pubescent leaves that are oblong-lanceolate, sessile or amplexicaul. Dark blue corolla, 5-6mm. long. Habitat: Dry places and uncultivated ground of lowland and sub-montane zones. Flowers April-May.

Mattiastrum

Perennial plants with flowers in terminal or axillary inflorescences. Blue, violet, or purple corolla, campanulate or with bell-shaped tube and lobes, on the whole spreading. Corolla tubes relatively long, with 5 scales at throat.

Echium plantagineum

Procopiana cretica
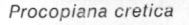

Procopiana insularis

Anchusa caespitosa

1. Mattiastrum lithospermifolium. A caespitose plant with stems 7-35(-50)cm. hairy or densely hairy. Basal leaves lanceolate or spathulate, stalked, the rest of the leaves are both sessile and smaller in size. Corolla bell-shaped, blue-violet, 3-5mm. A native of West Asia, it does not exist in any other part of Europe except Crete. Habitat: Montane zone. Flowers April-May.

Verbenaceae Family

Herbaceous plants or shrubs, with leaves opposite or in whorls. The flowers are zygomorphic, quadripartite or quinquepartite, with a very small calyx.

Vitex (Chaste Trees)

Shrubs with palmate leaves. Flowers in terminal, cymose, or spikelike inflorescences. Corolla bilabiate. The upper lip with two lobes, and the lower with three.

1. Vitex agnus castus. An aromatic plant, 1-6m. tall. Leaves with long stalks and 5-7 linear-lanceolate leaflets. Crowded inflorescences with flowers 8-10mm. long, blue, more seldom pink or white. Habitat: River-beds, shores and ditches in the lowest zone. Flowers May-July.

Verbena (Vervain)

Annual or perennial plants with leaves opposite, rarely in whorls of 3. Inflorescences in spikes or corymbs. Flowers small with 5-lobed corolla.

1. Verbena officinalis. Erect perennial, 30-60(-100)cm. tall. Stems quadrangular. Leaves rhomboidal at margin, pinnately-lobed, with the lobes dentate. Flowers tiny, pale pink, in 10-25cm. long spikes. Habitat: Lowland and sub-montane zones. Flowers June-October.
2. Verbena supina. Similar to 1 but annual and with stems as a rule spreading and much branched from the base. Spikes up to 8cm. with violet-coloured flowers.

The Callitrichaceae family, which includes plants that are insignificant from a decorative point of view - flowers having neither corolla nor calyx, - is represented in Crete by the species **Callitriche pulchra** that grows on the islet of Gavdhos.

Labiatae Family

Shrubs or herbaceous plants, often glandular and aromatic. Leaves usually simple, always opposite. Flowers zygomorphic with the corolla more or less 2-lipped, the upper lip 2-lobed and the lower 3-lobed; in rare cases there is only the lower lip which is five-lobed. Calyx usually five-lobed, often bilabiate.

Ajuga (Bugles)

Herbaceous annuals or perennials. Calyx five-lobed not bilabiate. Upper lip of corolla as a rule very small. The lower trilobate. The tube is hairy at throat.

1. Ajuga iva. A caespitose perennial with 5-20cm. long stems which are pubescent or hairy, and woody at base. Leaves linear or linear-oblong, pubescent or hairy, entire or with 2-6 shallow lobes. Flowers 2-4 at each node. They arise from bracts similar to the leaves. Corolla purple, pink, or yellow, 12-20mm. across, with protruding stamens. Habitat: Found in dry situations and in olive-groves. Flowers in springtime. **2. Ajuga chamaepitys - subsp. chia.** An annual or perennial of short duration, usually much-branched, 5-30cm. glabrous, pubescent, or hairy. Leaves trilobate with linear lobes. Bracts similar to the leaves. Flowers 2-4 at each node. Corolla yellow with red veins. Stamens protruding. Habitat: Scrub and meadows at a medium altitude. Flowers April-May.

Teucrium (Germanders)

Shrubs or herbs with bilabiate or actinomorphic calyx. Corolla lacking an upper lip, the lower one five-lobed.

1. Teucrium brevifolium. A small shrub up to 60cm. high. Leaves linear or oblong, entire with inrolled margin, greyish-green in colour, and pubescent on both sides. Blue corolla 10mm. long. Habitat: Arid, rocky areas near the sea. Flowers April-May. **2. Teucrium massiliense.** A small shrub, 30-60cm. with greyish-green hairs. Leaves ovate. Corolla

Anchusa undulata - s. sp. hybrida

Anchusa azurea

Cynoglossum creticum

Vitex agnus - castus

pink. Inflorescences in spikes arising from the axils of the leaves. Habitat: Stony, dry localities at medium and low altitudes. Flowers April-May. **3. Teucrium scordium - subsp. scordioides.** A hairy perennial with underground shoots. Leaves oblong or ovate, cordate and slightly amplexicaul at base, dentate. Purple corolla 7-20mm. hairy. It is a plant that exudes a smell of garlic. Habitat: Marshy sites and ditches. Flowers May-June. **4. Teucrium divaricatum subsp. divaricatum.** A small shrub 10-30cm. high. It is a hairy plant with ovate, dentate leaves 10-25mm. long. Flowers with pink or purple corolla about 1cm. Habitat: Scrub and heaths of lowland and sub-montane zones. Flowers May-June. **5. Teucrium flavum.** Small shrub with ovate, dentate leaves and a yellow corolla. It reaches a height of 50cm. Out of the 4 subspecies, the one most likely to grow in Crete is the **subsp. hellenicum,** however, it has not been possible to confirm it. Habitat: Rocky places in the montane and sub-montane zones. Flowers May-June. **6. Teucrium microphyllum.** A small shrub, 5-40cm. high, with whitish densely pubescent stems, and leaves 5mm. oblanceolate or ovate, dentate, and thickly pubescent and whitish underneath. Corolla hairy, pink, 10-12mm. Habitat: Rocky sites at medium and low altitudes. Flowers May-June. **7. Teucrium cuneifolium.** A small shrub, 10-25cm. greyish-green, and with dense down. Leaves 9-13mm. ovate or orbicular, cuneate at base, and with 3-4 teeth at tip. Corolla pale yellow. A Cretan endemic. Habitat: Rocky situations. Flowers May-June. **8. Teucrium alpestre.** A dwarf hairy dense shrub up to 20cm. Leaves obovate or linear, 4-10mm. Flowers in terminal heads. Pale yellow corolla. Endemic to Crete and to the Dodecanesian island of Carpathos. Habitat: Montane and sub-alpine zones. Flowers May-June. **9. Teucrium polium -subsp. capitatum.** A small shrub covered with thick white hair. Stems 10-25cm. Leaves oblong with shallow teeth and inrolled margins. Flowers in dense clusters, white or pink. Flowers May-June.

Scutellaria (Skullcaps)

Plants with perennial rhizomes, and herbaceous stems. Flowers in pairs arising from the axils of leaves or bracts. Calyx bilabiate with entire lips. Corolla bilabiate, too, with long more or less curved tube. Upper lip trilobate, curved. Bottom lip entire.

1. Scutellaria sieberi. Plant covered with velutinous down. Stems 20-60cm. on the whole erect, branching from their base. Ovate, crenate leaves, rather pointed at tip, 2-4(5,5)cm. long. Flowers in dense spikelike inflorescences. Corolla 10-14mm. whitish-cream in colour, the upper lip sometimes reddish. Endemic to Crete. Habitat: Rocks and gorges of lowland and sub-montane zones. Flowers April-May. **2. Scutellaria hirta.** Similar to 1 but a smaller plant with leaves 1-2cm. and not pointed. Inflorescences with fewer and smaller flowers. Endemic to Crete. Habitat: Rocks and stony situations of montane zone. Flowers May-June.

Prasium

Shrubs. Flowers solitary at the upper nodes of stem forming terminal inflorescences. Calyx bilabiate. The upper lip is trilobate while the lower is bilobate. Corolla, too, is bilabiate with the upper lip entire and curved, and the lower trilobate.

1. Prasium majus. Glabrous stems up to 1m, branching. Leaves glabrous, ovate or ovate lanceolate, acute, crenate. Corolla 17-20mm., usually white. Habitat: Medium and lower zones. Flowers March-April.

Marrubium (Horehound)

Perennial plants usually covered with velutinous hair. Calyx with 5-10 teeth. Corolla bilabiate. The upper lip bilobed, straight, the lower trilobed.

1. Marrubium vulgare. Stems up to 45cm. with numerous short nonflowering branches. Leaves orbicular or broadly ovate, crenate, densely hairy beneath but less hairy above. Flowers in crowded multi-flowered whorls. Calyx with 10 teeth. Corolla white. Habitat: Uncultivated waste land. Flowers May-June.

Sideritis

Perennial or annual plants. Flowers in whorls, at least two to a whorl. Calyx campanulate with 5 almost identical teeth. Corolla small, bilabiate, usually yellow. The upper lip straight, entire or bilobate, the lower trilobate.

1. Sideritis syriaca. A very hairy perennial plant, 10-25cm. Basal leaves oblong or narrowly obovate, entire or slightly crenate. The middle and upper leaves linear-lanceolate or

Ajuga chamaepitys - s. sp. chia   *Teucrium divaricatum - s sp divaricatum*

Teucrium polium - s. sp. capitatum   *Scutellaria sieberi*

oblong. 5-20 whorls, each bearing 6-10 flowers, each of which is surrounded by almost orbicular bracts. Corolla yellow, 9-15mm. Habitat: Rocky places of sub-alpine and montane zones. Flowers May-June. **2. Sideritis curvidens.** Annual with leaves oblong-ovate, crenate. Whorls with 6 flowers. Corolla yellow. Calyx with curved teeth, swollen at base. Habitat: Stony localities of montane and sub-montane zones. Flowers April-May.

Phlomis

Shrub-like plants, usually hairy. Flowers in whorls. Calyx tubular with 5 teeth. Corolla bilabiate, large, the upper lip very curved, like a helmet (hooded).

1. Phlomis fruticosa. Stems up to 130cm. covered with white down. Lower leaves elliptic, lanceolate or lanceolate-ovate, entire or slightly crenate, with petioles up to 4cm. Upper leaves sessile or shortstalked, rather lanceolate and rounded at tip. All the leaves are

195

greenish and sparsely hairy above, and densely hairy and whitish beneath. Whorls with 6-36 flowers. Corolla yellow, hairy, 23-35mm. long. Habitat: A rare sub-montane plant. Flowers March-May. **2. Phlomis cretica.** Very similar to 1 but up to 45cm. only. Upper leaves pointed, stalked, and calyx with ciliate teeth. Habitat: Submontane zone, mainly in Central and West Crete. Flowers March-May. **3. Phlomis lanata.** Similar to 2 but all the leaves are smaller, orbicular or obovate rounded at tip. Flowers smaller with corolla 20-23mm. and 2-10 flowers to a whorl. Habitat: Sub-montane and lowland zones, stony localities, mainly in Central and East Crete. Flowers March-April.

Lamium (Dead-Nettles)

Annual or perennial plants. Flowers in whorls; calyx campanulate or tubular, with 5 teeth. Corolla bilabiate with upper lip strongly compressed, and lower one obcordate or broadly obovate, with or without small lateral lobes.

1. Lamium garganicum - subsp. garganicum. A perennial with stems up to 50cm. Leaves cordate-ovate, crenate, 15-70mm., densely hairy. Corolla pink, with long tube and upper lip bilobular. Habitat: Montane and alpine zones. Flowers May-June. **2. Lamium moschatum.** An annual, sparsely hairy, 10-30cm. tall. Leaves ovate-orbicular or triangular-ovate, crenate. Corolla white, 16-25mm. Tube of corolla 6-12mm., shorter than the calyx. Upper lip crenate. Habitat: Lowland and sub-montane zones. Flowers March-April. **3. Lamium bifidum - subsp. albimontanum.** A hairy or hairless annual. Leaves cordate-ovate, crenate. Flowers pink. Corolla 12-25mm., with long tube. The bottom lip bilobular. A Cretan endemic. Habitat: Cultivated and fallow fields, and in meadows of montane and sub-montane zones. Flowers March-May. **4. Lamium amplexicaule - subsp. amplexicaule.** Annual, sparsely hairy or pubescent, up to 30cm. Leaves either orbicular or orbicular-ovate, crenate. Corolla purple, with long tube and upper lip entire. Length of corolla 14-15mm. Habitat: Uncultivated ground and meadows of lowland and montane zones. Flowers February-April.

Ballota (Horehounds)

Perennial plants with flowers in whorls. Calyx tubular with lips membraneous, entire, or dentate. Bilabiate corolla, with tube hairy inside. Upper lip straight or slightly curved, hairy on the outside. Lower lip trilobed.

1. Ballota acetabulosa. A perennial shrublet up to 60cm. high, woody towards the base. Stem and leaves with dense greyish-green down and hair. Middle and upper leaves broadly cordate, almost orbicular, crenate at margins. Flowers in whorls in bunches of 6-12. Corolla two-coloured - purple and white, 15-18mm. Calyx with broad membraneous lips. When ripe and dry it is used as a wick in oil-lamps. Habitat: In rocky situations of montane and sub-montane zones. Flowers May-June. **2. Ballota nigra - subsp. uncinata.** Perennial shrublet up to 80cm. in height, pubescent or almost glabrous and much-branched. Lower leaves 3-8mm. ovate or ovate-oblong. Flowers in crowded multiflorous whorls. Violet corolla 12-14mm. A plant with a very unpleasant smell. Habitat: Middle and lower zones by roadsides, and among rubble and rubbish. Flowers May-June. **3. Ballota pseudodictamnus.** Similar to 1 but smaller with yellowish down and both leaves and flowers smaller, and calyx with pointed lobes. Habitat: Sub-montane and lowland zones. Flowers April-May.

Stachys (Woundwort)

Annual or perennial plants. Flowers in whorls, rarely growing singly. Calyx usually bell-shaped with 5 teeth. Corolla bilabiate. The upper lip may be either flat or arched, entire or bilobed. The lower one trilobed.

Phlomis fruticosa

Phlomis lanata

Lamium garganicum - s. sp. garganicum   Stachys cretica - s. sp. cretica

1. Stachys tournefortii. Perennials with 30-100cm. high stems which, like the leaves, are covered with very dense white lanate hairs. Leaves 50-75mm, ovate or ovate-oblong, and cordate at base. Pink or purple corolla 15-20mm. hairy. A North African (Libyan) plant that occurs nowhere else in Europe except Crete. Habitat: Found in rocky situations of montane and sub-montane zones. Flowers April-May. **2. Stachys cretica - subsp. cretica.** Perennial with lanate stems, 20-80cm. and lanate leaves which are oblong with a cunate base. Corolla pink or purple, and hairy. Habitat: Stony localities in sub-montane and lowland zones. Flowers April-May. **3. Stachys mucronata:** A lanate perennial plant with stems 10-50cm. long. Leaves oblong, crenate, and rounded at both tip and base. Whorls with 2-4 flowers. Corolla 10-12mm., pale pink, densely hairy. Endemic to the islands of Crete and Carpathos. Habitat: Dry locations of submontane and lowland zones. Flowers April-May. **4. Stachys spinosa.** A perennial with branching stems and branches spiny at their tips. Leaves hairy, linear-lanceolate, entire or slightly crenate, 10-35mm. long.

Whorls with 1-6 flowers. Hairy corolla pale pink or white. Endemic to the South Aegean. Habitat: Dry, stony locations at a low altitude. Flowers April-May. **6. Stachys ocymastrum.** A pubescent annual with simple stem, 20-50cm. Leaves from oblong-ovate up to broadly ovate, margins crenate, and slightly cordate at base. Flowers in whorls of 4-6. Corolla either yellow or white with a yellow lower lip. A South-West Europe plant reaching as far as Italy, it has been observed only once in Crete. Flowers March-April. **6. Stachys spinulosa.** A glandular, pubescent annual with a simple stem, 10-60cm. high. Flowers in whorls of 4-6. Calyx with hard, pointed teeth. Corolla 10-20mm., white. Habitat: It grows in uncultivated places of sub-montane and lowland zones. Flowers: March-April.

Nepeta

Usually perennial plants. Flowers in multiflorous whorls that form terminal spikes at the tip of the stems. Calyx symmetrical with 5 teeth and 15 veins. Corolla bilabiate. Upper lip flat and bilobed. Lower lip trilobate, with the middle lobe the largest. The leaves surrounding the flowers (bracts) are much smaller than the others.

1. Nepeta scordotis. Stems simple 25-60cm. hairy or lanate. Leaves, 3-6mm. ovate-cordate, lanate and stalked. Inflorescences in closely-clustered spikes. Corolla blue, 13-16mm. long. Endemic to the South Aegean. Habitat: Dry locations of middle and lower zones. Flowers April-May. **2. Nepeta sphaciotica.** A much-branched plant with short stems 12-18cm. and very short spikes. Crenate, ovate-cordate, greyish-green leaves. The whole plant is hairy. Corolla white. Endemic to the White Mountains. Habitat: Montane and sub-alpine zones. Flowers May-June. **3. Nepeta melissifolia.** An erect plant, 20-40cm. high, pubescent or hairy. Leaves ovate, heart-shaped at base, and crenate at margins. Corolla 12-15mm. blue with red spots. Endemic to the South Aegean. Habitat: Sub-montane zone. Flowers April-May.

Prunella (Self-Heals)

Perennial plants with leaves entire, dentate, or pinnately-lobed. Bilabiate calyx with the upper lip trilobate and the lower with 2 broad teeth. Flowers in dense whorls that form a short compact spike. The leaves which surround the flower-bearing whorls are much smaller than the other leaves, and of a different shape. Corolla bilabiate, hairy at throat, the upper lip erect.

1. Prunella laciniata. A pubescent plant. Stems up to 15cm. erect or spreading. Leaves pinnately lobed, with narrow lobes. Corolla creamy-coloured or, more rarely, pink (varietas cretica), 15-17mm. long. Habitat: Montane zone. Flowers May-June. **2. Prunella vulgaris.** Similar to 1, but leaves ovate, slightly dentate, and flowers a deep violet colour. Habitat: Montane zone. Flowers May-June.

Melissa (Balm)

Perennial plants. Flowers in whorls, surrounded by leaves similar to the lower ones. Calyx bilabiate, the upper lip trilobed, the lower bilobed. Corolla, also, bilabiate, the upper lip bilobed and the lower trilobed.

1. Melissa officinalis - subsp. altissima. Stems 20-150cm. erect, branched, pubescent, glandular, and with sparse hairs. Leaves broadly ovate, rhomboidal or oblong, crenate, with dense white hair underneath. Whorls with 4-12 small flowers. Corolla pale yellow that turns white or pink when fully mature. It is a plant with a rather unpleasant smell. Habitat: Montane and sub-montane zones. Flowers May-June.

Stachys spinulosa

Nepeta melissifolia

Prunella laciniata

Satureja thymbra

Satureja (Savories)

Annual or perennial plants with flowers in whorls or in sparse cymes. Calyx campanulate or tubular, with 5 identical teeth and 10 veins. Corolla bilabiate. The upper lip is flat, entire or emarginate and smaller than the lower which is trilobed.

1. Satureja thymbra. A much-branched, aromatic, perennial shrublet, pubescent, 20-35cm, tall. Leaves oblong or obovate, acute, 7-20mm. long. Flowers in multi-flowered whorls. Calyx hairy. Corolla, 8-12mm., pink or purple. Habitat: Sub-montane and montane zones. Flowers April-June. **2. Satureja spinosa.** Similar to 1 but the branches are prickly at tip. Whorls with 2 flowers only, and leaves smaller up to 10mm. Endemic to Crete. Habitat: Alpine and sub-alpine zones. Flowers May-June.

Acinos

Plants similar to **Satureja** but flowers always in whorls and calyx bilabiate, saccate, and with 13 veins.

1. Acinos alpinus - subsp. meridionalis. A pubescent, aromatic, perennial plant with either creeping or ascending stems. Leaves small, elliptic or almost orbicular. Calyx with crisped hairs. Corolla violet-coloured. Habitat: Montane and alpine zones. Flowers May-June. **2. Acinos rotundifolius.** Similar to 1 but annual. Leaves obovate or orbicular, awned at tip. Habitat: Sub-montane zone. Flowers April-May.

Calamintha (Calaminths)

Perennial plants with flowers in opposite, stalked cymes. Calyx more or less bilabiate. Corolla like those of **Acinos** and **Satureja.**

1. Calamintha grandiflora. A perennial with sparse hairs and a stem 20-60cm. high. Leaves ovate or ovate-oblong, dentate-crenate, 30-80mm. Cymes with 1-5 large flowers. Corolla pink or pinkish-violet, 25-40mm. Habitat: Montane zone in shady and cool sites. Flowers June-July. **2. Calamintha nepeta - subsp. glandulosa.** A pubescent, greyish-green plant, with stems 30-50(-80)cm. Leaves ovate, slightly dentate, 10-20mm. Inflorescences with 5-11 flowers. Corolla small, white or violet. Flowers August-October. **3. Calamintha cretica.** A densely pubescent, greyish-green plant, woody at base, with stems 10-30cm. long. Leaves 6-10mm. broadly ovate. Cymes with 1-3(-6) flowers. Corolla 10mm., white. It is endemic to Crete. Habitat: Montane and sub-alpine zones. Flowers June-August.

Chinopodium (Wild Basil)

Plants similar to **Calamintha** but flowers in closely-packed, almost sessile cymes. Calyx curved.

1. Chinopodium vulgare - subsp. arundanum. Pubescent or hairy, perennial plants, 30-80cm. Leaves 20-65mm., ovate-lanceolate or ovate. Flowers pink or purple. Whorls of inflorescences very distant. Habitat: Montane and sub-montane zones. Flowers July-September.

Micromeria

Perennial plants. Calyx tubular. Corolla bilabiate with straight tube, with the upper lip straight, entire or emarginate, the lower lip trilobed.

1. Micromeria microphylla. Shrublet almost glabrous or just slightly pubescent, 10-30 cm. with slender, ascending or trailing stems. Leaves 3-6mm., triangular-ovate or elliptic. Whorls with 1-6 flowers. Corolla 5-8mm., purple. Habitat: Rocks in the montane and sub-montane zones. Flowers April-June. **2. Micromeria hispida.** Similar to 1 but stems erect and densely pubescent; whorls with more flowers. A Cretan endemic. Habitat: Rocks in the lowest zone. Flowers April-May. **3. Micromeria nervosa.** Much-branched shrublet, 10-40cm. Leaves 7-10cm. ovate or ovate-lanceolate. Whorls with 4-20 flowers. Corolla 4-6mm., purple. Habitat: Stony localities in lowest zone. Flowers May-June. **4. Micromeria juliana.** A pubescent shrublet, 10-40cm. Numerous erect stems. Leaves 3-8mm. linear-lanceolate or oblong, entire, not acute, with rolled margins. Whorls have from 4 to 20 flowers. Purple corolla 5mm. Habitat: Among rocks in the sub-montane zone. Flowers April-June. **5. Micromeria myrtifolia.** Very like 4 but the calyx is hairy inside, and has small

Calamintha grandiflora

teeth. Habitat: Rocks of low altitude. Flowers In springtime. **6. Micromeria graeca - subsp. graeca.** A pubescent or hairy shrublet, 10-50cm., with many stems. Leaves 5-12mm., the lower ones ovate and acute, the remainder lanceolate with rolled margins. Whorls with 4-18 flowers. Corolla 6-8(-13)mm purple. Habitat: Rocks in the montane zone. Flowers in springtime.

Micromeria tapeinantha has been described as a plant growing in Crete, however, it is more likely to be a natural hybrid between 3 and 6.

Thymbra

Small shrublets. Flowers in dense whorls that form crowded spike-like inflorescences.

Both calyx and corolla bilabiate, upper lip of latter flat and entire, while the lower is trilobed. Leaves similar. Inflorescence leaves alternately overlapping.

1. Thymbra calostachya. Stems up to 40cm, erect or ascending, densely pubescent. Leaves 5-12mm, oblong-lanceolate, entire with thick grey down. Calyx 3mm. Corolla 5,5-6mm, white. Endemic to Crete in the Seteia area. Habitat: Calcareous rocks in submontane zone. Flowers Springtime.

Origanum (Oreganos, Wild Marjorams and Dictamnums)

Perennial, biennial, or annual plants. Flowers in whorls forming dense spikelets. Several spikelets together make up corymb-like apical inflorescences. The 5-toothed calyx is bilabiate or actinomorphic. The upper lip of the bilabiate corolla is entire or slightly bilobed whilst the lower is trilobed. Aromatic plants.

1. Origanum heracleoticum. A woody perennial with pubescent stems up to 60cm., branching at the upper part. Leaves 15-22mm, ovate or oblong, entire or slightly dentate, and sparsely hairy. Spikelets 5-20mm. Corolla 4-5mm, white, seldom pink. Habitat: Montane, sub-montane, and lowland zones. Flowers June-July. **2. Origanum onites.** Shrublet up to 60cm., similar to 1 but the leaves are smaller, broader, with cordate base, and very compact spikelets up to 10mm. Habitat: Sub-montane and lowland zones. Flowers May-June. **3. Origanum microphyllum.** Similar to 1 and 2 but leaves very small, 4-8mm., pubescent or hairy; slender quadrangular reddish stems, and purple corolla. Endemic to Crete. Habitat: Lower zone. **4. Origanum dictamnus.** A perennial with stems up to 20cm. Leaves either orbicular or broadly ovate, 13-25mm. long, covered with dense white hairs. Spikelets nodding, with large, reddish bracts, almost glabrous. Corolla pink. Endemic to Crete. Habitat: Montane zone. Flowers May-June. **5. Origanum tournefortii.** Similar to 4 but glabrous to sparsely hairy. Leaves glaucous, ciliate. Endemic to Crete and to the Cyclades Islands. Habitat: Rocky localities at a low altitude. Flowers April-May.

Origanum minoanum is a natural hybrid between 1 and 3, with intermediate characteristics.

Thymus (Thymes)

Small shrubs or perennial herbaceous plants, woody, at least at base. Two-lipped calyx, the upper lip with 3 teeth and the lower with 2. The upper lip of the bilabiate corolla is flat, entire or emarginate, while the bottom one is divided into 3 lobes. Flowers small in closely packed head-shaped inflorescences.

1. Thymus capitatus. Much-branced, thick and aromatic shrublet. Leaves linear, up to 10mm, almost hairless. Corolla up to 10mm, too, pink or purple. Habitat: Common in stony areas of the submontane zone. Flowers May-June.

Mentha (Mints)

Aromatic plants with creeping, perennial rhizomes. Small flowers with actinomorphic or bilabiate calyx, and corolla 4-lobed with the top one emarginate or bilobed. Leaves next to flowers are more or less similar to the lower leaves but smaller.

1. Mentha pulegium - subsp. pulegioides. An either sparsely or densely-haired plant. Erect stems, 30-60cm high. Flowers in packed whorls distant from one another. Leaves elliptic or nearly round, slightly dentate, green or greyish-green in colour, and 16-35mm. in length. Calyx 2,5-3,5mm. Corolla violet, on rare occasions white. Habitat: Damp areas near the sea. Flowers June-August. **2. Mentha aquatica.** A hairy plant. Stems (10) 20-

Clinopodium vulgare

Thymus capitatus

Mentha aquatica

Mentha spicata

100cm, erect and much-branched. Leaves 30-90mm, ovate-lanceolate or cordate, dentate. Corolla 6-7mm, pink or violet. Flowers in tightly-packed whorls forming closely-clustered terminal heads. Habitat: Damp locations, swamps, river-banks, lakesides of montane and sub-montane zones. Flowers July-September. **3. Mentha suaveolens.** A hairy plant with stems 40-100cm. Leaves 25-45mm, olive-green, oblong-ovate, heart-shaped at base, crenate. Corolla white or pale pink, 3.5-4mm. Multi-flowered whorls the lower distant, the upper forming an almost continuous spike. Habitat: Damp regions at a low altitude in West Crete. Flowers July-September. **4. Mentha longifolia - subsp. petiolata.** A hairy or glabrous plant with branched stems 30-130cm. Flowers pink or pale pink, small, in successive oblong spikes. Leaves oblong-lanceolate, dentate, green and with a short petiole. Habitat: Damp locations of montane and sub-montane zones. Flowers July-September. **5. Mentha spicata.** A plant with either dense or sparse hair.

Stems 30-150cm, often much-branched. Leaves 28-80mm, green above and olive-green or greyish-green beneath, oblong-lanceolate or oblong-ovate, dentate. Flowers about 3-5mm, white, pink, or lilac in spike-like, often branched, inflorescences. Habitat: Damp sites of sub-montane and montane zones. Flowers June-September. **6. Mentha piperita.** A natural hybrid between 2 and 5 with intermediate characteristics. It has been observed at Platania in the prefecture of Chania, and at Ambelouzo in the prefecture of Heraclion. It is sterile. **7. Mentha villoso-nervata.** A very varied sterile hybrid between 4 and 5. One of its forms is the common mint that is widely cultivated. **Mentha villosa-nervata** has been observed in the prefecture of Heraclion.

Rosmarinus (Rosemary)

Evergreen shrubs. Flowers in few-flowered whorls. Calyx two-lipped, the top lip being entire and the lower two-lobed. Corolla bilabiate, too, the upper lip curved, deeply bipartite, and the lower one three-lobed.

1. Rosmarinus officinalis. A shrub reaching from 50 to 200cm. in height. Leaves linear, green above and whitish beneath, with rolled margins. Corolla 10-12mm, pale blue. A much-cultivated aromatic plant. Habitat: Stony localities in sub-montane and lowland zones. Flowers May-June.

Lavandula (Lavender)

Small shrubs. Flowers in either sparse or dense spikes. Bracts very different from the leaves. Calyx with 5 small teeth. The top one occasionally different and larger. Corolla bilabiate with the upper lip bilobed and the lower trilobed.

1. Lavandula stoechas - subsp. stoechas. An evergreen plant up to 60cm. high. Leaves linear or narrowly oblong, covered with a grey pubescence. Spike short and compact, 2-3cm. Dark purple flowers 6-8mm. Bracts violet-coloured, rhomboidal-cordate. At the apex of the spike there are some larger, sterile bracts. Habitat: Sub-montane scrub and stony localities. Flowers February-April.

Salvia (Sages)

Herbs or shrubs, perennials or annuals. Flowers in whorls arising from the axils of upper leaves. Bilabiate calyx, the lower lip with 2 teeth and the upper with three. Corolla two-lipped. The upper lip either straight or curved, the lower trilobate, the middle lobe being the largest.

1. Salvia triloba. A perennial shrub up to 1m. Stems with dense, white down. Leaves simple, trifoliate or pinnate with two pairs of lateral leaflets. The central leaflet being the largest. All ovate or elliptic. Leaflets green and pubescent above, densely pubescent and grey beneath. Flowers 16-25mm, pale pink or lilac, more rarely white. Habitat: Sub-montane and montane scrub and stony locations. Flowers April-May. **2. Salvia pomifera - subsp. pomifera.** A shrub up to 1m high. Leaves simple, ovate, with thick velutinous down, greenish or greyish-green. Flowers in whorls of 2-4, bluish-violet, with the lower lip a lighter colour. Corolla about 35mm. Habitat: Found in sub-montane and lowland scrub and stony localities in West Crete. Flowers April-May. **3. Salvia verbenaca - subsp. multifida.** An annual. Stems 10-50cm, erect, simple or branching, pubescent, glandular at their upper section. Leaves pinnately lobed. Flowers 6-10mm, blue or violet. Habitat: Arid, waste lands in montane and sub-montane zones. Flowers April-May, and frequently right up to September. **4. Salvia viridis.** A 10-50cm high annual with an erect stem which may be simple or branching, hairy, hairs glandular or not. Leaves simple ovate or oblong, slightly

Rosmarinus officinalis

Lavandula stoechas

Salvia viridis

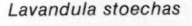
Lycium barbarum

crenate, pubescent. Pink or violet flowers, 14-18mm. Frequently at the tip of the spike there are sterile bracts, violet-coloured, more rarely they may be green or white. Habitat: Stony situations in sub-montane and lowland zones.

Solanaceae Family

Shrubs or herbaceous plants. Leaves simple or pinnately-lobed, alternate or verticiliate, rarely opposite. Calyx usually with 5 lobes or teeth. Corolla tubular, campanulate, or rotate, with lobes folded when in bud.

Lycium (Duke of Argyll's and Tea-plants)

As a rule spiny shrubs. Leaves entire, alternate, or in whorls. Flowers in axils of leaves, singly or several together. Calyx with 5 teeth. Corolla tubular or tubular at base, with 5 spreading lobes at end.

1. Lycium barbarum. Up to 2,5m tall. Branches arcuate. Leaves narrowly elliptic, or narrowly lanceolate. Calyx 4mm, slightly bilabiate. The 9mm corolla with spreading lobes is, initially, violet-coloured but turns brown when full-blown. Fruit an orange-red berry. This plant is a native of China which has become naturalised in Crete. Habitat: Sporadically occurring in the sub-montane and lowland zones. Flowers June to September. **2. Lycium intricatum.** A very many-branched, and very prickly shrub. Leaves oblanceolate, 3-5mm, Its flowers are a bluish-violet, purple, pink, or white, with patent lobes. Fruit a black berry. The Cretan plants differ from the typical ones of the West Mediterranean which produce red fruit. They are often considered a variety of **Lycium persicum.** Habitat: Low altitude seaside localities. Flowers June-September.

Lycium europaeum with its pink or white flowers, and leaves up to 50mm, is mentioned as occurring in Crete but with some doubt.

Hyoscyamus (Henbane)

Perennial or annual plants with flowers in axillary inflorescences. Calyx campanulate-tubular. Corolla also campanulate, oblique, with 5 broad lobes.

1. Hyoscyamus albus. Perennial or annual, hairy, glandular, with stems 30-90cm high. Leaves orbicular-ovate, dentate, with broad teeth. Flowers creamy-coloured with a yellow or brown throat, hairy on the outside, and 3cm long. Habitat: Rocks, walls of old house, rubble, and rubbish-dumps, all at a low altitude. Flowers April-May. **2. Hyoscyamus aureus.** Similar to 1 but leaves with dentate teeth, and flowers a golden-yellow with a purple throat. Habitat: Rocks, and old castle walls. Flowers August-October. It is a South-West Asia species, probably established in Crete in modern times.

Wilhania

Shrubs with leaves alternate or opposite, and entire. Flowers arise from the axils of leaves singly or in clusters. Calyx campanulate, so is the 5-lobed corolla. Fruit a spherical berry surrounded by the calyx that swells as it ripens.

1. Wilhania somnifera. Stems 60-120cm, erect, branched, and pubescent. Downy leaves, 3-10cm long, ovate, obovate or oblong, with a wedge-shaped base. Flowers in clusters of 4-6. Calyx 5mm. Corolla 5mm, too, greenish-yellow in colour. Fruit a shiny, red, berry, 5-8mm. Habitat: Verges of roads, ruins and rocks, from the lower right down to the littoral zone. Flowers August-October.

Solanum

Herbs or shrubs. Leaves alternate or opposite, simple or pinnately-lobed. Inflorescences arise from the axils of the leaves. Calyx small, campanulate. Corolla rotate, 5-lobed. Stamens with convergent protruding anthers.

1. Solanum nigrum: Annual, almost glabrous, pubescent or hairy, up to 1m. high. Leaves up to 7cm. ovate, rhomboidal or lanceolate, with large teeth. Flowers with corolla 10-14mm., white with yellow anthers. Fruit a black or greenish-yellow berry. Habitat: Both arable and waste ground, olive groves and rubble at a low altitude. Flowers in summer. **2. Solanum luteum:** Similar to 1 but flowers somewhat larger, and berry reddish, orange-coloured or yellow. Habitat: Arable and waste ground, among rubble and rubbish, at a low altitude. Flowers in summer.

Hyoscyamus albus

Hyoscyamus aureus

Withania somnifera

Solanum nigrum

Mandragora (Mandrake)

Perennial plants with fusiform taproot. Leaves large, simple, forming rosette at base. Flowers arising direct from the base of the plant, without any stem; long-stalked and large; corolla and calyx campanulate, 5-lobed. Fruit a berry.

1. Mandragora autumnalis: Leaves ovate or ovate-lanceolate, almost hairless. Corolla 3-4cm. long, violet or lilac. Fruit a yellow or orange-coloured berry. Habitat: Uncultivated ground and meadows at a low altitude. Flowers October-November or February-March. Bears fruit November-December or March-April.

Datura (Thorn Apple)

Annual, large plants, with leaves entire or notched. Flowers large with funnel-shaped corolla and 5-10 lobes.

1. Datura stramonium: A pubescent plant 50-200cm. high. Leaves 5-18cm. notched-dentate. Corolla white, rarely purple, 5-10cm. long. Fruit a large capsule, egg-shaped and prickly. Of American origin established in Crete. Habitat: Ditches, among rubble and rubbish, and roadsides in the lowland and sub-montane zones. Flowers July-September.

Nicotiana (Tobacco)

Annuals or perennials. Leaves alternate, simple. Corolla tubular or with tubular base and broad, spreading lobes at tip.

1. Nicotiana glauca: A glabrous shrub. Leaves lanceolate or ovate, glaucous-green. Flowers in lax inflorescences. Calyx small. Corolla yellow, 30-40mm. long, tubular. A plant of Argentina and Bolivia established in the Mediterranean area. Habitat: Among rubbish, rubble, ruins and in ditches in the lower zone. Flowers May-October.

Scrophulariaceae Family

Herbaceous plants, rarely shrubs. Leaves simple, seldom pinnately-lobed, usually alternate or opposite. Flowers zygomorphic. Calyx with 4 or 5 lobes, often bilabiate. Corolla usually with 5 lobes or else two-lipped.

Verbascum (Aaron's Rods, Mulleins)

Plants usually biennial, more rarely perennial or annual. Inflorescences large, terminal, spike-shaped or panicle-like. Calyx with 5 lobes. Corolla usually yellow, zygomorphic, with a short tube and broad spreading lobes.

1. Verbascum spinosum: A perennial spiny shrub, up to 50cm. Leaves oblong-lanceolate, dentate, up to 5cm. long, covered with white down. Corolla yellow, 10-18mm. across. Endemic to Crete. Habitat: Hills and dry places of the montane and sub-montane zones. Flowers in spring. **2. Verbascum arcturus:** A perennial with a woody base. Stems 30-70cm., simple, erect. Basal leaves green and sparsely hairy on upper side, very hairy on underside, lyrate, with one large, ovate, entire lobe and 2-4 much smaller lateral ones. Stem leaves few and much smaller. Inflorescences spike-like, thickly pubescent-glandular. Flowers yellow, 25-30mm. across. Endemic to Crete. Habitat: Rocks of the sub-montane and lowland zones. Flowers April-May. **3. Verbascum macrurum:** Biennial, 40-150cm., with dense, white hairs. Basal leaves 20-50cm., oblong-oblanceolate, stalkless. Stem leaves smaller. Inflorescence spike-shaped, compact, lanate. Flowers 25-40mm., yellow. Habitat: Sub-montane zone. Flowers May-July. **4. Verbascum sinuatum:** A densely pubescent biennial, often lanate, glandular towards top. Stems 50-100cm. Basal leaves 15-35cm., pinnately-lobed or undulate. Inflorescence branched, lax. Corolla yellow, 15-30mm. Habitat: Low altitude. Flowers May-July.

Verbascum mucronatum, A plant of W. Asia Minor and of the islands of the E. Aegean, it is a matter of conjecture whether it occurs in Crete. It is a very lanate plant, up to 2m. in height, with branching inflorescence.

Scrophularia (Figworts or Water Betonies)

Herbs or small shrubs, with leaves opposite, entire, either pinnately-lobed or pinnate. Flowers in cymes in the axils of the upper leaves or bracts. Corolla small, with a rather spherical tube and a two-lipped mouth. The upper lip being larger and covering the lower one when in bud.

1. Scrophularia peregrina: Annual, glabrous, 15-90cm. Leaves up to 10cm., ovate-cordate, dentate. Flowers 9mm., dark red or brown. Habitat: Cool gardens and damp

Mandragora autumnalis

Nicotiana glauca

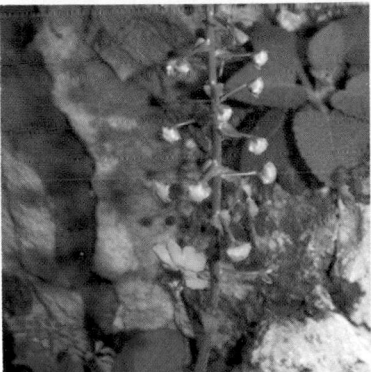

Verbascum arcturus

Verbascum sinuatum

situations of the sub-montane and lowland zones. Flowers February-April. **2. Scrophularia auriculata:** Similar to 1 but a perennial. Stems quadrangular. Leaves longer than they are broad, usually with 2 small, lateral leaflets, and greenish flowers, the upper lip brown. Habitat: Situations with plenty of soil, in the medium and lower zones. Flowers March-May. **3. Scrophularia lucida:** A glabrous, perennial plant, with simple stem 10-100cm. high. Leaves pinnately-lobed or pinnate with crenate-dentate lobes. Corolla 4-9mm., greenish-brown. Habitat: Rocks from a low altitude down to the coastal zone. Flowers February-April. **4. Scrophularia heterophylla - subsp. heterophylla:** Glabrous or glandular, perennial, 10-70cm. Leaves up to 5cm., more or less fleshy, glaucous-green, crenate or almost pinnately-lobed, with the lobes rounded. Corolla 6-9mm., reddish-purple or greenish. Habitat: Rocks of the lowland and sub-montane zones. Flowers March-April.

Antirrhinum (Snap dragons)

Small shrubs or perennial herbs. Leaves entire usually opposite at the higher part and alternate at the lower. Flowers zygomorphic in terminal racemes. Calyx 5-lobes. Corolla with a broad swollen tube, saccate at base. At edge two-lipped, the upper lip being upcurved, bipartite, and the lower lip down-curved, 3-lobed.

1. Antirrhinum majus - subsp. tortuosum: Perennial with erect stems, up to 80cm. Leaves narrow, linear, 10-60 X 1,5mm. hairless. Corolla purplish-pink, yellow or white at opening. Habitat: Both cultivated and self-seeding among rocks, on walls of buildings and among ruins. Flowers April-June, very often much later, right up to October. The **subsp. tortuosum** which is a native of S. Spain and Sicily is widely distributed throughout the E. Mediterranean region.

Antirrhinum siculum, a smaller plant with smaller yellowish flowers is mentioned as existing in Crete, but its existence has not been verified in recent times. It has very possibly become extinct.

Misopates

Plants similar to **Antirrhinum** but annual. The lobes of the calyx are longer than the corolla.

1. Misopates orontium: Stem 20-50cm., with few branches, glabrous or slightly pubescent towards the lower part while glandular towards the higher part. Leaves linear or oblong. Flowers pink. Corolla 10-15mm. Habitat: Lowland and sub-montane zones. Flowers February-April.

Chenorhinum

Plants similar to **Antirrhinum** but flowers with a straight spur at the lower part of the corolla.

1. Chenorhinum minus subsp. minus: Annual, glandular, 10-40cm. Leaves linear or oblong. Corolla 6-9mm., lilac, yellow at the opening. Habitat: Montane and sub-montane zones. Flowers April-June. **2. Chenorhinum minus subsp. idaeum.** Similar to 1 but up to 5cm., and corolla 5mm., pale yellow. Endemic to Crete. Habitat: Montane and sub-alpine zones. Flowers May-June.

Linaria (Toadflaxes)

Plants similar to **Chenorhinum** but upper leaves in whorls.

1. Linaria triphylla. A glaucous-green annual, 10-45cm. high. Leaves up to 35mm., elliptic-obovate. Flowers 20-30mm., white with yellow mouth and violet spur. Habitat: Uncultivated ground and meadows in the lowland and sub-montane zones. Flowers February-April. **2. Linaria chalepensis.** Annual with spreading stems 20-40cm. Leaves linear. Inflorescences (racemes) very lax. Corolla 12-16mm., white. Habitat: Dry locations at a low altitude. Flowers February-March. **3. Linaria pelisseriana.** Annual with slender erect stems, 15-40cm. Leaves linear, 1mm. wide. Inflorescences dense, corolla 15-20mm., purplish-violet. Habitat: Montane, sub-montane and lowland zones. Flowers March-May. **4. Linaria simplex:** Annual, glaucous-green with leaves linear or linear-lanceolate. Corolla

Scrophularia lucida

Antirrhinum majus - s. sp. tortuosum

Linaria triphylla

Linaria chalepensis

5-9mm., pale yellow, often with violet veins. Habitat: Dry localities at a low altitude. Flowers March-April. **5. Linaria micrantha.** Similar to 4 but leaves broader and flowers smaller, lilac-coloured. Habitat: Low altitude cultivated and fallow fields. Flowers March-April.

Cymbalaria (Ivy-leaved Toadflaxes)

Plants similar to **Linaria** but leaves kidney-shaped, or almost orbicular, with palm-shaped veins and trailing stems.

1. Cymbalaria muralis - subsp. muralis. A usually glabrous plant. Corolla violet-coloured, with yellow opening, 9-15mm. long. Spur 1,5-3mm. Leaves 12X15mm., rarely larger, up to 55X65mm., with 5-9 obtuse lobes. Habitat: Rocks, walls of houses, ruins, in flowerpots in gardens, ranging from the montane to the littoral zone. Flowers March-June, often later if watered. **2. Cymbalaria longipes:** Similar to 1 but leaves never broader than 20mm., and spur 4-5mm. Habitat: Rocks in the littoral zone. Flowers March-May. **3. Cymbalaria microcalyx subsp. dodekanesi:** Similar to 1 and 2 but a smaller plant, hairy, with leaves at most 15mm. wide, entire or with 3—5 shallow lobes. Spur 2-3mm. Habitat: Rocks of the montane and sub-montane zones. Flowers April-July.

Kickxia (Fluellens)

Plants similar to **Cymbalaria** but leaves lanceolate, ovate or arrow-shaped. Flowers arise singly from the axils of the leaves.

1. Kickxia commutata - subsp. graeca: Perennial, hairy-glandular, with creeping stems. leaves lanceolate, with arrow-shaped base, the upper leaves very small. Corolla 11-15mm. whitish, the upper lip violet, the lower yellowish and the opening with purple spots. Habitat: Sandy soil at medium and low altitudes. Flowers May-September. **2. Kickxia elatine - subsp. crinita:** Similar to 1 but the corolla is yellowish, while the upper lip is similarly violet. Main stems ascending, with many short branchings that bear the flowers. Habitat: They grow on both cultivated and uncultivated land at low and medium altitudes. Flowers June-October. **3. Kickxia spuria - subspecies integrifolia:** Similar to 1 and 2 but leaves ovate, not arrow-shaped at base. Main stems producing small secondary stems with very small leaves. Corolla yellow, the upper lip dark purple. Habitat: Both cultivated and uncultivated land and sandy soil of medium and lower zones. Flowers May-October.

Veronica (Speedwells)

Plants with lower leaves opposite, and upper leaves alternate. Flowers in terminal or axillary inflorescences or arising singly from the axils of the leaves. Calyx with 4 lobes. Corolla rotate or broadly bell-shaped, with 4 lobes, usually dissimilar.

1. Veronica thymifolia: Perennial with dense hairs. Stems spreading, woody at base. Leaves 4-6mm., oblong or oblanceolate-spathulate. Inflorescences 1-2 on each stem, very short and with few flowers. Flowers 7-8mm. across, blue, violet or pink. Endemic to S. Greece and Crete. Habitat: Rocks of the montane and sub-montane zones. Flowers May-June. **2. Veronica anagallis-aquatica:** Usually a perennial. Stems 30-60cm., erect, simple or branching from the base, glabrous or pubescent-glandular. Leaves 20-100mm. pale green, hairless, ovate or ovate-lanceolate, more or less crenate. Flowers in axillary racemes, up to 3 times longer than the corresponding leaves. Corolla 5-10mm. across, blue with violet veins. Habitat: Banks of streams, swamps and other damp situations of the montane and lowland zones. Flowers May-July. **3. Veronica acinifolia:** Annual 5-15cm., pubescent glandular. Leaves 4-10mm. ovate, entire or slightly crenate, pubescent or almost glabrous. Flowers in racemes. Corolla 2-3mm., blue. Habitat: Both cultivated and uncultivated land, at medium and low altitudes. Flowers February-April. **4. Veronica praecox:** Similar to 3 but leaves deeply crenate. Habitat: Dry and sunny places, low and medium altitudes. Flowers February-April. **5. Veronica kavusica:** Similar to 4. It differs mainly in the capsule which is smooth and truncate on the upper part (whereas it is hairy glandular and bilobed in 4). Endemic to E. Crete. Habitat: Montane zone. Flowers March-April. **6. Veronica arvensis:** Similar to 3 but leaves triangular-ovate, with base more or less cordate, crenate at margin. Habitat: Cutlivated land and dry, open spaces. Flowers March-April. **7. Veronica sartoriana:** Very similar to 6 but dwarf-like (up to 5cm.) **7. Veronica sartoriana:** Very similar to 6, but dwarf-like (up to 5cm.) densely hairy-glandular. Endemic to the Greek mainland and Crete. Habitat: Montane zone. Flowers April-May. **8. Veronica agrestis:** A pubescent annual. Stems 3-30cm. spreading. Flowers arising singly from axils of leaves, with pedicel 5-15mm. long, curved at maturation. Flowers 3-6mm. across, white with a blue or pink upper lobe. Habitat: Cultivated places in the medium and

Cymbalaria muralis - s. sp. muralis

Kickxia spuria - s. sp. integrifolia

Veronica thymifolia

Veronica cymbalaria

lower zones. Flowers Feb-April. **9. Veronica polita:** Similar to 8 but leaves more deeply crenate and flowers blue. Habitat: Cultivated ground. Flowers Feb-April. **10. Veronica persica:** Similar to 8 and 9, but leaves larger, flowers 8-12mm. blue with pedicels 5-30mm. long. A species of S.W. Asia that has become naturalised in Crete. Habitat: Cutlivated fields. Flowers Feb-April. **11. Veronica cymblararia:** Annual with hairy leaves that are 5-9 lobed. Flowers white with pedicels longer than the corresponding leaves. Numerous spreading stems. Habitat: On rocks and walls in medium and lower zones. Flowers Feb-March.

Veronica hederifolia, with 5-7 lobed leaves and blue or violet flowers is mentioned doubtfully as existing in Crete.

213

Sibthorpia

Perennial plants with creeping stems, rooting at nodes. Leaves long-stalked, orbicular, alternate or in clusters. Corolla rotate with 4 to 8 lobes.

1. Sibthorpia europaea: Stems slender and up to 40cm. in height. Leaves 8-25mm. wide, crenate or with broad teeth pubescent-hairy. Flowers arising singly from axils of leaves. Corolla 1.5-2,5mm., 5-lobed, white, flushed with pink. Habitat: Damp, shady sites, in alpine zone. Flowers May-July.

Euphrasia (Eyebright)

Annual, dwarf plants. Leaves opposite or the upper ones alternate, all of them dentate. Flowers on terminal spike-like racemes, surrounded by leaf-like bracts. Calyx with 4 lobes. Corolla bilabiate. The upper lip curved like a helmet, the lower three-lobed.

1. Euphrasia salisburgensis: Stem up to 20cm., often branching. Leaves 3-13mm., glabrous, usually purple-hued. Corolla 5-7,5mm., white. Habitat: Montane and alpine zones. Flowers May-June.

Odontites (Bartsias)

Annual or perennial semi-perasitic plants. Leaves opposite, commonly narrow and terminal. Flowers on terminal spike-like racemes. Calyx 4-lobed. Corolla with cylindrical tube and two-lipped apex. Upper lip entire or slightly bilobed. The lower lip is 3-lobed.

1. Odontites linkii: A small shrub with slender branches, reaching up 50cm. Leaves linear, up to 4mm. wide. Inflorescence rather lax. Corolla 7mm. long, yellow. Endemic to the Greek mainland and Crete. Habitat: Rocks of the montane zone. Flowers September-November.

Parentucellia

Annual plants with dentate, opposite leaves. Flowers on terminal spike-like racemes. Calyx tubular, slightly curved, with 4 lobes. Corolla with one long cylindrical tube and a bilabiate apex. The upper lip which is entire or wavy is longer than the lower one. Lower lip 3-lobed.

1. Parentucellia viscosa: Stem 10-50cm. Leaves oblong or lanceolate crenate. Flowers yellow, rarely white, 16-24mm. The whole plant is hairy-glandular. Habitat: Seaside sandy locations. Flowers March-April. **2. Parentucellia latifolia:** Similar to 1 but a smaller plant with leaves deeply dentate and the flowers smaller and purple. Habitat: Littoral, lowland and sub-montane zones.

Bellardia

Plants resembling **Parentucellia** but the calyx is swollen and split into 2 dentate segments. Lower lip of corolla longer.

1. Bellardia trixago: Pubescent, glandular, 15-70cm. Leaves 15-90mm., linear-lanceolate, crenate. Corolla 20-25mm., either two-coloured - white and purple, or all-white. Habitat: Uncultivated sites at a low altitude. Flowers April-May.

Globulariaceae Family

Perennial plants with simple leaves, alternate or in clusters. Flowers 5-segmented, zygomorphic, blue.

Odontites linkii

Parentucellia viscosa

Bellardia trixago

Acanthus spinosus

Globularia (Globularia)

Evergreen plants. Flowers in heads. Corolla two-lipped. The upper lip usually bilobed and small, and the lower lip 3-lobed.

1. Globularia alypum: Shrub up to 1m. high. Leaves small, oblanceolate or obovate. Heads 1,5cm. across, with numerous, acute hypanthium bracts. Habitat: Bushy, and scrub land in the sub-montane and montane zones. Flowers May-June.

Acanthaceae Family

Herbaceous plants or shrubs. Leaves opposite. Flowers zygomorphic on spikes.

Acanthus

Sturdy, perennial herbaceous plants. Stems simple, erect. Most of the leaves are at the base. Leaves large, pinnately-lobed or pinnate. Flowers large, in compact spikes. Corolla two-lipped the lower lip being tripartite, and the upper almost entire. Bracts large, dentate-spiny. Calyx 4-lobed, the lateral lobes being much smaller.

1. Acanthus spinosus: Stems 20-80cm. Flowers white. Leaves large. Leaves and bracts very prickly. Habitat: Roadsides, olive groves, uncultivated ground in the lowland and sub-montane zones. Flowers May-June.

Orobanchaceae Family

Perennial or annual herbs, lacking chlorophyll, parasitic on the roots of other plants, usually on dicotyledonous herbs. Leaves small, bract-like. Corolla 5-lobed or bilabiate.

Orobanche (Broomrapes)

Stems simple or branching. Flowers in dense spikes or racemes. Calyx with 4 teeth or two-lipped, with two lateral segments. Corolla bilabiate; the lower lip 3-lobed.

1. Orobanche ramosa: Stems 5-30cm., swollen at base, simple or branching, pubescent and glandular. Leaves 3-8mm., ovate or lanceolate acute. Corolla 10-22mm., almost erect in relation to the stem, swollen and whitish at base, yellowish, violet or blue at mouth. Habitat: Common in the medium and lower zones, particularly the subsp. **mutelli** and **nana** that are parasitic on various species of the Papilionaceae. Flowers April-June. **2. Orobanche oxyloba:** Stems 12-30cm., slightly swollen at base. Leaves 5-15mm., ovate-lanceolate. Corolla 15-20mm., white at base, lilac at tip. Parasitic on Anthemis chia and other plants. Habitat: Montane and sub-montane zones. Flowers March-April. **3. Orobanche cernua:** Stems up to 40cm. Leaves 5-10mm., ovate-lanceolate. Corolla 12-20mm., swollen and whitish at base, blue-violet at edge. Multiflowered inflorescence. Parasitic on species of the genus Artemisia, as well as on Helianthus annuus. Habitat: Medium and lower zones. Flowers May-June. **4. Orobanche crenata:** Stems up to 80cm. Leaves 15-25mm., linear-lanceolate, dense at lower part of stem, few at upper part. Corolla 20-30mm., white or with lilac veins. A common parasite on Papilionaceus plants, particularly on the broad bean plant. Habitat: Medium and lower altitude. Flowers April-May. **5. Orobanche alba:** Thick stem up to 35cm. high. Corolla 15-25mm., purple yellow or whitish. Parasitic on the genus **Thymus** and other plants of the Labiatae family. Habitat: Medium and low altitudes. Flowers April-May. **6. Orobanche pubescens:** Stems 15-50cm., pubescent-glandular, pale yellow or with light purple hue. Corolla 10-20mm., pale yellow, flushed with violet at mouth. Parasitic on plants of the Compositae and Umbelliferae families, rarely on Leguminosae. Habitat: Medium and lower zones. Flowers March-May. **7. Orobanche canescens:** Stem 10-70cm. Leaves ovate. Corolla 12-18mm., glandular-pubescent or almost glabrous, yellow with reddish tints. Stigma yellow. Parasitic on plants of the Compositae family, rarely on other species. Habitat: Medium and lower zones. **8. Orobanche grisebachii:** Similar to 7 but leaves ovate-lanceolate, corolla smaller, whitish tinged with violet, stigma purple. Parasitic on Papilionaceus plants and occasionally on Compositae. Habitat: Medium and lower zones. Flowers March-May. **9. Orobanche loricata:** Similar to 7 but its leaves are narrowly lanceolate, and its corolla are larger, white or pale yellow, violet-tinted and with veins the same colour. Parasitic on the Artemisia, Picris and other Compositae genera, also on Daucus (carrot) and Orlaya of the Umbeliferae family. Habitat: Medium and lower zones. **10. Orobanche gracilis:** Stems 15-60cm., yellow or reddish. Leaves 7-15mm., ovate-deltate or lanceolate. Corolla 15-25mm., yellow outside and reddish inside. Parasitic on many Papilionaceus plants and occasionally on the Cistus genus. Habitat: Montane and sub-montane zones. Flowers

Orobanche ramosa

Orobanche pubescens

Orabanche gracilis

Putoria calabrica

April-June. **11. Orobanche sanguinea:** Similar to 10 but smaller. Corolla smaller, 10-15mm., dark red or purple, and yellow towards the base. Parasitic on plants of the Lotus genus. Habitat: Montane zone. Flowers May-June.

Two more species **Orobanche purpurea** and **Orobanche schultzii** are noted as occurring in Crete, but with reservations.

Equally doubtful is the existence there of two species of the **Utricularia** genus: **Utricularia vulgaris** and **Utricularia australis.** Both grow in stagnant water; and have not been observed in recent years.

Rubiaceae Family

Herbs or dwarf shrubs, with leaves entire, small, opposite or in whorls, and stipules at the base of leaves. Flowers small with a corolla tubular towards the base and divided into lobes (usually 4) towards the lips. Ovary inferior. Calyx either with 4 lobes or absent.

Putoria

Small, perennial shrubs with opposite leaves. The small corolla has a long tube and the calyx 4 lobes.

1. Putoria calabrica: A many-branched, woody, thick shrublet, spreading over rocks. Leaves ovate or elliptic-lanceolate, with rounded tip, up to 20mm. long. The corolla is pink with linear lobes. The plant has an unpleasant smell. Habitat: Rocks in the montane and sub-montane zones. Flowers May-June.

Sherardia (Field Madders)

Annual plants. The leaves are in whorls, in bunches of 4-6. The tiny flowers form heads at the apex of the stems. The corolla is 4-lobed and long-tubed.

1. Sherardia arvensis: Stems up to 40cm. Leaves oblanceolate, terminating in awns. Flowers violet-coloured, in bundles of 4-10, 4-5mm. in length.

Asperula

Dwarf shrubs or perennial herbs or, more rarely, annual plants. The leaves are usually small, linear and whorled. The flowers are small, the calyx as a rule lacking, and the corolla is tubular at the base, divided into 4 lobes at mouth.

1. Asperula idaea: A dwarf shrub, with green or glaucous stems, sparsely hairy. The leaves are linear, 5-8mm. long. Crowded inflorescence with pink flowers, hairy on the outside. Endemic to the Cretan mountains. Habitat: Sub-alpine zone. Flowers in June. **2. Asperula incana:** A thick dwarf shrub, up to 40cm. high. The stems are hairy. The leaves covered with dense hairs. Inflorescences in compact heads. Flowers purple, hairy on the outside. Endemic to Crete. Habitat: Rocky locations from the littoral up to the montane zone. Flowers April-June. **3. Asperula taygetea:** Similar to 2 but its stems are velvety, its leaves up to 10mm., and the flowers whitish, densely hairy on the outside. Endemic to the South Peloponnese and to W. Crete. Habitat: Rocks, from the littoral to the sub-alpine zone. Flowers April-June. **4. Asperula rigida:** A small shrub with stems up to 30cm. Leaves linear, in whorls of 6. up to 10mm. long, and inflorescences lax, with hairless, reddish or yellowish flowers. Endemic to Crete. Habitat: Dry, rocky sites. Flowers April-May. **5. Asperula tournefortii:** A dwarf shrub or a shrublet up to 30cm. high, with tough, sturdy branchlets and obovate leaves rounded at tip, in bundles of 6-7. Inflorescences rather closely-packed, with pale yellow flowers. It is a plant of West Asia, extending as far as the South Aegean. Habitat: Rocky places of the montane zone. Flowers April-June.

Crucianella

Perennial or annual, woody or herbaceous plants. The leaves are in whorls, in bunches of 4-8. The flowers on spikes, very small with a long tube and 4-5 lobes, arising from conspicuous bracts.

1. Crucianella macrostachya: An annual, with stems up to 60cm. high. Leaves 10-25X1,5-3mm., the lower are elliptic, the upper lanceolate or linear, in whorls of 6-8. The spike is 4-10cm. long and rather sparse. Flowers are yellow or greenish, more rarely reddish. It is a

Asperula taygetea

Sherardia arvensis

Callium verum - s. sp. verum

Gallium tricornutum

plant of West Asia, occurring sporadically in Crete, and not anywhere else in Europe. Flowers in Spring. **2. Crucianella angustifolia:** Similar to 1, but all its leaves are narrow, linear, glaucous and its spike is tightly-clustered, with yellow-coloured flowers. Habitat: Rocks and dry stony places. Flowers April-May. **3. Crucianella imbricata:** An annual with slightly pubescent stems, 8-20cm. in length. The lower leaves are obovate-elliptic, the remainder are linear or lanceolate. The spike is rather crowded with yellowish flowers. It is a plant of West Asia; Crete is the only place in Europe where it occurs. Flowers in spring.

Galium (Bedstraws)

Plants similar to Asperula but their stems are hollow-tubular or winged. Leaves in whorls.

Group A. Perennial dwarf, woody shrubs or with perennial tapruroots and herbaceous stems. Leaves in whorls of 4.

219

1. Galium rotundifolium: A plant with many herbaceous stems. The leaves are ovate or almost orbicular. Flowers white, small in corymb-like inflorescences. Habitat: Woods of the montane zone. Flowers May-June. **2. Galium fruticosum:** A plant that is woody towards the base, with many green, slender rod-like ascending stems, 35-90cm., quadrangular, at intersection. Leaves oblong, wedge-shaped at base. Flowers cream-coloured in ovate inflorescences. Endemic to Crete. Habitat: Calcareous slopes. Flowers April-May.

Group B. Perennial plants, with slender, creeping roots. Leaves in whorls of 4-6.

Calium debile: Stems 20-60cm. more or less erect. Leaves linear or linear-lanceolate, pointed. Whitish, multi-flowered inflorescences. Habitat: Marshy regions. Flowers May-June.

Group C. Perennial plants with woody roots and herbaceous stems. Leaves in whorls of 8-12.

1. Galium verum - subsp. verum: Leaves narrow, linear, acute, hairy up to 30mm. Ovate inflorescence with yellowish flowers. Habitat: Meadows and glades of montane zone. Flowers May-June. **2. Galium pomernicum:** Similar to 1 but leaves slightly broader, narrowly lanceolate and less hairy. Flowers bright yellow or white.

Group D. Perennial with woody base. Leaves up to 10 on each whorl. Multi-flowered inflorescences.

1. Galium heidreichii: Stems up to 150cm., glabrous or hairy, often reddish towards base, erect and branching. Leaves oblong or oblanceolate, occasionally tinged with red. Flowers whitish, geenish or, rarely, reddish. Habitat: Montane zone. Flowers May-July. **2. Galium album:** Similar to 1 but the flowers are either whitish or yellowish. Habitat: Open spaces and glades at a medium altitude. Flowers May-June. **3. Galium incurvum:** A glaucous-green hairless plant. Stems 20-40cm. Leaves linear, 10-20mm. long. Rather dense inflorescence with yellowish or reddish flowers. Endemic to the islands of the South Aegean. Habitat: Rocky sites at medium and low altitudes. Flowers April-June. **4. Galium incanum - subsp. creticum.** Dense, caespitose plant with woody root and stems 2-15cm. Leaves in clusters of 4-7, narrowly oblanceolate and somewhat rounded at tip, densely hairy. Flowers whitish or pink, in ovate or oblong inflorescences. A Cretan endemic. Habitat: Rocks and meadows of the montane and sub-alpine zones. Flowers May-June.

Group E. Perennial or annual plants, frequently caespitose. Leaves in whorls of 5-8.

1. Galium graecum - subsp. graecum: Stems up to 15cm., more or less woody at their base. Green, linear, hairy leaves. Inflorescence narrow and oblong. Flowers a purple-brown. Habitat: Calcareous rocks at medium and low altitudes. Flowers May-June. **2. Galium graecum - subsp. pseudocanum:** Similar to 1 but stems are up to 8cm. only, and with longer hairs; the leaves have denser hair, and the inflorescences are somewhat ovate. Endemic to East Crete. Habitat: Littoral locations. Flowers April-May. **3. Galium setaceum - subsp. decaisnei:** An annual with slender, erect stems, 5-30cm. high. Leaves in whorls of 6-8, narrowly linear or filiform, glabrous or slightly hairy. Inflorescence sparse, with tiny purple flowers. Habitat: Heath and scrub. Flowers April-May.

Group F. Annual plants. Leaves in whorls of 4-11.

1. Galium spurium: Stems 10-100(-160)cm. Leaves 30-35mm. long, oblanceolate, with very acute tip, in clusters of 6-10. Inflorescence narrowly ovate or cylindrical. Flowers yellowish-green. Habitat: Low altitude cultivated land, roadsides, and ditches. Flowers

Sambucus ebulus

May-June. **2. Galium tricornutum:** Similar to 1 but a little shorter (10-80cm.) with 6-8 leaves to each whorl, and with white flowers. Habitat: Along the verges of cultivated ground, ditches etc. Flowers May-June. **3. Galium verrucosum:** Similar to 1 and 2, but shorter than either (5-50cm.) Leaves lanceolate, awned, glabrous and in whorls of 5-6. Flowers greenish-white. Habitat: Cultivated land and hedges at a low altitude. Flowers May-June. **4. Galium incrassatum:** Stems up to 35cm. Leaves usually in whorls of 6, the lower oblanceolate, the upper almost linear. Flowers reddish, in rather closely-packed inflorescences. Endemic to Crete. Habitat: Dry localities at a low altitude. Flowers April-May. **5. Galium divaricatum:** Stems 5-30cm. Leaves in whorls of 6-8, narrowly lanceolate or linear. Lax inflorescence with very tiny, yellowish-red flowers. Flowers April-June. **6. Galium verticiliatum:** Stems 8-18cm., hairy or almost glabrous. Leaves lanceolate or oblong in whorls of 6-7, 4-8mm. long. Flowers yellowish-red, in dense clusters along the upper leaves and bracts. **7. Galium murale:** Stems up to 20cm., spreading or ascending. Leaves in whorls of 4-6, oblanceolate, pointed, more or less hairy 4-10mm. long. Cylindrical inflorescence, with small yellowish flowers. Habitat: Rock crevices, waysides, walls at a low altitude. Flowers April-May.

Valantia

Plants similar to **Galium.** Leaves in whorls of 4. 3-flowered inflorescences arranged in whorls, along the upper leaves.

1. Valantia aprica: A caespitose perennial with stems 5-20cm. Leaves oblanceolate, 3-6mm. long. Flowers cream-coloured or pink. Habitat: Rocks in the montane and sub-alpine zones. Flowers May-June. **2. Valantia hispida:** Annual with stems 6-20cm. long. Leaves obovate or oblanceolate, pointed, up to 10mm. Flowers yellowish. Habitat: Dry, rocky places at medium and low altitudes. Flowers April-June. **3. Valantia muralis:** Similar to 2 but smaller. Leaves up to 6,5mm., and rounded at tip. Habitat: Rocks and gullies at a low altitude. Flowers April-May.

Rubia (Wild Madder)

A perennial plant that is either herbaceous or woody. The leaves are in whorls, in clusters of 4-8. Flowers very like those of **Galium** and **Asperula** but with 5 lobes. Inflorescences in the axils of leaves.

1. Rubia peregrina: Ascending stems, 30-120cm. high. Leaves in bundles of 4-8, usually 5, ovate-elliptic and towards the top narrower, linear-lanceolate. Multiflorous inflorescences with yellowish-green flowers. Habitat: Rocky scrub of the montane and sub-montane zones. Flowers May-June.

The **Plantaginales** to which the various species of the genus **Plantago** belong, is not described because its plants are of no special decorative importance. We mention only that the following species exist in Crete: **Plantago major, P. coronopus, P. amplexicaulis, P. lanceolata, P. altissima, P. lagopus, P. albicans, P. bellardii, P. cretica, P. squarrosa, P. arenaria** and **P. afra.**

Dipsacales

Caprifoliaceae Family

Perennial woody shrubs, or climbing plants, seldom herbaceous. Flowers with inferior ovary, small calyx and corolla that is tubular at base, with 5 lobes at apex. Leaves opposite.

Sambucus (Elder)

Small trees, shrubs or perennial herbs, with symmetric actinomorphic flowers. Flowers in multi-flowered corymbs. Leaves pinnate with stipules.

1. Sambucus ebulus: A plant with a perennial rhizome and annual stems, 60-200cm. tall. Large leaves with 5-13 leaflets, oblong or oblong-lanceolate, pointed, crenate. Flowers white in umbrella-like corymbs that are 5-16cm. across. Fruit black. Habitat: Edges of forests, roadsides, river banks in the montane zone. Flowers June-July. **2. Sambucus nigra:** Similar to 1, but it is either a shrub or a small deciduous tree, up to 10m. high, with

Viburnum lantana

woody boles. Habitat: It is both cultivated and semi-self-seeding in the montane zone. Flowers May-June.

Viburnum (Wayfaring tree)

Shrubby plants, evergreen or deciduous, with entire, or palmately lobed leaves. Flowers symmetrical, actinomorphic, in corymb-like inflorescences.

1. Viburnum lantana: Leaves ovate-lanceolate, 4-15cm. long, with small teeth at margins. Inflorescence 6-10cm. across and the white flowers 5-9mm. across. The fruit is a drupe, initially reddish that becomes black at maturation. Habitat: Valleys and plateaus of montane and sub-alpine zones. Flowers May-June.

Lonicera (Honeysuckle)

Shrub-like or climbing plants, deciduous, very rarely evergreen. Leaves entire and without stipules. Flowers in axillary pairs, or in terminal heads, or in whorls. The corolla is usually bilabiate, with a long tube. The upper lip is 4-lobed, the lower simple. The fruit is a red or black berry.

1. Lonicera nummulariifolia: An evergreen shrub, with leaves that are ovate or almost orbicular, and usually pubescent underneath. The flowers are in pairs, and arise from the axils of the leaves. The bilabiate corolla is pink and small. Habitat: Rocks in the montane and sub-alpine zones. Flowers May-June. **2. Lonicera etrusca:** A climbing shrub. The hairless leaves are entire, dark green on the upper side and glaucous-green beneath. They are up to 8cm. long, elliptic or obovate, and rounded at tip. The uppermost pairs of leaves are fused together in a single blade (perforate). Flowers 3,5-4,5cm., two-lipped, with a long tube; white or yellowish, tinged with pink. The inflorescences are at the tip of the stems, forming 1 or more heads. Habitat: Montane and sub-alpine zones. Flowers May-June.

Valerianaceae Family

Annual or perennial plants. The leaves are opposite or in whorls or occasionally forming a rosette at the base. The flowers which are in dense cymose inflorescences, are small and usually zygomorphic. The corolla is tubular, and as a rule has 5 unequal lobes at the mouth. The tube often has a small or a large spur at its base. The calyx is small. Ovary inferior.

Valerianella (Lamb's Lettuces, Corn Salads)

Annual herbaceous plants, dichotomously branching. The flowers are very tiny, and have a small projection at the base of the tube. The inflorescences are arranged dichotomously. Leaves opposite.

1. Valarianella coronata: The bottom leaves are spathulate or ovate, rounded at tip, entire or slightly concave-dentate. The uppermost leaves are linear-lanceolate, except at their base, where they are pinnately-lobed. The flowers are violet or blue, on spherical, closely-packed inflorescences. Habitat: Dry places at a low altitude. Flowers March-April. **2. Valerianella hirsutissima:** Similar to 1, but with narrower leaves, a hairy stem and the flowers lilac-coloured or nearly white. Habitat: Found on both cultivated and uncultivated land. Flowers April-May. **3. Valerianella discoidea:** Similar to 1 but leaves are pinnately-lobed, the lobes being narrow, and the flowers lilac. Habitat: On cultivated and uncultivated land. Flowers March-April. **4. Valerianella obtusifolia:** All the leaves either ovate or lanceolate, entire or slightly dentate, and somewhat pinnately-lobed at base. The flowers which are lilac-coloured or almost white, are in compact inflorescences. Habitat: Uncultivated fields and meadows. Flowers March-April. **5. Valerianella echinata:** The lower leaves are spathulate, rounded at tip, the other are spathulate-lanceolate, dentate or pinnately-lobed. Flowers in dense inflorescences, whitish-pink or rosy-violet. Features of this plant are; in the first place, the prickly protuberances of the calyx that give the inflorescence a spiny appearance, and secondly the thick peduncle of the inflorescence. Habitat: Common in low altitude fields and meadows. Flowers March-April. **6. Valerianella eriocarpa:** Flowers pink. Leaves lanceolate or oblong, entire or dentate, at least towards base. Habitat: Uncultivated land, and roadsides at a low altitude. Flowers March-April. **7. Valerianella microcarpa:** Similar to 6 but uppermost leaves are narrow, entire and the flowers pink or violet. Habitat: Low altitude fields. Flowers March-April.

Fedia

Plants similar to **Valerianella.** Two terminal head-like inflorescences on the top of stems.

Lonicera etrusca

1. Fedia cornucopiae: A hairless annual plant, with broadly spathulate or elliptic leaves. Flowers pink or purple, in heads surrounded by two small leaves. Habitat: It grows on cultivated and uncultivated land and at waysides, at a medium or low altitude. Flowers March-April.

Valeriana (Valerians)

Plants with perennial rhizomes and annual stems. The leaves are opposite, entire or pinnate. The flowers are in dense cymes, at the ends of the stems. The flowers are small with a small protuberance (sac) at the base of the tube.

1. Valeriana asarifolia: A plant with a short rhizome and with erect hairy stems, 25-50cm.

225

The long-stalked basal leaves are simple, discoid or reniform. The stem leaves are pinnate. The flowers are in dense apical, pale pink inflorescences. Endemic to Crete and Carpathos. Habitat: Rocks in the middle montane zone. Flowers April-May.

Centranthus (Red Valerians)

Hairless rhizomatous, perennial or, occasionally, annual plants. The flowers similar to those of **Valeriana** are in dense inflorescences. The tube of the corolla has a spur or a small sac.

1. Centranthus ruber: Stems up to 80cm., ascending, and as a rule branching. The leaves are lanceolate or ovate, glaucous-green, opposite. The flowers are purple with long slender spurs at their base. It has been cultivated in Crete for a long time, and now it has become almost self-seeding in certain regions. Habitat: On walls and rocks. Flowers April-May. **2. Centranthus nevadensis - subsp. sieberi:** A caespitose plant with stems 7-20cm. The leaves are elliptic or spathulate, rounded at tip, and 20-40mm. long. Inflorescences with pink or purple flowers. Spur 13-17mm. long. Endemic to the Cretan mountains. Habitat: Rocks of the alpine and sub-alpine zones. Flowers May-June. **3. Centranthus calcitrapae - subsp. calcitrapae:** An annual plant very like Valeriana. The flowers are white or pale pink and have a small spur or sac. The leaves are pinnately-lobed or lyrate, the apical lobe a little or much larger. Habitat: Stony and rocky sites of the montane zone. Flowers March-April.

Dipsacaceae Family

Perennial or annual plants, with leaves opposite or in whorls. Small flowers with a tubular corolla with 4-5 unequal lobes. Flowers zygomorphic or two-lipped, clustered in a capitula.

Cephalaria

The heads are egg-shaped or spherical with large membranous, stiff bracts among the flowers. The corolla is 4-lobed and the leaves opposite.

1. Cephalaria squamiflora - subsp. squamiflora: A shrub up to 90cm. Leaves ovate-lanceolate or oblanceolate, entire, crenate or, rarely, lyrate, 4-17cm. long. Heads with white or yellowish flowers.

Scabiosa (Scabious)

Annual or perennial plants, with leaves opposite, simple, pinnately-lobed or pinnate. Many conspicuous bracts forming a "hypanthium" under the head. The bracts among the flowers are small and hidden inside the inflorescence. The corolla is 5-lobed, with unequal lobes. The outer flowers are usually larger than those in the centre.

Group A. Perennial plants with thick stems, woody towards the base.

1. Scabiosa albocincta: Leaves entire, broadly elliptic, covered with long, straight hairs, denser at the margin. The peduncles of the inflorescences are 30-40cm. The heads, 4cm. across, are composed of violet-coloured flowers. It is a rare plant, endemic to West Crete. Habitat: Rocks in gorges of the montane zone. Flowers May-June. **2. Scabiosa minoana - subsp. minoana:** Similar to 1 but the leaves are elliptic-obovate, slightly rounded at tip, with dense silvery hairs. The peduncles of the inflorescences are shorter. Endemic to Mount Dhikti (East Crete). Habitat: Rocks and gorges of the montane zone. Flowers May-June. **3. Scabiosa minoana - subsp. asterusica:** Similar to 2 but with broader flowers and

Valerianella echinata

Valeriana asarifolia

Centranthus ruber

Centhranthus calcitrapae - s. sp. calcitrapae

denser hairs. An extremely rare plant, endemic to Mount Cofinas in South Crete. Habitat: Mountain rocks. Flowers May-June. **4. Scabiosa sphaciotica:** Many slender, leafless stems or with 1 pair of leaves at base. Leaves up to 20mm. long, linear or linear-lanceolate at margin, pinnate, covered with dense hairs. Heads 10-15mm., with only a few pink-violet flowers. Endemic to Crete. Habitat: Mountainous, stony locations. Flowers May-June.

Group B. Biennial or annual plants with few long stems.

1. Scabiosa atropurpurea: A hairless or pubescent, biennial plant. Branching stem 20-60cm. high. Lower leaves oblong-spathulate, entire or lyrate, long-stalked. The remainder are pinnately-lobed. Heads 20-30mm., with violet or deep purple flowers. Habitat: Dry bare sites. Flowers April-May. **2. Scabiosa sicula:** A hairy, annual plant. The

227

lower leaves are entire or dentate. The others are lyrate-pinnate, with narrow lobes. Heads 10-15mm., with reddish flowers.

Knautia (Field Seabious)

Plants similar to Scabiosa, but the corolla has only 4 lobes.

1. Knautia integrifolia. An annual plant with stems 20-80cm., pubescent-hairy towards base, almost glabrous towards top. Basal leaves entire dentate or lyrate, forming rosette. The upper leaves are linear or lanceolate. Heads 30cm., with violet-coloured or bluish-violet flowers. Habitat: Meadows and garrigue of medium and lower zones. Flowers April-May.

Pterocephalus

Plants similar to Scabious and Knautia, differing only in botanical details difficult to distinguish. Corolla with 5 lobes.

1. Pterocephalus papposus: An annual with an erect stem, up to 60cm. Leaves oblong, dentate-crenate, or lyrate or pinnately-lobed, with the topmost lobe the largest. Heads with pink or purple flowers. Habitat: Barren areas at medium and low altitudes. Flowers April-May.

Tremastelma

Plants resembling Scabiosa, with botanical differences not easy to discern.

1. Tremastelma palaestinum: An annual hairy plant with stems up to 50cm. Basal leaves lyrate or entire, up to 8cm. The remainder are smaller, usually entire. Pale lilac flowers in heads surrounded by large bracts.

Campanulales

Campanulaceae Family

Perennial or annual plants. Leaves alternate. Calyx usually with 5 sepals. Corolla as a rule with 5 or more lobes of various shapes.

Campanula (Bellflowers or Campanulas)

Herbaceous plants, perennial, biennial or annual. Corolla campanulate or tubular, more rarely crateriform or entirely open - rotate with 5 or more lobes. The calyx has 5 sepals, frequently with leaf-like appendages between the sepals. Stamens fused, around the style. Fruit a capsule with holes found at the base, at the middle or at the top. Flowers usually blue or bluish-violet, very seldom white.

Group A. A capsule with 5 holes at base. Calyx with or without leaf-like appendages between the sepals. Biennial plants that grow in rock crevices, the first year producing only one rosette of leaves, or perennials.

1. Campanula pelviformis: Basal leaves ovate, pointed, hairy, crenate, stalked. The stem leaves are similar but stalkless. Stems ascending, simple or branching and hairy. The corolla is blue-violet-coloured, occasionally white, broadly campanulate, more swollen in the middle, about 30mm. long. The sepals are oblong-ovate, 3 times longer than the ovary. Endemic to Central and East Crete. Habitat: Rocks of medium and low altitudes. Flowers

Knautia integrifolia

Tremastelma palaestinum

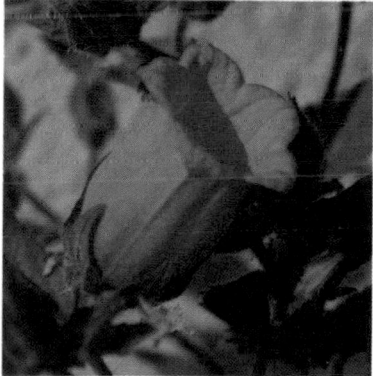

Campanula pelviformis

Campanula tubulosa (common form)

April-May. **2. Campanula tubulosa:** Similar to 1 but stem dichotomous, pubescent, with the middle and bottom leaves oblong-ovate, long-petioled; calyx lobes twice the size of ovary, and corolla tube-like, up to 20mm. long, always blue-violet. An endemic to Central Crete. A colony discovered by the author in South-East Crete, among the rocks in the gorge of Moni Capsa, differs from the typical form, mainly in the shape of the corolla which is in all probality a local subspecies. It is in all probality a local subspecies. Habitat: Rocks and gorges of middle and low altitudes. Flowers April-May. **3. Campanula saxatilis - subsp. saxatilis:** Similar to 1 and 2 but with numerous stems which are almost erect, fragile, simple or branching; the basal leaves are usually spathulate and the corolla narrowly tubular, 14-20mm. Endemic to West Crete. Habitat: Rocks at medium and low altitudes. Flowers April-May. **4. Campanula hierapetrae:** A small velutinous perennial. Stems 5-10cm., ascending or spreading slender. Basal leaves 8-10mm., ovate-spathulate stalked.

The stem leaves are ovate or almost orbicular, with short petioles. The corolla measures 12-15mm. Endemic to East Crete. Habitat: Rocks at a medium and low altitude. Flowers March-May. **5. Campanula laciniata:** Biennial, with stems as a rule simple up to 60cm. Inflorescence with many large flowers. Corolla campanulate, 40-50mm. wide. Basal leaves about 30cm. long, ovate at margin, pinnately-lobed, and dentate. Stem leaves smaller and less cleft. Endemic to the South Aegean, rare in Crete. Habitat: Rocks at medium and low altitudes. Flowers April-June.

Group B. Biennial plants with capsule holes at the sides or at the upper part. Calyx without leaf-like appendages.

1. Campanula aizoon - subsp. aizoides. A glabrous plant. The basal leaves are spathulate with a small arista at tip. The stem leaves are acute, triangular, sessile. Erect stem 10-30cm. long and rather thick. Flowers with campanulate-tubular, pale blue corolla, 12-15mm. forming a branched inflorescence. Endemic to the White Mountains in West Crete. Habitat: Rocks of the sub-alpine zone. Flowers June-July.

Group C. Annual plants with capsule opening with holes at the base.

1. Campanula drabifolia - subsp. creutzburgii: A hairy plant. Branching stems. Leaves dentate, oblong, the basal ones have short stalks. A small tubular, bell-shaped, rather narrow violet-coloured corolla. Habitat: Hills and mountain slopes at a medium and low altitude, all over the island. Flowers March-April. **2. Campanula erinus:** Similar to 1 but the leaves are ovate or obovate, dentate-crenate, sessile. The flowers are very small (3-5mm.), pale blue in colour. Habitat: Dry situations at a low altitude all over the island. Flowers March-April.

Group D. The corolla is cleft almost to the base, into 5 linear lobes.

1. Campanula trichocalycina: A perennial plant, almost glabrous, with one or more stems which are usually simple. The basal leaves are ovate or oblong, sparsely dentate, pointed and almost stalkless. Stem leaves smaller. Flowers blue, 15mm., with narrow, linear lobes. Habitat: Rocks in the montane zone. Flowers May-July.

Symphyandra

Plants resembling campanulas. Flowers in erect racemes and leaves mainly concentrated round the base.

1. Symphyandra cretica - subsp. cretica: A glabrous perennial plant. The basal leaves the large, cordate or reniform, dentate, long-stalked, the length reaching up to 14cm. (which includes the stalk). Stem leaves small, bract-like. Calyx lobes linear. Corolla blue or occasionally white, bell-shaped, about 30mm. Endemic to Crete. Habitat: Rocks and gorges of the middle montane zone. Flowers July-August.

Legousia (Venus' Looking-glass)

Plants similar to Campanulas but corolla always rotate or broadly bell-shaped. The flowers form racemes or panicles and the leaves are alternate.

1. Legousia speculum veneris: A pubescent, annual plant, as a rule much-branched, with stems 10-40cm. The leaves are small, obovate or oblong, with margins slightly cymose. The violet corolla is rotate, up to 12mm. across. Habitat: Grows on both uncultivated and cultivated land, at medium and low altitudes. Flowers April-May. **2. Legousia hybrida:** Resembles 1, but the corolla is smaller (5-6mm) and shorter than the linear lobes of the calyx. Habitat: Medium and low altitudes. Flowers March-April. **3. Lagousia pentagonia:**

Campanula tubulosa (Kapsá Monastery)

Legusia speculum veneris

Legusia pentagonia

Petromarula pinata

Similar to 1, but the flowers are larger, up to 18mm. Habitat: Medium and low altitudes. Flowers April-May. **4. Legousia falcata.** Similar in appearance to 1 but corolla very small, and lobes of calyx 3 times longer than the corolla, arcuate and turned outwards. Habitat: Uncultivated and cultivated sites. Flowers March-April.

Trachelium

Small flowers, with corolla tubular towards base, and 5 narrow lobes at mouth. Flowers in head-shaped corymbs.

1. Trachelium jacquinii - subsp. jacquinii: Flowers a bluish-violet. Leaves alternate, crenate-dentate, oblong or ovate. Stems up to 15cm. Habitat: A rare plant, found in the montane and sub-alpine zones. Flowers June-October.

Petromarula

Flowers with corolla divided almost to the base into 5 linear lobes. Inflorescence in a long raceme. Leaves pinnately-lobed or pinnate.

1. Petromarula pinata: A biennial plant with a rosette of pinnately-lobed or pinnate leaves, up to 30cm. high and hairless stems, up to 80cm. Flowers blue. Endemic to Crete. Habitat: Rocks and gorges from sea-level to the montane zone. Flowers April-May.

Laurentia

Flowers with 5-lobed calyx and bilabiate corolla. The upper lip with 2 lobes and the lower with 3.

1. Laurentia gasparinii: An annual or perennial pubescent plant, up to 25cm. Leaves obovate or oblong-spathulate, crenate or entire. Flowers 4-11mm blue, violet or white. Habitat: Medium and low altitudes. Flowers in springtime.

Compositae Family

Plants with small flowers called florets, always arranged on a common flat receptacle and forming a characteristic head: the Capitulum. The florets are all alike, either tubular, or the outer ones are all on one side, lingulate or all lingulate.

Eupatorium (Hemp Agrimony)

Perennial plants. Leaves alternate. Flowers in very tiny heads, all the florets tubular. Heads in densely clustered inflorescences.

1. Eupatorium adenophorum: Leaves rhomboid or triangular, dentate. Heads white, 5-10mm across. Stems 1-2m. It is a Mexican plant that has become established and grows sub-spontaneously in Crete. Habitat: Damp localities and banks of streams in the montane zone. Flowers April-May.

Bellis (Daisies)

Leaves alternate, entire, dentate or crenate. Heads with disk florets in the centre and ray florets at the margin. Ray florets narrow (linear) and closely-packed.

1. Bellis perennis: A perennial plant with leaves 10-60mm. long, oblanceolate, obovate or spathulate, sparsely crenate at margin. Leaves pubescent with 1 vein, clustered into basal rosettes. Flower pedicels 4-15cm. without leaves. Capitula 15-30mm. with white ray florets, often purple flushed beneath. Habitat: Damp meadows of the sub-alpine, montane and sub-montane zones. Flowers February-June. **2. Bellis annua:** Similar to 1 but a tiny annual plant with smaller leaves and capitula. Habitat: Meadows and fields of the middle and lower zones. Flowers December-April. **3. Bellis hybrida:** Very similar to 1 but the flower pedicels usually have leaves at their lower section; leaves with 3 veins. Habitat: Damp situations of the montane and sub-montane zones. Flowers February-April. **4. Bellis longifolia:** Similar to 1, perennial, with leaves longer and narrower, oblong-oblanceolate, with 1 vein. Capitula smaller, up to 18mm. across. Endemic to Crete. Habitat: Alpine and sub-alpine meadows. Flowers May-June. **5. Bellis silvestris.** Perennial similar to 1, with longer leaves (30-180cm.) narrower, oblong or narrowly obovate.

Eupatorium adenophorum

Bellis perennis

Bellis annua

Bellis hybrida

Habitat: Meadows and clearings in the montane and sub-montane zones. Flowers October-December.

Bellium

Plants similar to Bellis, but leaves very small, entire and few ray florets.

1. Bellium minutum: A downy annual plant, with numerous stems. Leaves elliptic-obovate, 5-8mm, clustered at base. Capitula 6-7mm. with 7-10 pink ray florets. Habitat: A rare plant that grows among seaside rocks. Flowers February-April.

Aster (Asters)

Usually perennial plants with alternate leaves or all at base. Capitula with florets of 2 kinds, tubular and ray, or all tubular.

1. Aster tripolium - subsp. pannonicus. Annual or perennial, with stems 20-60(-115)cm., erect or branching, glabrous. Leaves lanceolate or linear, the bottom ones stalked, the others sessile. Numerous capitula, in corymb-like inflorescences, with 10-30 ray florets, bright blue or violet. Habitat: Brackish water and lagoons. Flowers September-November.
2. Aster squamatus: Similar to 1 in appearance but the ray florets are much smaller. It is an American species established in Crete and in other Mediterranean regions. Habitat: Usually in brackish water near the sea. Flowers August-October. **3. Aster creticus:** A plant with patent or erect stems, 15-40cm. high, with arachnoid hairs and linear-lanceolate leaves. Capitula few with no ray florets. Endemic to East Crete and to the island of Carpathos. Habitat: Medium and low altitudes. Flowers April-May.

Filago (Cudweeds)

Annual plants with dense hair. Capitula small without ray florets clustered in dense inflorescences.

1. Filago vulgaris: A greyish-white plant. Erect stems 5-35ch. high. Leaves linear or lanceolate, slightly cymose. Capitula in bunches of 15-35, in spherical inflorescences. Habitat: Meadows and sandy stretches at a low altitude. Flowers June-September. **2. Filago eriocephala:** Similar to 1 but the inflorescences are more compact, ovoid, with 30-50 capitula together. Habitat: Environment similar to that of 1, Flowers in summer. **3. Filago aegaea:** Dwarf-like, up to 6cm. with dense white hair. Capitula 5-15. Habitat:Low and seaboard sites. Flowers in spring. **4. Filago cretensis:** Similar to 3, but fewer capitula (5-7) and leaves almost glabrous on the upper surface. Habitat: It grows under the same conditions as the previous plant. **5. Filago pyramidata:** A greyish-green plant with stems 5-30(-40)cm. long. The leaves are linear-oblong or spathulate. Capitula in clusters of 5-20. Habitat: Sites at a low altitude. Flowers in spring. **6. Filago eriophaera:** A caespitose, multibranched and densely hairy plant, with very short stems, very tiny leaves and a great many inflorescences bearing small capitula. It is a plant of South West Asia that occurs as far west as the islands of Carpathos and Crete. Habitat: Low altitude.

Logfia

Plants similar to Filago but the capitula are solitary or in few-flowered, sparse inflorescences.

1. Logfia arvensis: A hairy plant. Stems 5-70cm., branching. Leaves oblong or linear-lanceolate, 10-20mm. Capitula very small, in bunches of 3-12, in a sparse inflorescence. Habitat: Montane and sub-montane zones. Flowers June-August. **2. Loglia gallica:** Similar to 1 but greyish-green, with linear or filiform leaves. Habitat: Sandy stretches and uncultivated meadows. Flowers July-August.

Evax

Plants similar to Filago but the capitulum inflorescences are surrounded by many, large leaf-like bracts.

1. Evax pygmaeae - subsp. pygmaea: A dwarf plant 2-4cm. high, silvery or whitish. Many dense leaf-like bracts surround the comparatively few capitula that are clustered in a dense inflorescence. Habitat: Dry, bare locations near the sea. Flowers April-May.

Gnaphalium

Plants similar to Filago but with few capitula at the tips of the stems, surrounded by leaves.

Bellis silvestris   *Aster tripolium - s. sp. pannonicus*

Helichrysum stoechas - s. sp. stoechas   *Inula crithmoides*

1. Gnaphalium luteo-album: Stem 8-40cm. high, simple or branching. Leaves oblong or linear, 2-5cm. Capitulum inflorescences small and dense. Habitat: Sandy stretches at a low altitude. Flowers July-September.

Helichrysum (Elichrysum)

Plants that are usually perennial, densely hairy-pubescent. Leaves alternate. Capitula small, usually yellowish, with all the florets tubular. Capitula as a rule many together in dense corymbs. Capitula persist even after they have dried out, and are used to make bunches of dried decorative flowers.

1. Helichrysum stoechas - subsp. barrelieri: A perennial plant with a white, dense down. Numerous stems, up to 50cm. in height, with linear or linear-spathulate leaves. Spherical capitula yellow, 4-6mm. across in dense corymbs at the tips of the stems. Habitat: Stony hillsides at medium and low altitudes. Flowers April-June. **2. Helichrysum heidreichii:** Very similar to 1 but its capitula are conical and all the leaves are linear. Endemic to West Crete. Habitat: Stony slopes at medium and low altitudes. **3. Helichrysum italicum - subsp. microphyllum.** A plant similar to 1 and 2 but smaller (10-30cm.) with thicker stems. The non-flower-bearing stems have numerous clusters of leaves. Capitula 3mm., in dense corymbs. Habitat: Seaboard rocks. Flowers April-May. **4. Helichrysum orientale:** Similar to 1 but it is a sturdier plant with leaves 20-60mm., oblong-spathulate, obtuse. Capitula larger, in dense inflorescences. Habitat: Stony hillsides at a low altitude. Flowers April-May. **5. Helichrysum doerfleri:** Perennial with many short stems (up to 8cm) and lower leaves oblanceolate-spathulate, acute, while the upper ones are narrower. Large capitula in small bundles of 2-4. Endemic to East Crete. Habitat: Rocks of the montane zone. Flowers May-June.

Phagnalon

Densely hairy-pubescent plants, similar to Helichrysum, with capitula almost always solitary, at apices of stems. Capitula made up wholly of yellow ray florets. Involucral bracts brown.

1. Phagnalon graecum: A perennial, with many erect stems, up to 30cm. Leaves oblanceolate or obovate, densely hairy beneath, sparsely hairy above. Capitula solitary, about 5mm. Habitat: Stony slopes, of medium and low altitudes. Flowers April-May. **2. Phagnalon pumilum:** A dwarf-like, caespitose perennial, up to 15cm. Leaves oblong-spathulate, densely pubescent or glabrous. Capitula solitary. Endemic to Crete. Habitat: Rocks of the montane zone. Flowers May-June.

Inula

Perennial plants with simple, alternate leaves. Capitula solitary or in inflorescences with florets of 2 kinds. Those of the centre being tubular, while those at the margin are ray florets, but often tiny, not easily seen.

Group A. Whitish-silvery plants, with dense white down or hair.

1. Inula candida - subsp. candida: Slender stems up to 30cm. Basal leaves ovate or lanceolate, 3-9cm. Capitula medium-sized with yellowish florets. Ray florets very tiny, difficult to be observed. Endemic to West Crete. Habitat: Rocks of the middle and lower zones. Flowers May-June. **2. Inula candida - subsp. decalvans:** Similar to 1 but stems up to 10cm. , and the basal leaves up to 3,5cm. Endemic to East Crete.

Group B. Green plants with fleshy leaves.

1. Inula crithmoides. A hairless perennial with linear, fleshy leaves, 2-4,5cm. Capitula yellow, with narrow, linear, large, easily discernible florets. Habitat: Stony seaboard places. Flowers August-October.

Ditrichia

Plants greatly resembling Inula, characterised by botanical details that are not easily distinguished.

1. Ditrichia graveolens: An annual with densely glandular stems, 20-50cm. Small yellow heads in the axils and at apices of the stems. Small ray florets. Leaves lanceolate or oblong. Habitat: Waysides and somewhat damps fields. Flowers August-October. **2. Ditrichia viscosa:** Similar to 1 but it is a larger plant (40-130cm.) with a perennial root. The leaves are linear of oblong-lanceolate. Narrow ray florets 10-12mm. long. Habitat: Waysides, damp fields. Flowers August-October.

Pulicaria odora

Pulicaria dysenterica

Pallenis spinosa - s. sp. microcephala

Asteriscus aquaticus

Pulicaria (Fleabane)

Plant similar to Inula and Ditrichia that differ only in barely discernible botanical details.

1. Pulicaria odora: Perennial with stems simple or slightly branching, lanate or hairy, 20-40cm. Basal leaves lanceolate or ovate-lanceolate, hairy and large. Stems leaves few, narrower and much smaller. Capitula few, large, golden-yellow with narrow ray florets, sparse and large. Habitat: Meadows of the montane zone. Flowers June-August. **2. Pulicaria dysenterica:** A plant with a perennial rhizome, and annual stems up to 60cm. that are hairy and branching. Leaves oblong-lanceolate. Heads smaller, about 1,5cm. Habitat: Low altitude. Flowers in autumn. **3. Pulicaria sicula:** A plant with an erect stem, up to 60cm., pubescent, usually reddish. Uppermost leaves linear. Heads small, with small ray florets. Habitat: Seaboard meadows and waysides. Flowers August-October.

Pallenis

Annual or biennial plants. Capitula with ray and disk florets. Leaves acute at tip. Capitula surrounded by pointed leaves which are spiny at the tip.

1. Pallenis spinosa - subsp. microcephala: A hairy plant with branching stems. Heads pale yellow, about 1,5cm. across. Habitat: Garrigue and uncultivated land, at a low altitude. Flowers April-May.

Asteriscus

Plants similar to Pallenis, occasionally perennial, differing only in undiscernible botanical details.

1. Asteriscus aquaticus: Similar to Pallenis spinosa but the stem is usually simple and shorter. Often dwarf-like, almost stemless. Habitat: Garrigue, meadows, uncultivated land and seaside locations. Flowers March-May. **2. Asteriscus maritimus:** Similar to 1 but perennial, with large golden-yellow capitula. Habitat: Seaboard rocks. Flowers April-May.

Ambrosia (American Wormwoods)

Plants with leaves largely alternate. Heads small, numerous, without ray florets.

1. Ambrosia maritima: An erect, branching, strong-scented annual plant up to 125cm. The stems are woody near their base. Leaves bipinnate, covered with grey hair beneath. Yellowish capitula of two kinds: 1) With male florets, in which case they form spikes at the tips of the stems and 2) with female florets arising from the axils of the leaves. It is a medicinal plant and considered effective as a tonic, and for stomach ailments or hysteria. Habitat: Sandy seaboard tracts. Flowers in summer.

Unimportant plants from a decorative point of view, are the species of the **Xanthium** genus with tiny barely discernible heads and prickles in the axils of the leaves. In Crete there are two species **Xanthium strumarium** and **Xanthium spinosum.**

Tagetes

Usually annual aromatic plants, with pinnate leaves. Heads of various sizes with two kinds of florets, ray and disk florets, yellow, orange, brown or cream-coloured.

1. Tagetes minuta: An annual plant, 1-2m high, on rare occasions reaching a height of 3m. Leaves with narrow crenate leaflets. Inflorescence composed of several very small capitula arranged in corymbs. Capitula cream-coloured. A plant of South America, established in Mediterranean countries and West Crete. Habitat: Gardens, roadside ditches, irrigation trenches, at a low altitude. Flowers September-November.

Anthemis (Chamomile)

Perennial or annual herbs or small shrubs, more or less hairy. The alternate leaves are usually divided into lobes. Flowers in apical solitary heads. The bracts surrounding the inflorescence form a hemispherical hypanthium. The outer capitulum florets are usually ray-florets, the others disk-florets.

Group A. Usually perennial plants, with simple stems and capitulum pedicels not swollen beneath the head. Ray-florets sometimes absent.

1. Anthemis abrotanifolia: A dwarf caespitose, perennial shrub, with stems 3-15cm.

Tagetes minuta

Anthemis arvensis - s. sp. arvensis

Anthemis rigida

Anthemis chia

Oblong leaves 2-3cm., pinnate or bipinnate, dotted with glands, hairy. Lobes linear, or oblong-obovate, prickly at tip. Capitula 4-7(-9)mm. Small white, ray-florets, often absent. Endemic to Crete. Habitat: Sub-alpine zone about 1900m above sea-level. Flowers at end of springtime.

Group B. Annual plants, with stems branching or simple, and Capitula pedicels frequently swollen beneath heads. There may or may not be ray-florets present.

1. Anthemis arvensis - subsp. arvensis: An annual with branching stems reaching a height of 80cm. Leaves 1,5-5cm. with oblong or linear lobes. Capitula pedicels slightly or not at all swollen. Ray-florets 5-14mm. Habitat: Cultivated ground at a low altitude. Flowers March-May. **2. Anthemis rigida:** A slightly fleshy annual. Crowded stems up to 15cm. and usually simple. Leaves oblong, pinnate or bipinnate with lanceolate or linear-spathulate lobes, cuneate at their base. Capitula 3-9mm. Ray-florets as a rule absent. Habitat: Sandy beaches. Flowers in early spring. **3. Anthemis chia:** Numerous stems 5-40cm., simple or branched a little, erect or ascending. A scantily pubescent plant. Leaves pinnate or bipinnate. Lobes either triangular or ovate. Capitula up to 45mm., with large white ray-florets, always present. Capitula pedicels not swollen. Habitat: Both uncultivated and cultivated land at a low altitude. Flowers February-April. **4. Anthemis altissima.** A robust annual with stems 20-120cm., simple or, often, branched at its upper section. Leaves ovate, bipinnate or thrice pinnate, with linear lobes, so acute as to be almost spiny at tip. 25-40mm. capitula composed of white ray-florets. Habitat: Fallow and cultivated fields at a low altitude. Flowers April-May. **5. Anthemis syriaca:** A sparsely haired plant with simple stems, branched from their base. Oblong, pinnate or bipinnate leaves. Capitula up to 35mm. of white ray-florets (occasionally tinged with pink or purple) 10mm. long and 2,5mm. wide. A West Asia plant. Habitat: Low altitude dry localities and cultivated ground. Flowers in spring. **6. Anthemis cotula:** A strong-smelling plant, pubescent or nearly hairless, 20-70cm. with branching stems. Leaves twice or thrice-pinnate with linear mucronate lobes. Capitula 12-30mm. with white florets 5-14mm., or on rare occasions absent. Habitat: Lowland and sub-montane zones. Flowers April-May.

Group C. Delicate plants, always annuals, with a rosette of leaves at the base whence numerous simple or branched stems rise. Ray-florets, if any, tiny.

1. Anthemis filicaulis: Stems 2-14cm., ascending or patent, very slender, purple-coloured and usually simple. Rosette leaves up to 3cm., pinnate with two lanceolate or elliptic lobes on either side, either entire or trilobate. 5-7 ray-florets, practically orbicular. An endemic of North-East Crete. Habitat: Calcareous maritime rocks. Flowers March-May. **2. Anthemis tomentella:** Resembles 1 but ray-florets are absent. An East Crete endemic. Habitat: Dry, stony slopes at a low altitude. Flowers In spring. **3. Anthemis ammanthus - subsp. ammanthus:** Similar to 1 and 2, but as a rule bigger, up to 35cm. with more or less branched stems, rather slender and stiff. Ray-florets are absent. Seeds (achenes) not persisting on disk after blooming. Habitat: A South Aegean endemic it is to be found in Crete only at the furthest North-Eastern end of the island. Flowers in springtime. **4. Anthemis ammanthus - subsp. paleacea:** Similar to 3 but the achenes persist on disk long after flowering is over. A North-Eastern Crete endemic. Flowers In spring. **5. Anthemis glaberrima:** Similar to 1 and 2 but capitula with pink ray-florets, 2mm. It is endemic to the islet of Gramvoussa of North West Crete. Habitat: Calcareous rocks.

Achillea (Yarrows)

Herbaceous plants with perennial rhizomes, and entire leaves, winged, or twice or thrice-winged. Flowers in tiny heads, like very small daisies. Several capitula clustered together at the tops of the stems, in umbels, rarely solitary.

1. Achillea ligustica: Simple, erect stems 50-100cm. high. Middle leaves 2-3 X 1,5cm., ovate in outline bipinnately-lobed or bipinnate, downy. Bottom leaves larger, while top ones are smaller. Inflorescence an umbel. Capitula 2,5-3mm. with marginal ray-florets white. Habitat: Dry montane meadows. Flowers May-June. **2. Achillea cretica:** Stems up to 40cm., simple. White capitula, small less than 10mm. Leaves of two kinds. The fully developed leaves are winged, narrow, and 2-8cm. long, the new ones very small, cylindrical, covered with thick down. Habitat: Medium altitude, rocky situations. Flowers April-May.

Anthemis altissima

Anthemis filicaulis

Achillea ligustica

Achillea cretica

Chamaemelum

Plants similar to Anthemis with botanical differences barely discernible.

1. Chamaemelum mixtum: A 10-60cm. high pubescent annual, as a rule many-branched. Leaves marginally oblong, pinnate or bipinnate. Capitula 30mm. across with 10mm. white ray-florets, yellowish at their base. Habitat: Cultivated meadows, verges of roads, and seaside sandy tracts. Flowers March-May.

Chamomila

Annual similar to Anthemis but with capitulum disk convex-hemispherical. Ray-florets white.

1. Chamomila recutita: Stems 10-60cm. high, branching. Leaves bipinnate, or thrice-pinnate with linear-filiform segments. Many capitula on each plant, 10-25mm. across. An aromatic and medicinal plant, suitable for skin maladies, stomach trouble, etc. Habitat: Uncultivated fields and meadows in sub-montane and lowland zones. Flowers March-May.

Otanthus (Cottonweed)

Perennial herbs, with thick white hair. Capitula without any ray-florets.

1. Otanthus maritimus: Thick, ascending stems, woody towards base, up to 50cm. high. Leaves oblong-lanceolate, 5-17mm. Spherical capitulate with whitish involucre, and florets of capitulum disk yellow. Habitat: Sandy beaches. Flowers June-September.

Chrysanthemum (Crown Daisies, Corn Marigolds)

Annuals with large capitula. Both ray - and disk-florets.

1. Chrysanthemum coronarium: Hairless stems, 20-80cm. high. Leaves bipinnately-lobed. Disk-florets yellow. Ray-florets yellow or white with yellow at the base. (**bicolor** variety). This variety is the prevailing and very usual one all over Crete. Large capitula, 5-6cm. across. Habitat: Common to fallow fields bare tracts, and along the roadsides, at a low altitude. Flowers March-May. **2. Chrysanthemum segetum:** Similar to 1 but ray-florets always yellow, and leaves less cleft, the lower one pinnately-lobed, the upper dentate only.

Tanacetum (Tansy)

Aromatic plants with alternating pinnately-lobed leaves. Capitula in corymbs. Marginal florets present or absent.

1. Tanacetum parthenium: A herbaceous, aromatic perennial, with capitula about equal in size and shape with those of the **Chamomila recutita** in tightly-packed corymbs of from 5 to 20 capitula. Light green pinnately-lobed leaves, with the lobes elliptic or ovate. A medicinal plant. Habitat: Stream banks, roadside ditches, rock crevices and wet and cool localities in general, in the montane zone. Flowers May-August.

Coleosteophus

Plants similar to Chrysanthemum but with simple leaves.

1. Coleostephus myconis: Stems 10-45cm. high, slightly branched. Lower leaves obovate-spathulate, dentate, stalked; the remainder narrower and sessile. Capitula 2mm. across, with yellow, white or two-coloured ray-florets. Habitat: Cultivated land and gardens. Flowers April-May.

Chlamydophora

Glabrous plants with entire leaves. Capitula with no ray-florets.

1. Chlamydophora tridentata: Plants up to 15cm. with oblong or linear leaves and usually with 3 teeth at tip. Capitula 5-8mm. A North Africa native found in Crete only on the islet of Gavdhos, to the south of the island. Habitat: Barren areas of low altitude. Flowers in spring.

Otanthus maritimus

Chrysanthemum coronarium - var. bicolor

Chrysanthemum segetum

Tanacetum parthenium

Artemisia (Wormwood)

As a rule aromatic plants. Small capitula without any ray-florets clustered in inflorescences of a variety of shapes at the apices of stems.

1. Artemisia arborescens: A perennial aromatic shrub, covered with whitish silvery down. Stems 50-100cm. high. Leaves pinnately-lobed or bipinnately-lobed with narrow lobes, obtuse at apex. Capitula 6-7mm., erect or nodding in big, multi-flowered panicles. Habitat: Uncultivated ground at a low altitude. Flowers May-June.

Senecio (Groundsel)

Perennials or annuals with alternating leaves. Capitula usually yellow with both disk - and ray-florets, rarely with only disk-florets.

243

Group A. Annuals

1. Senecio gallicus: An almost hairless plant or just a little lanate, with a stem up to 40cm. usually branching from the base. Capitula golden-yellow, 15-22mm. across, with about 13 large ray-florets. Habitat: Fallow and cultivated fields, and sandy areas always close to the sea. Flowers March-April. **2. Senecio vulgaris:** Smaller than 1 and with smaller leaves. Small capitula without ray-florets or, more rarely, with 6-12 ray-florets, small and curved downwards.

Group B. Perennials.

1. Senecio gnaphalodes: A dwarf shrub, 20-50cm. high, thickly hairy-pubescent, silvery white in colour. Linear leaves entire or with a few linear lobes. Heads 12-15mm. across, in packed corymbs. Capitula with 10-13 ray-florets. Habitat: Stony positions. Flowers May-June. **2. Senecio rupestris:** A perennial or annual plant, practically hairless with numerous stems. Leaves pinnae. Capitula 15-20mm. across in lax corymbs. Circa 13 large ray-florets. Habitat: Montane and sub-montane stony sites. Flowers May-June. **3. Senecio fruticulosus:** Similar to 2 but smaller leaves, dentate. Habitat: Montane and sub-alpine zones. Flowers May-June.

Calendula (Marigolds)

Annual or perennial plants. Alternate, entire leaves. Capitula with ray- and disk-florets. Ray-florets large, yellow or orange-coloured. Disk-florets orange, yellow or dark brown.

1. Calendula arvensis: An annual up to 30cm., multi-branched, thinly lanate stems. Pubescent, oblong-obovate leaves. Capitula 1,5-2cm. seldom any larger. Ray-florets yellow or orange. Disk-florets orange-yellow-or dark brown. Habitat: Cultivated and uncultivated fields at a low altitude. Flowers March-May. **2. Calendula officinalis:** Similar to 1 but a bigger plant with capitula 4-5cm. across. Widely cultivated, and frequently sub-spontaneous. Up to the present it has not been spoken of as self-seeding in Crete. Yet the writer has come upon it in the sub-montane zone of West Crete, growing along roadsides and in uncultivated fields. Habitat: Fallow and cultivated fields at a low altitude. Flowers March-May.

Carlina

Annuals or perennials with leaves as a rule pinnately-lobed, and spiny. Capitula with all florets tubular, surrounded by shiny, dry bracts giving the impression of ray-florets.

1. Carlina corymbosa - subsp. curetum: A nearly glabrous perennial, 20-40cm. high. Capitula 12-18mm. with bright yellow or brownish-yellow bracts. Prickly pinnately-lobed leaves. Endemic to Crete and Carpathos. Habitat: Low altitude. Flowers June-August. **2. Carlina diae:** A plant with dense white hair and stems 40-60cm. high. Leaves entire without any spines. Capitula 15-20mm. Bracts a bright yellow. Endemic to Dhia and other islets off the North coast of Crete. Habitat: Seaside rocks. Flowers June-August. **3. Carlina barnebiana:** A perennial almost glabrous or else slightly arachnoid lanate, and stems up to 8cm. Spiny pinnately-lobed leaves. Solitary capitula, 15-20mm. Bracts entirely purple or, at least so, towards edges. An East Crete endemic. Habitat: Low altitude. Flowers May-June. **4. Carlina lanata:** A 5-40cm. high annual. Leaves pinnately-lobed, spiny and lanate underneath. Capitula 15-40mm. Pink bracts. Habitat: Low altitude barren areas. Flowers June-July.

Senecio gallicus

Senecio rupestris

Carlina lanata

Echinops spinosissimus - s. sp. bithynicus

Cardopatium

Plants with very prickly pinnately-lobed leaves. Small capitula, all florets tubular. Capitula in crowded inflorescences, surrounded by spiny leaves.

Cardopatium corymbosum: A short-stemmed and branching plant. Capitula with blue florets, rarely white. Habitat: Beaches. Flowers June-July.

Echinops (Globe-Thistles)

Perennial or annual plants with pinnately-lobed spiny leaves. Large spherical and prickly capitula with only tubular florets.

1. Echinops spinosissimus - subsp. bithynicus: Stems 50-80cm. in height, branched and

245

covered with dense arachnoid hair. Leaves usually bipinnately-lobed, green above and whitish lanate beneath. Capitula with light blue florets. Habitat: Low altitude. Flowers July-September.

Staechelina

Small caespitose shrubs with entire leaves, as a rule, forming rosettes at the apices of the stems. Heads in cymose inflorescences, medium-sized, all florets tubular.

1. Staechelina arborea: Stems up to 100cm., silvery-coloured. Ovate leaves, obtuse at tips, dark green above and silver-coloured beneath. Oblong capitula about 30mm. long, florets pink. A Cretan endemic. Habitat: Low altitude rocks and gorges. Flowers May-September. **2. Staechelina fruticosa:** Similar to 1 but a larger plant. Stems up to 150cm. high, slightly pubescent-glandular. Leaves smaller, lanceolate, acute or not, practically hairless, all one colour. Capitula smaller with white florets. Habitat: Rocks and gorges of medium and low altitudes. Flowers June-September.

Carduus (Thistles)

Plants with leaves dentate or pinnately-lobed, more or less spiny, and stems winged and spiny. Heads spherical or cylindrical, spiny. All florets tubular, pink or purple.

1. Carduus argentatus: An annual plant up to 1m. high. Stems covered with lanate hair, and with very narrow wings. Leaves with obtuse, dentate lobes, green and almost smooth above, silvery and thickly pubescent beneath. Small capitula 15-18 X 10-13mm., with long, slender pedicels. Pink florets. A South-West Asia plant spread down to Carpathos and Crete. Habitat: Rocky sites. Flowers in spring. **2. Carduus pycnocephalus:** Stems with broader wings than those of 1. Leaves with 2-5 pairs of lobes which are palmately divided. Leaves slightly hairy above, and thickly so beneath. Capitula 15-20 X 7-13mm., solitary or in bunches of 2-3. Pink florets. Habitat: Lonely barren regions. Flowers in springtime.

Cirsium (Thistle)

Plants similar to Carduus. Stems winged or not. Florets pink, purple or yellowish, rarely white.

1. Cirsium morinifolium: A biennial 30-100cm. high. With multi-branched stem. Leaves almost glabrous on top, hairy beneath, deeply cleft into prickly lobes. Numerous capitula on many-branched corymbs, about 30mm. Large, with white florets. Endemic to Crete. Habitat: Barren, waste pasture-land. Flowers Spring. **2. Cirsium creticum - subsp. creticum:** A branched winged stem, with spiny wings. Deeply undulating leaves, prickly, thinly hairy above, more densely hairy underneath. Capitula about 20mm., with purple florets. Flowers Spring.

Picnomon

Resembles Cirsium in appearance, with botanical differences not manifest.

Picnomon acarna: Annual, 10-50cm. high, arachnoid lanate. Stem much-branched, with spiny wings. Leaves pinnately-lobed, prickly. Capitula circa 25-35mm., cylindrical, numerous, in corymbose inflorescences. Florets rosy-purple. Habitat: Both uncultivated and cultivated fields at medium and low altitudes. Flowers April-June.

Notobasis syriaca

Notobasis

Plants similar to Cirsium. Capitula surrounded by the upper leaves. Stems without wings.

Notobasis syriaca: Annuals reaching a height of 60cm. or even over. Leaves pinnately-lobed, spiny with narrow lobes, and white veins. Taproot branched. Capitula quite large, in lax inflorescences. Florets rosy-purple. Habitat: Low altitude fields cultivated or not. Flowers April-May.

Ptilostemon

Small perennial shrubs, rarely annuals, either without any spines or with only a few. Capitula with tubular florets only.

1. Ptilostemon chamaepeuce: A 30-100cm. high shrub, dense, with linear leaves, silvery lanate beneath. Capitula in few-flowered corymbs on long stems with few, small leaves. Capitula about 25mm., with pink or purple florets. Habitat: Rocks and gorges of middle and low altitudes. Flowers May-June. **2. Ptilostemon gnaphaloides - subsp. pseudofruticosus:** Similar to 1 but upper leaves very small, slightly spiny at tip, and with 1-2 narrow lobes at their base. Habitat: Rocky situations. Flowers May-June. **3. Ptilostemon stellatus:** An annual 15-30(-70)cm. high. Leaves linear or linear-lanceolate, sparsely hairy, with 1-3 spines at base. Capitula about 25mm. with pink florets. Habitat: Dry and barren sites. Flowers in spring.

Lamyropsis

Plants similar to Ptilostemon. Leaves pinnately-lobed.

1. Lamyropsis cynaroides: A 20-50cm. high perennial. Stem with white arachnoid hair. Leaves pinnately-lobed or almost pinnate, white-haired beneath and, above hairy only along the veins. Capitula solitary, or few together on bare pedicels. Length of capitula circa 35mm. Florets purple.

Galactites

Annual plants resembling Cirsium, covered with white hair or down.

1. Galactites tomentosa: Stems 15-100cm. high. Leaves pinnately-lobed. Capitula 30-35mm. with pale pink florets. Habitat: Roadsides and cultivated ground at low altitude. Flowers April-May.

Tyrimnus

Slender, hairy or lanate annuals or biennials, with very prickly oblong leaves. Florets tubular.

1. Tyrimnus leucographus: Stems 20-60cm. Leaves dentate-concave with white veins, and thickly spined along margins. Capitula 14-16mm., with pink or violet florets. Habitat: Dry, bare places. Flowers in spring.

Onopordon (Scotch Thistles)

Big biennial plants with large heads. Stems winged, with spiny wings (alae). Leaves dentate, pinnately-lobed or pinnate, with prickles. All florets tubular.

1. Onopordon tauricum: A yellowy-brown stem up to 200cm; wings up to 15mm. broad. Large, dark green pinnately-lobed leaves, with a few hairs above, and hairier beneath. Capitula almost spherical 35-45 X 55-70mm. Rose-purple florets. Habitat: Ditches along roads, meadows, and rocky places. Flowers May-July. **2. Onopordon bracteatum - subsp. creticum:** Stem hairy. Leaves with dense white hair beneath, greyish-green above pinnate or pinnately lobed, lobes palmately-lobed. Purple capitula 50-70mm. Habitat: Calcareous, stony expanses. Flowers June-July. **3. Onopordon illyricum - subsp. cardunculus:** Plant up to 130cm. in height. Yellowish, hairy stems. Leaves pinnately-lobed or pinnate with triangular-wedge-shaped lobes. Capitula 30-50mm. with purple florets. Habitat: Barren regions, uncultivated fields, roadsides. Flowers June-July. **4. Onopordon majorii:** Stem up to 150cm. covered with white hair. Wings narrow. Leaves large up to 45cm., pinnate, a greyish-green, sparsely haired above and thickly beneath. Capitula 70-80mm., with purple florets. Habitat: Barren areas at a low altitude. Flowers May-July.

Ptilostemon chamaepeuce

Cynara cardungulus

Cynara cornigera

Centaurea raphanina - s. sp. raphanina

Cynara (Cardoons or Artichokes)

Perennial plants with erect stems. Most of the leaves in a rosette, the remainder alternating, all deeply cleft and spiny. Large apical capitula solitary or few. All florets tubular.

1. Cynara cardunculus: Stems 20-100cm. high. Leaves pinnately-lobed up to 50 X 35cm. Greenish above and white haired beneath. Capitula about 60mm. with blue, violet or, rarely, white florets. Habitat: Seaboard stetches of sand. Flowers May-June. **2. Cynara cornigera:** Similar to 1 but stems up to 30cm. only. Leaves up to 40cm. with light-coloured veins on upper surface. Capitula up to 50mm., and yellowish floroto. Habitat: Maritime localities. Flowers May-June.

Silybum (Milk-Thistles)

Plants similar to onopordon. Alternating, spiny, white-veined leaves. Medium sized capitula with large, spiny involucral bracts.

1. Silybum marianum: Stem 20-150cm. Basal leaves pinnately-lobed, hairless, 25-50cm. The stem leaves are smaller, and less cleft. Capitula 2,5-4cm. with purple florets. Habitat: Cultivated and uncultivated ground, roadsides. Flowers May-July.

Serratula (Saw-worts)

Perennial plants without any spines. Slender stems. Capitula solitary on few-flowered inflorescences, and similar to Centaurea with all florets tubular.

1. Serratula cichoracea - subsp. cretica: A pubescent plant up to 70cm. high. Stem leaves dentate, linear-lanceolate. Basal leaves similarly dentate, oblanceolate or elliptic. Capitula 30-40mm. with purple florets and involucral bracts bearing spine at tip. Endemic to Crete. Habitat: Low altitude scrub. Flowers April-June.

Centaurea (Knapsweeds)

Perennial or annual plants. Leaves entire, lyrate, pinnately-lobed, or pinnate. Capitula solitary or in small clusters of 2-3 at the end of stems. Hypanthium cylindrical or spherical with bracts which are frequently fimbriate, or spiny along margin. All florets tubular, marginal ones larger and sterile with long narrow lobes.

Group A. Perennial plants, with erect stems, on rare occasions biennial. Basal leaves usually pinnate, upper leaves entire. Hypanthium bracts pinnately fimbriate, as a rule with an apical spine, which is at least 15mm. long.

1. Centaurea redempta: Erect stems 10-20cm. high, simple or little-branched, covered with dense arachnoid lanate hair. Leaves almost glabrous with slightly Arachnoid lanate hair. Lower leaves stalked pinnate, with ovate-lanceolate lobes, dentate or lobate. Spherical hypanthium 30-40mm. Hypanthium bracts black with or without apical spine 15-20mm. long. Florets dark purple, outer ones practically the same as the inner. Endemic to Crete. Habitat: Montane rocks. Flowers May-July. **2. Centaurea spruneri - subsp. minoa:** Similar to 1 but taller up to 30cm. with stems that are always branched at their upper section. Basal leaves either lyrate-pinnate, or entire. Florets pink or purple, the outer manifestly larger. Hypanthium bracts a brownish-yellow. A Cretan endemic. Habitat: Low altitude fields and hills. Flowers April-June.

Group B. Perennials either with short stems or else stemless. Leaves form rosette at base. Hypanthium bracts entire, fimbriate or dentate, with apical spine.

1. Centaurea raphanina - subsp. raphanina: Practically a stemless plant. Rosette leaves entire or lyrate-pinnate, with entire lobes. Flower heads usually 2-4, with pink or purple florets, the outer ones slightly bigger than the inner. Hypanthium bracts entire with an apical spine 2-9mm. Endemic to Crete, Cassos and Carpathos. Habitat: Middle and low zones. Flowers April-June. **2. Centaurea aegialophila:** Similar to 1 but rosette leaves heart-shaped at base, heads single or 2 together, florets always purple. The whole plant covered with arachnoid lanate hair. Hypanthium bracts with small spines, 1-3mm. long. Habitat: Sandy beaches. Flowers April-May. **3. Centaurea pumilio:** Very similar to 2, with no discernible differences except in the apical spines of the hypanthium bracts which are longer (5-9mm.). Habitat: Sandy beaches in West Crete. Flowers April-May.

Group C. Perennial or annual plants. Stems as a rule erect and much-branched. Capitula

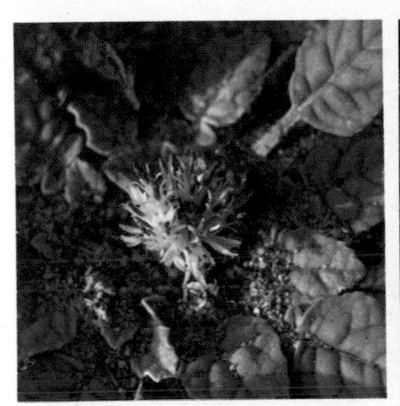

Centaurea aegialophila

Centaurea solstitialis

Centaurea idaea

Centaurea melitensis

small. Leaves usually pinnate with narrow lobes. Hypanthium bracts usually fimbriate with an apical spine.

1. Centaurea argentea. A grey-green-whitish, hairy perennial, with stems up to 45cm., and basal leaves lyrate, lobes oblong. Capitula solitary. Florets yellow. Habitat: Montane and sub-montane rocks. Flowers May-July. **2. Centaurea spinosa - subsp. spinosa.** A dwarf, dense, multi-branched shrub with spiny branches. Leaves covered with grey hair or almost glabrous, lobes prickly. Single capitula. Pale pink or white florets. Habitat: Sandy beaches. Flowers April-May.

Group D. Plants biennial. Leaves pinnate. Hypanthium bracts with one long spine and a few much smaller ones at tip.

1. Centaurea hyalolepis. Stems reach a height of 40cm., and are branched from the base.

Capitula single with yellow florets. Hypanthium bracts with one very long spine and 2-3 much smaller ones. Habitat: Uncultivated land at a low altitude. Flowers April-June. **2. Centaurea calcitrapa.** Similar to 1 but taller, up to 1m. Florets a light purple. Habitat: Waste ground at a low altitude. Flowers April-June.

Group E. There are annuals, biennials, and perennials among this group of plants. Lower leaves pinnate, upper ones entire or dentate. Hypanthium bracts with one long and a few shorter spines at tip.

1. Centaurea solstitialis - subsp. solstitialis. A biennial with much-branched stems, 30-100cm. high. Capitula single with yellow florets. Hypanthium bracts with 3-5 spines, the centre one much longer than the others. Leaves a greyish-green, arachnoid lanate, the lower ones as a rule lyrate or pinnate with oblong-triangular lobes. Habitat: Arid localities at a low altitude. Flowers June-August. **2. Centaurea idaea.** Similar to 1 but branching stems 10-15(-30)cm; basal leaves in rosettes, and smaller capitula. Hypanthium bracts with black lateral spines. Endemic to Crete. Habitat: Dry, barren areas in montane zone. Flowers May-July. **3. Centaurea melitensis:** Similar to 1 but frequently an annual, with fewer branches. Capitula 1-3. Hypanthium bracts with shorter apical spines. Leaves greenish, downy.

Group F. Perennial or annuals with leaves either entire or pinnate. Hypanthium bracts fimbriate.

1. Centaurea baldaccii. A perennial plant with a very short, thick stem. Leaves narrow, entire or lyrate, arachnoid lanate, whitish. Hypanthium bracts dark brown. Florets cream. A Cretan endemic. Habitat: Alpine zone. Flowers June-July.

Crupina

Slender, erect annuals with stems branching at their upper part. Capitula small, just like those of **Centaurea.** Florets only tubular.

1. Crupina crupinastrum. Stem up to 80cm., leafless at its upper part. Leaves pinnate, segments slender, linear, dentate. Capitula 15-25mm., florets purple. Habitat: Low altitude garrigue. Flowers April-May.

Wagenitzia

Perennial plants with thick, woody rhizomes. Alternating leaves. Large capitula, a single one at the top of each stem. Florets, tubular uniform.

1. Wagenitzia lancifolia. Stems erect or spreading, thinly branched. Leaves entire, lanceolate, and pointed. The capitula are surrounded by the upper leaves. Capitula 15-25mm., with yellow florets. Endemic to Crete. Habitat: Montane and sub-montane zones. Flowers May-June.

Cnicus (Blessed Thistle)

Annual plants with hairy, pinnately-lobed leaves. Capitula surrounded by the upper leaves. Florets tubular the outer ones very small. The involucral bracts of the capitula are of two kinds: - the outer bracts bear simple apical spines, whereas the inner ones bear an pinnate apical spine.

1. Cnicus benedictus. Stem 10-60cm., covered with arachnoid lanate hairs. Leaves bright green with white veins, hairy. Habitat: Both cultivated and uncultivated fields at a low altitude. Flowers April-May.

Cnicus benedictus

Carthamus

These plants are as a rule annuals, rarely perennials, and very spiny. Leaves pinnately-lobed or pinnate. Stems branched. Capitula solitary, surrounded by prickly leaves and bracts, florets tubular.

1. Carthamus dentatus - subsp. ruber. A hairy plant. Capitula bear lilac, pink, or purple florets. The leaves are greyish-green. Involucral bracts with long spines. Habitat: Barren areas of low and middle altitudes. Flowers May-June. **2. Carthamus boissieri.** Similar to 1 but with greyish leaves. Lower leaves with more than 10 pairs of lobes. Stems with thick, arachnoid lanate hair. Capitula florets rosy-purple. Endemic to the South Aegean. Habitat: Low altitude waste localities. Flowers April-May. **3. Carthamus leucocaulos.** Similar to 1 and 2 but almost glabrous; leaves green, and stems whitish or reddish. Lilac-coloured florets on the capitula. This, too, is endemic to the South Aegean. Habitat: Low altitude uncultivated ground. Flowers May-June. **4. Carthamus lanatus - subsp. baeticus:** Similar to the previous three species; greyish-green. Capitula with yellowish or, occasionally, almost white florets. Habitat: Barren situations at middle and low altitudes. Flowers May-June.

Scolymus (Spanish Oyster Plants)

These plants resemble **Carthamus** in appearance but the capitula have only ray-florets. Stems winged and prickly.

1. Scolymus maculatus. An annual 15-90cm. high, with a winged-spiny stem, and big pinnately-lobed or pinnate, prickly leaves. Capitulum florets yellow. Habitat: Uncultivated ground at a low altitude. Flowers May-June. **2. Scolymus hispanicus.** Similar to 1 but a hairy biennial or perennial. Habitat: Barren expanses at a low altitude. Flowers May-June.

Cichorium (Chicory)

Annual or perennial plants with pinnately-lobed or dentate leaves. All florets rayed always blue.

1. Cichorium intybus. A glabrous or slightly hairy plant with a perennial rhizome. Basal leaves pinnately-lobed or dentate, large. Those of stem smaller and less cleft. The capitula which measure about 4cm. across open in the morning. Habitat: Found in fields both cultivated and fallow and in montane meadows. Flowers June-July. **2. Cichorium endivia - subsp. divaricatum.** Similar to 1 but an annual or biennial with the lower leaves hairy. Some of its varieties are cultivated. Habitat: Cultivated and fallow fields at a low altitude. Flowers May-July. **3. Cichorium spinosum.** Stems short, 4-18cm., branching from the base and bearing either pinnately-lobed or dentate leaves. The capitula are similar to those of the two previous plants. Habitat: Maritime regions. Flowers May-June.

Catananche (Cupidone)

Annual or perennial plants having most of their leaves at the base. 1 or more stems which are practically bare. Capitula with all their florets ray-florets.

1. Catananche lutea - subsp. lutea. An annual with hairy linear or oblanceolate leaves, entire or very slightly dentate, 3-veined, 30-150mm. long. All the leaves basal and numerous. Stems leafless up to 20cm. Capitula, solitary or only a few, with yellow florets. Habitat: Stony sites at a low altitude. Flowers in the Spring.

Tolpis

Perennial or annual plants with stems as a rule branching. Varied leaves. Capitula with all ray-florets, yellow-coloured, sometimes their inner surface is a brownish-purple.

1. Tolpis barbata. An annual, 6-90cm. high. Leaves ovate, lanceolate or linear, entire or sparsely dentate, acute. Capitula one or only a few at the tips of the stem and its branches. Outer involucral bracts ending in a long arista. Habitat: Uncultivated and seaboard sites. Flowers May-June. **2. Tolpis virgata.** A pubescent biennial or perennial plant, 30-100cm. high. Leaves oblong-lanceolate, or elliptic, entire, crenate or dentate. Capitula with small exterior bracts, lacking awns. Habitat: Uncultivated and seaboard sites. Flowers May-June.

Scolymus maculatus

Hyoseris

Plants with rosette of leaves at base, and simple, leafless stems. Capitula solitary. Only ray-florets always yellow in colour. Leaves pinnately-lobed.

1. Hyoseris scabra. An annual with hairless leaves. Stems 1-7cm., erect or patent, quite thick and hollow. Habitat: Barren localities near the sea. Flowers February-April. **2. Hyoseris radiata.** A perennial with big, rather erect leaves, 5-25cm. Stems 6-36cm. long, erect and usually glabrous. Capitula larger than those of 1. Habitat: Stony, barren places at a low altitude. Flowers April-May.

255

Hedypnois

Annuals with many, branched stems. Leaves entire, dentate, or pinnately-lobed. Capitula composed of ray-florets, small in size.

1. Hedypnois cretica. A hairy plant 3-45cm. high. Leaves narrowly elliptic or oblanceolate, entire or dentate. Capitula either solitary or in clusters of several, bearing yellow florets. Head peduncles thick, slightly inflated near head. Habitat: Dry, barren locations. Flowers March-April.

Rhagadiolus

Annuals with branched stems. Leaves dentate or pinnately-lobed. Capitula with all ray-florets, yellow in colour.

1. Rhagadiolus stellatus. A hairy plant, 7-40cm. high, with numerous leaves, 2,5-14cm., oblong-obovate, dentate, concave, lyrate, or pinnately-lobed. Small capitula with but a few ray-florets. Fruit (achenes) develops considerably when flowering is over, turning outwards in a stellar arrangement. Habitat: Found on cultivated and uncultivated ground. Flowers April-May.

Urospermum

Plants with one or few stems which are as a rule branched. Capitula few and big. Yellow ray-florets only present.

1. Urospermum picroides. An annual, 30-45cm. high, covered with bristly hairs. Leaves pinnately-lobed or dentate, large. Capitula 4cm. across, 1-9 on long stalks. Pale yellow florets. Habitat: Fallow fields at a low altitude. Flowers April-May.

Hypochoeris (Cat's Ears)

Annual or perennial plants with a rosette of leaves at base, and one or a few stems, usually leafless or else with only a few small ones. Capitula solitary or more than yellow ray-florets only present.

1. Hypochoeris achyrophorus. An annual, 8-35cm. high. Stems branching. Leaves from spathulate to ovate in shape, entire or lobate with bristly hairs. Capitula up to 15mm. in breadth. Habitat: Uncultivated fields at a low altitude. Flowers April-May. **2. Hypochoeris cretensis:** A perennial plant 10-85cm. high. Stem as a rule branching. Leaves pinnately-lobed, hairless or sparsely hairy. Capitula up to 22mm. Habitat: Heaths and cultivated ground. Flowers April-June. **3. Hypochoeris tenuiflora.** A practically hairless perennial with stems 2-9cm., simple or little-branched. Leaves 1,5-10cm., linear to oblanceolate, almost entire or pinnately-lobed. Small capitula, 5-9mm. An endemic of Crete. Habitat: Rocks in the montane and sub-alpine zones. Flowers June-August. **4. Hypochoeris glabra.** An annual or perennial, with stems usually branching, 1-40cm. Leaves dentate or pinnately-lobed, hairless or pubescent. Capitula 5-15mm., with pale or golden-yellow florets. Habitat: Heaths and barren areas at a low altitude. Flowers May-June. **5. Hypochoeris radicata.** A hairy perennial with stems 20-60(-100cm.) high, branched. Leaves dentate-pinnately lobed. Capitula 20-35mm. Florets a bright yellow. Habitat: Dry pastures at middle and low altitudes. Flowers May-July.

Leontodon (Hawkbits)

Annual or perennial, with a rosette of leaves at base. Leaves entire or pinnately-lobed. Stems one or more, simple or branched, leafless. Only ray-florets present on capitula. Florets yellow.

Hypochoeris achyrophorus

1. Leontodon tuberosus. A hairy perennial with long, slender tubers at its roots. Simple, hairy stems, 1-6, 7-35cm. Leaves 2-14cm., dentate or pinnately-lobed. Capitula solitary. Habitat: Montane and sub-montane zones. Flowers May-June.

Picris (Ox-Tongue)

Annuals or perennials covered with bristly hair. Leaves usually dentate or emarginate. One stem, as a rule branching. Only ray-florets present on capitula. Florets yellow.

1. Picris pauciflora. An annual with stems 10-50cm. high. Leaves oblong-elliptic or oblanceolate, entire or emarginate-dentate, tho upper leaves amplexicaul. Few, small capitula. Habitat: Barren, stony situations at a low altitude. Flowers April-May. **2. Picris**

altissima. Similar to 1 but capitula numerous. Habitat: Stony, uncultivated ground and way-sides. Flowers April-May.

Scorzonera (Scorzoneras)

As a rule perennials. 1 or many stems. Leaves entire or pinnately-lobed. Capitula have only ray-florets which may be yellow, whitish, pink, or purple in colour.

1. Scorzonera idaea. A perennial whose rhizome is erect, thick, and cylindrical. Stems up to 4cm. Leaves linear, 3-6cm., sparsely hairy, and all at the base of the plant. Small, yellow capitula. Endemic to Crete. Found on the mountains of Crete in the alpine and sub-alpine zones. **2. Scorzonera cretica.** A perennial with a cylindrical rhizome. Stems 3-45(-60)cm., lanate or almost glabrous. Linear leaves up to 30cm. Big capitula up to 50mm., across, bearing yellow florets. A very varied species. Habitat: Rocky and barren localities of montane and sub-montane zones. Flowers April-May.

Tragopogon (Goatsbeard)

Annual, biennial, or perennial plants. A single stem. Linear leaves. Capitula bearing yellow, pink, or purple ray-florets. Involucral bracts about equal in length with the florets.

1. Tragopogon porrifolius. A sparsely lanate biennial with cylindrical rhizome. Stems 20-50(-125)cm. high. Leaves broadly linear, wider at base. Big pink or pinkish-violet capitula. Habitat: Meadows, heaths, uncultivated fields of montane and lowland zones. Flowers April-May. **2. Tragopogon lassithicus.** A dwarf perennial, with linear leaves, and simple stems, 6-8cm. high. Capitula with yellow florets. Endemic to the mountains of East Crete (Dhikti). Habitat: Montane zone rocks. **3. Tragopogon hybridus.** A small, fragile, hairless annual plant with stems 10-30(-50)cm. high, and a few florets (as a rule only 5), pink or purple. Habitat: Uncultivated fields and pastures at a low altitude. Flowers March-April.

Reichardia

Annuals or perennials. Leaves concentrated largely at the base, entire, dentate, or pinnately-lobed. Branched stems with few, small leaves. Capitula composed entirely, of ray-florets which are yellow.

1. Reichardia tingitana: A glabrous annual or perennial plant. Leaves covered with white down, dentate or pinnately-lobed. Stems 4-35cm. high. 1-4 capitula to a stem, these heads are 20-40mm. across. Habitat: Barren tracts and scrub. Flowers March-May. **2. Reichardia picroides.** A glabrous perennial, 5-45cm. Dense, entire or pinnately-lobed leaves. Slender stems. 1-5 capitula circa 30mm. across. Habitat: Barren localities, and uncultivated fields. Flowers March-May. **3. Reichardia intermedia.** Similar to 3 but usually an annual. Habitat: Uncultivated fields and scrub. Flowers March-May.

Aetheorhiza

Perennial plants, frequently producing round tubers. Leaves in rosettes. Simple stems. Leaves entire, dentate, or emarginate. Capitula entirely of yellow ray-florets.

1. Aetheorhiza bulbosa - subsp. microcephala. A glaucous-coloured plant. Leaves emarginate or deeply dentate. Stems 7-40cm. in height. Capitula circa 2,5cm. Habitat: Maritime regions. Flowers In spring.

Sonchus (Sow-Thistles)

Annual, biennial, or perennial plants. Leaves dentate or pinnately-lobed, occasionally

Leontodon tuberosus

Tragopogon porrifolius

Tragopogon hybridus

Hypochoeris glabra

prickly, those of stem amplexicaul. Stem branched.

1. Sonchus asper - subsp. asper. An annual or biennial plant, 10-120mm. high, hairless, except for the apices of the stems which are hairy-glandular. Lower leaves entire or pinnately-lobed, lower ones entire or pinnate. Large capitula, 20-30mm. across. Habitat: Common to cultivated land, waysides, and ditches. Flowers April-June. **2. Sonchus oleraceus.** Similar to 1 but often a white down covers the upper section of the stems. Lower leaves always entire, upper always pinnately-lobed or pinnate, lyrate. Capitula slightly smaller. Habitat: Cultivated expanses and roadside ditches. Flowers April-June.

Lactuca (Lettuce)

Annuals or perennials with tough, branched stems. Leaves entire or pinnately-lobed. Small capitula with only ray-florets present, which are yellow in colour, and on rare occasions blue.

1. Lactuca viminea - subsp. viminea. This is either a perennial or a biennial plant. Stems, 30-80cm. branching at their upper section. Leaves glaucous-coloured with large auricles at their base, the lower-deeply pinnately cut into narrow lobes while the upper ones are often entire. Inflorescence multi-flowered, with small heads and pale yellow florets. Habitat: Rocky situations at middle and low altitude. Flowers June-August. **2. Lactuca viminea - subsp. alpestris.** Similar to 1 but stems 7-25cm., and little-branched. Endemic to Crete. Habitat: Alpine and sub-alpine zones. Flowers July-September. **3. Lactuca acanthifolia.** Similar to the previous two plants but taller reaching up to 1m, very sparsely lanate towards the petioles of leaves. Capitula in an oblong inflorescence, florets yellow. Habitat: Shady rocky localities. Flowers June-September. **4. Lactuca serriola.** A tall plant up to 180cm. Leaves with coarse, prickly hair on veins, and usually pinnately-lobed. Small capitula, florets a pale yellow. Habitat: Uncultivated ground, roadsides, and on walls. Flowers June-August. **5. Lactuca saligna.** Stem 30-100cm. high. Lower leaves entire or pinnately-lobed. Upper ones entire, narrow, with sagittal base. Inflorescence oblong. Capitula of pale yellow florets. Habitat: Both cultivated and uncultivated fields. Flowers June-August.

Streptoramphus

These plants resemble **Lactuca,** but have tuberous roots.

1. Streptoramhus tuberosus. Stem 40-60cm., occasionally branched. Lower leaves entire or pinnately-lobed, the upper entire. Involucral bract of capitula reddish and smooth. Florets yellow. Habitat: Cultivated and fallow fields. Flowers June-August.

Taraxacum (Dandelions)

Plants with perennial roots. Leaves form rosette. Simple, short, leafless stems. Capitula solitary. Only yellow ray-florets present.

1. Taraxacum megalorhizon. Thick, woody root. Leaves oblanceolate or obovate, entire or slightly lobed, glabrous or hairy only underneath, appearing before the flowering. Capitula 10-25mm. Florets short and broad, pale yellow, with a reddish or brown stripe. Habitat: Stony and rocky places at a low altitude. Flowers October-November. **2. Taraxacum gymnanthum.** Very similar to 1 but leaves appear together with the flowers. Habitat: Stony meadows at middle and low altitudes. Flowers September-November.

Chondrilla

Perennial or biennial plants. Leaves entire or dentate-pinnately-lobed. Most of the leaves are concentrated at base. Stem leaves much smaller or bractlike. 1-5 stems, much-branched. Only ray-florets present on the capitula. Florets yellow.

1. Chondrilla juncea. A greyish-green plant with a 50-100cm. high stem, glabrous or hairy, branches erect. Leaves deeply pinnately-lobed dentate. Numerous capitula, 1cm., with 9-12 florets. Habitat: Uncultivated ground and meadows at middle and low altitudes. Flowers April-June. **2. Chondrilla ramosissima.** Very similar to 1 but stems and branches with white down and bristly hairs. Endemic to the South Aegean islands. Habitat: Middle and low altitudes. Flowers April-June.

Reichardia picroides   Sonchus oleraceus

Crepis rubra   Crepis neglecta - s. sp. neglecta

Crepis (Hawksbeards)

Annual or perennial plants with leaves usually dentate or pinnately-lobed. Stems as a rule branched. Capitula made up of ray-florets only, the colour of which is as a rule yellow, more rarely it may be orange or pink.

1. Crepis fraasii - subsp. mungieri. Basal leaves hairy, pinnately-lobed-lyrate with the terminal lobe broadly ovate, sparsely toothed. The upper leaves are small, bractlike. Capitula small in lax corymbs. Florets yellow, reddish on the outside. Endemic to Crete and Carpathos. Habitat: Montane and sub-alpine zones. Flowers June-July. **2. Crepis**

auriculifolia. A perennial with a rosette of dentate or slightly emarginate leaves, hairy or glabrous. Few, small, yellow capitula, frequently a little reddish on outer surface. Endemic to Crete. Habitat: Rocks and stony slopes of middle and low altitudes. Flowers May-June. **3. Crepis sibthorpiana.** A perennial with pubescent or glabrous leaves, which are dentate or pinnately-lobed. Stems 3-12cm. Few small capitula with yellow florets, purplish-red on the outside. A Cretan endemic. Habitat: Rocks in the alpine and sub-alpine zones. Flowers May-June. **4. Crepis rubra.** Leaves dentate or pinnately-lobed. Stems, 4-40cm., simple or with 1 branch. Capitula quite large with pink florets. Habitat: Montane and sub-montane uncultivated fields. Flowers April-June. **5. Crepis foetida - subsp. foetida.** Hairy leaves, dentate, pinnate or bipinnately-lobed. Stems, 10-50cm. branching starting from low down. Capitula rather large, with yellow florets, reddish outside. Flowers Spring. **6. Crepis foetida - subsp. commutata.** Very similar to 5 differing only in the involucral bracts of the capitula, and in the achenes. Habitat: Middle and low altitudes. Flowers in the spring. **7. Crepis sancta.** An annual. Leaves either with yellow hairs or hairless, dentate or lyrate-pinnately-lobed. Numerous stems, 3-35cm. Capitula 15-20mm., with yellow florets. Habitat: Fields and heaths in the middle and low altitudes. Flowers May-June. **8. Crepis dioscorides.** An annual plant with stems, 10-60cm. high, usually branching. Leaves almost hairless, dentate or pinnately-lobed, with 6-8 broad, triangular lobes. Capitula 15-20mm. with yellow florets, reddish on the outside. Habitat: Montane and sub-montane zones. Flowers May-June. **9. Crepis multiflora.** An annual with 7-35cm. high stems branching from the base. Leaves glabrous, dentate or pinnately-lobed. Many capitula, yellow, and measuring about 15mm. Habitat: Middle and low altitudes. Flowers April-May. **10. Crepis zacintha.** An annual plant. Stems, 20-30cm., branched from the base. Leaves hairy, pinnately-lobed, - lyrate, with the ending lobe large, ovate, and obtuse. Small capitula up to 15mm., with yellow florets that have a purple stripe on the outer surface. Habitat: Middle and low altitudes. Flowers April-May. **11. Crepis pusilla.** This plant is almost stemless, or else with a very short one. Leaves 2-7cm., narrow, entire or pinnately-lobed, and glabrous. 2-8 capitula in the middle of the rosette of leaves, very small and yellow. **12. Crepis micrantha.** Leaves with dense, rather coarse, hairs, the lower lanceolate, acute, entire or slightly dentate, sagittal-involucral at base. Stems one or more, branching from the base upwards. Small, yellow capitula. Habitat: Middle and low altitudes. Flowers April-June. **13. Crepis neglecta - subsp. cretica.** A hairy dwarf plant with many short, branched stems. Leaves pinnate, pinnately-lobed or deeply dentate, up to 7cm. long. Small, yellow capitula. Endemic to Crete. Habitat: Middle and low altitudes. Flowers April-May. **14. Crepis neglecta - subsp. neglecta.** Resembles 13 but is larger with one or more stems, 10-50cm., and leaves up to 14cm. Habitat: Middle and low altitudes. Flowers April-May. **15. Crepis vesicaria - subsp. vesicaria.** A perennial with stems 3-100cm. high. Leaves glabrous or pubescent, very varied in shape, ranging from dentate to deeply pinnately-lobed or pinnate. Much-branched stems. Many capitula, 15-25mm., with yellow florets, red on the outside and, occasionally, entirely red. Habitat: Barren places at a middle altitude. Flowers May-June. **16. Crepis tybakiensis.** Many simple stems up to 15cm. high. Many leaves, all at the base of the plant, dentate or pinnately-lobed, up to 7cm. Medium-sized solitary capitula, 15-25mm. Yellow florets, reddish on the outside. It is endemic to Central and East Crete, and to the nearby island of Cassos. Habitat: Fallow and cultivated fields at a low altitude. Flowers April-May.

Hieracium (Hawkweeds)

These plants are always perennials. Leaves entire or dentate, rarely pinnately-lobed. The basal leaves as a rule form a rosette. Only ray-florets on capitula, usually yellow.

1. Hieracium pallidum. A hairy plant with one stem up to 50cm. high, leafless or with only a single leaf. Rosette leaves many, ovate-lanceolate, and dentate. Capitula 20-30mm.

Asphodelus fistulosus

Habitat: Stony locations in montane and sub-montane zones. Flowers May-June. **2. Hieracium frivaldii.** 10-60cm. high stems, hairy, without a rosette at base. Big leaves, 4-20cm. entire or dentate, obovate, oblanceolate, or elliptic, with thick hair. Capitula quite large, 25-40mm. Habitat: Montane zone. Flowers May-June. **3. Hieracium leithneri.** Stems hairy, up to 20cm. high. Leaves glabrous or with sparse hairs. Basal leaves dentate or emarginate, with broad petiole. Capitula medium-sized, circa 20mm. Habitat: Alpine and sub-alpine zones. Flowers May-July. **4. Hieracium parnassi.** Rosette leaves obovate, hairy. Stem with a single leaf and 1-2 capitula. Habitat: Alpine and sub-alpine zones. Flowers May-July.

Helobiae

Alismataceae Family

Aquatic plants, usually perennials. Leaves alternate or forming rosette at base. Flowers with 3 small sepals and 3 petals, as a rule much larger.

Alisma (Water Plantains)

Leaves growing under water, floating, or rising above the surface. Stamens 6. Flowers in compound racemes.

1. Alisma plantago-aquatica. A simple stem ending in a rich, compound raceme with numerous, small flowers, white, light purple, or lilac coloured. Leaves above water, ovate, elliptic or lanceolate, with cordate or truncate base. Habitat: Swamps and marshes at a low altitude. Flowers June-November. **2. Alisma lanceolatum.** Similar to 1 but a smaller plant, and leaves cuneate at base. Rarely found in swamps and marshes. Flowers June-October.

Potamogetonaceae Family

Aquatic plants with long stems, growing under water or floating. Leaves alternating, or opposite, or in whorls of 3. Flowers with 4 sepals and 4 stamens, and without petals.

Potamogeton (Pondweeds)

Alternating leaves. Greenish flowers in simple spikes.

1. Potamogeton nodosus. Floating leaves elliptic or ovate, cuneate or completely rounded at base, up to 15cm. The submerged leaves are elliptic or lanceolate, obtuse at tip, and larger. Habitat: Low altitude marshes. Flowers in summer. **2. Potamogeton lucens.** Similar to 1 but all the leaves are submerged, and they are elliptic or obovate, and wedge-shaped at their base. Habitat: Stagnant waters at a low altitude. **3. Potamogeton trichoides.** A plant with no rhizome, and completely floating. Stems slender. Leaves hairlike up to 1,5mm. in width. Habitat: Marshes and stagnant waters at a low altitude. Flowers In summertime.

There are some more aquatic plants of Crete that belong to the **Helobiae** Order; these, however, are of no decorative interest. They are **Ruppia cirrhosa, Posidonia oceanica, Zostera marina, Zannichella palustris,** and **Cymodocea nodosa.** They all grow in the sea or in brackish waters.

Liliflorae

Liliaceae Family

These plants are usually perennials, rarely annuals, with bulbous, rhizomatous, or tuberous roots; they are seldom climbers. Flowers solitary, or in simple or compound racemes, or in umbels. Flowers as a rule 6-segmented, consisting of three petals and three sepals, almost identical, all of them coloured, and which are designated as "perianth segments". Ovary superior. Stamens 6.

Asphodelus (Asphodels)

Plants with erect stems, frequently branched and leaves always at the base.

Asphodeline lutea

Inflorescences simple or branching racemes. Flowers white or pale pink. Usually perennials but a few species are annuals.

1. Asphodelus aestivus. A perennial with tuberous roots like those of dahlias. Leaves 1-2cm. width. Stems 1-2m tall. Branched inflorescence. Flowers 20-30mm. across. Petals white or flesh-coloured, with midvein green. Habitat: Bare, waste land at a low altitude. Flowers April-May. **2. Asphodelus fistulosus.** Similar to 1 but a much smaller plant, annual, only rarely perennial. Inflorescence up to 70cm. long. Leaves up to 4mm. wide. Flowers 10-24mm. Habitat: Common to hills, waysides, and cultivated land at a low altitude. Flowers April-May.

Asphodeline

Very similar to Asphodels but with yellow flowers, very rarely white. Fleshy roots. Leaves

265

linear, flattened at base and covering stem, at least up to the middle. Inflorescences in dense, oblong racemes.

1. Asphodeline lutea. Sturdy stem up to 80cm. in height, leafy up to the inflorescence. Habitat: To be found in stony sites of the montane and sub-montane zones. Flowers April-June. **2. Asphodeline liburnica.** Similar to 1 but the stem is slender and the leaves reach only to the middle. Habitat: Montane zone. Flowers May-June.

Colchicum (Autumn Crocus)

Bulbous plants with pink or white flowers, with or without darker-coloured dots on the perianth segments. Flowers with a long throat, the bottom part of which is in the earth. Underground stem very short or non-existent at the time of flowering, growing in length during fruiting. Flowering usually autumnal, rarely in spring. Leaves appearing with the flowers or much later. 3 styles and 6 stamens.

1. Colchicum macrophyllum. Large flowers, autumn flowering segments up to 45mm. long, and extremely long tube. Pink segments have violet-coloured dots, at least towards the tip. Anthers 8-10mm. purple with greenish pollen. Styles slender, curved at tips. 3-4 spring leaves, very big, up to 35cm. long and 14cm. broad, elliptic, with strong parallel grooves. Ovoid capsule up to 5cm. Bulb large, chestnut-like, up to 6cm., with brown tunic and a long tuber. Habitat: In middle and lower montane zone. **2. Colchicum pusillum.** A dwarf plant with a 2cm. bulb, and pink or white flowers. Segments 10-20mm. long. Anthers blackish-purple or brown, pollen yellow, styles straight, and leaves 3-8, very narrow (1-2mm. broad, rarely up to 5mm.). Leaves appear with the flowers in autumn. Habitat: Rocky places at a low altitude. **3. Colchicum cretense.** Very similar to 2 but a mountain plant, with leaves appearing, as a rule, after flowering. Endemic to Crete. Habitat: Montane zone. **4. Colchicum coustorieri.** Small pink flowers with parallel lengthwise purple streaks. 2 canaliculate leaves. A Cretan endemic but found only on the islets of Gaidhouronissi and Coufonissi off the coast of South Crete. It is considered a form of the widespread **Colchicum cupanii.**

Androcymbium

Plants similar to **Colchicum.** Perianth segments 6, divided down to their base without fusing into a tube, but terminating in exceedingly long and fine claws. Leaves together with flowers. Stem short.

1. Androcymbium rechingeri. Stem 2-7cm. long. 1-8 pink flowers with small pedicels. Segments narrow, acute, up to 20mm. long and 4mm. wide. Leaves linear or lanceolate, up to 15cm. long, existing at the time of flowering and forming a rosette that encircles the flowers. Habitat: Seacliffs or sandy coasts. Flowers In wintertime. It is a member of the North-African flora. The only known place in Europe where it can be found is on the small islet of Elafonissi just off the coast of South-West Crete.

Gagea (Yellow Stars-of-Bethlehem)

Bulbous plants, Leafy, erect stems, non-branching. Flowers on the small side, usually yellow, more rarely white, solitary or in few-flowered umbels. Perianth segments 6.

1. Gagea reticulata. Simple bulbs, frequently many together in groups, rarely produce stolons which bear at their apex bulblets. Stem 10-15cm. Stem leaves linear; basal leaf solitary, pubescent, linear, in fact, almost tubular. As a rule 1 yellow flower, seldom any more, with its segments 14-20mm. long. Habitat: Middle and low altitude meadows. Flowers March-April. **2. Gagea peduncularis.** Similar to 1 but bulbs always solitary, basal leaves 2, filiform or linear, canaliculate; stem leaves lanceolate-spathulate. 1-3 flowers.

Colchicum macrophyllum (flowers)   *Colchicum macrophyllum (leaves)*

Gagea reticulata   *Gagea graeca*

Habitat: Low altitude hills and dry localities. Flowers March-April. **3. Gagea amblyopetala.** Similar to 1 and 2 but flowers 1-7. Perianth segments up to only 10mm., obtuse at tip, and stem leaves lanceolate. Basal leaves 2, linear, canaliculate. Habitat: Montane meadows. Flowers May-June. **4. Gagea bohemica - subsp. bohemic.** Stems only 2 cm. long. Basal leaves lanceolate. 1-3 yellow flowers. Perianth segments up to 17mm. long, not acute. Habitat: Dry meadows at a low altitude. Flowers March-May. **5. Gagea graeca.** This plant can be distinguished by its white flowers. Perianth segments up to 15mm. 2-4 linear basal leaves. Stem leaves linear-lanceolate. 1-7 flowers. Habitat: Middle and low altitude stony sites. Flowers March-May.

Tulipa (Tulips)

Bulbous plants, with simple bulbs covered with a brown tunic, glabrous or hairy inside.

Leaves few, alternate, assembled largely about lower half of stem, which is simple and, as a rule, bearing one flower, more rarely 2-3. Flowers erect. 6-segmented perianth.

1. Tulipa orphanidea. A bulb with hairless tunics. 3-7 glaucous-green leaves, linear-lanceolate or linear, canaliculate and hairless. Stem carries 1 flower, rarely 2. Flowers orange-coloured or reddish with acute segments, 30-50mm. long. Anthers and filaments usually black. Habitat: Montane meadows in West Crete. **2. Tulipa saxatilis.** Similar to 1 but perianth segments pink or light pink, golden-yellow at base, anthers and filaments golden-yellow, 2-4 grass-green, broader leaves (oblong-lanceolate). Flowers 40-55mm., 1-2, rarely up to 4. Habitat: Mainly in East Crete, in meadows, and on hills and rocks of the middle zone. **3. Tulipa bakeri.** Similar to 2 but leaves glaucous-green and perianth segments tricoloured pink or purple at tip, white in the middle, and golden-yellow at their base. A West Crete endemic. Habitat: Montane meadows. **4. Tulipa cretica.** Similar to 2 but with 2-3 narrower, glaucous, canaliculate leaves. Perianth segments smaller (15-30mm.), white on the inside, pink, purple or greenish on the outside. Anthers yellow. Endemic to Crete. Habitat: Scattered all over the island in stony and rocky situations.

Fritillaria (Fritillaries)

Plants similar to **Tulips** but with flowers nodding, and with no bright colours (they are usually brown, yellowish-green, or black). Alternating leaves all along the stem, or opposite, or verticiliate. Bulb small and spherical.

1. Fritillaria graeca - subsp. graeca. A simple stem up to 20cm., bearing 1-2 (-3) flowers, which are broadly campanulae, segments brownish-purple or brownish-black, usually with a light-coloured streak down the middle, and frequently with darker dots. Glaucous-green leaves, ovate or lanceolate. The lower opposite, the others alternate. Habitat: Middle and low altitude stony slopes. **2. Fritillaria messanensis - subsp. messanensis.** Similar to 1 but stem taller and more slender, leaves linear, and flowers a lighter colour with many more dots. Perianth segments usually curved outwards at the tip. Habitat: Montane glades and clearings. Flowers May-June.

Urginea (Sea Squills)

Plants with a large bulb, and a stout, tall stem. Inflorescence many flowers in a simple raceme.

1. Urginea maritima. Stem 50-150cm. tall. Flowers white, about 2cm. across. The lanceolate leaves, which appear after flowering time, are 30-100cm. long, and 30-100mm. broad. Bulb 5-15cm. Habitat: Hills and slopes in middle and low altitudes. Flowers July-September.

Chionodoxa

Bulbous plants with two leaves, a simple stem, and 1, or more, 6-segmented flowers, with segments arranged in an open rotate form.

1. Chionodoxa nana. Stem 5-10cm. high. Leaves 3-5mm. broad linear, rounded at tip. Flower one, whitish seldom violet at the tips of the segments, 9-12mm. across. A Cretan endemic. Habitat: Stony sites at a middle altitude (1700-2300m.) Flowers May-June. **2. Chionodoxa cretica.** Similar to 1 but stem 8-18cm., flowers 1-3, rarely up to 5. They are both larger and blue in colour, (14-19mm.) and leaves 4-10mm. broad. Habitat: Montane zone (1300-1700m). Flowers April-May.

Tulipa orphanidea

Tulipa saxatilis

Tulipa bakeri

Fritillaria graeca - s. sp. graeca

Scilla (Squills)

Bulbous plants with 1 or several 6-segmented flowers to each stem. Stems leafless. Basal leaves appearing with or after the flowers.

1. Scilla autumnalis. A slender stem, 5-20cm. high. Small lilac-coloured flowers in clusters of 6-20, forming an oblong raceme. 5-10 linear leaves appearing after the flowers are over. Habitat: Dry pastures and uncultivated land at a low altitude. Flowers October-November.

Lilium (Lilies)

Plants with scaly bulbs. Numerous leaves, all along the length of stem. Large flowers, solitary or in racemes. Perianth segments more or less recurved at tip.

1. Lilium candidum. Basal leaves big, up to 30cm., lanceolate with 3-5 parallel veins. Stem leaves gradually tapering upwards. Flowers a brilliant white; segments recurved only slightly at tip. Anthers yellow. It was known to grow subspontaneously in one locality only -- on the Chania Promontory, but whence it has, in all probability, disappeared in recent times. Habitat: Common as a cultivated species all over Crete.

Ornithogalum (Star-of-Bethlehem)

Plants with a simple bulb, or one surrounded by bulblets, or scales. Flowers white, cream, or whitish-green, with 6-segmented perianth, usually greenish on outer surface. Stamens either simple or with a 3-toothed filament.

Group A. Inflorescence cylindrically oblong. Leaves without white midvein. Flowers with pedicels spreading during flowering.

1. Ornithogalum creticum. Plant with a 20-60cm. stem. Flowers yellowish-green, and leaves appearing after flowering. Endemic to Crete. Habitat: Arid, rocky localities. Flowers July-September. **2. Ornithogalum narbonense.** Similar to 1 but flowers white, flowering in spring or in summer, leaves appearing together with flowers. Habitat: Middle and low altitude meadows, roadsides, uncultivated fields.

Group B. Inflorescence more or less a corymb, with flower pedicels ascending at time of flowering. Leaves with a white midvein.

1. Ornithogalum sibthorpii. Plant 5-15cm. high, with 3-11 glaucous leaves, 1,5-4,5mm. wide, and longer than inflorescence. Habitat: Barren hills at a low altitude. Flowers February-March. **2. Ornithogalum divergens.** Similar to 1 but leaves 5-8, and not glaucous. Habitat: Dry meadows at middle and low altitude. Flowers March-April. **3. Ornithogalum commosum.** Similar to 1 and 2 but leaves 4-15, and reaching a length of 20(-40)cm. Habitat: Low altitude fields. Flowers March-April.

Bellevalia

Bulbous perennials with leaves forming rosette at base and stem leafless. Inflorescence a rather lax raceme. Flowers white or blue-violet that, as they mature, turn brown, greenish, or yellowish. In shape they are tubular or campanulate, and 6-segmented.

1. Bellevalia brevipedicellata. Stem 6-17,5cm. in height. Leaves 2-3, linear-lanceolate. Racemes cylindrical with 9-25 flowers, which are tubular, 7mm., with perianth segments white and greenish-pink at edge. Endemic to Crete. Habitat: Low altitude meadows. Flowers March-May.

The species **Bellevalia trifoliata** with its flowers initially violet-coloured then brown when mature, and **Bellevalia dubia** with its perianth segments violet or greenish and whitish at the edges, have also been mentioned as occurring in Crete, however, their existence there has not been authenticated in later years.

Muscari (Grape Hyacinthus)

These are plants similar to **Bellevallias** but, as a rule, the flowers are smaller, and more or less spherical or cylindrical, and with their perianth segments fused, except for their apices. The flowers are generally in crowded inflorescences, deep violet, blue, brown or yellow. All leaves are basal.

Group A. Racemes with sterile flowers at the top and of a different colour and size to the rest, and as a rule with longer pedicels.

1. Muscari macrocarpum. Leaves linear-lanceolate, 5-15mm. broad, and 10-20cm. long.

Urginea maritima

Lilium candidum

Ornithogalum narbonense

Ornithogalum divergens

Stem shorter than leaves, up to 15cm. Raceme up to 6cm., early on dense but becoming lax as it matures. Flowers 8-12mm., purple when buds, yellow when they open. At the apex of the raceme there are small, purple, sterile flowers. Habitat: Uncultivated land and bare situations at a low altitude. Flowers April-May. **2. Muscari cycladicum.** Similar to 1 but leaves 8-25mm. broad, canaliculate, flowers two-coloured, brown at top and yellow at the base. Sterile flowers violet-coloured. Habitat: Meadows and arable land at a low altitude. Flowers March-April. **3. Muscari speitzenhoferi.** Similar to 1 and 2 but leaves narrower, 8-12mm., and flowers brownish-green at their base and golden-yellow at their top. Sterile flowers at the tip of the raceme violet, pedicels short. It was once considered a Cretan endemic, it seems, however, that it occurs in Algeria as well. Habitat: Montane and sub-alpine zones. Flowers May-June. **4. Muscari weicoii.** Similar to the foregoing but flowers two coloured, at the bottom brownish-yellow or greenish, and towards the top dark

271

brown. Sterile flowers violet or purple. Habitat: Stony locations at a low altitude. Flowers March-April. **5. Muscari commosum.** Like the previous ones but leaves linear, shorter than the stem which is 30-50 (-80)cm. high; Large raceme, cylindrical, flowers a light brown, and sterile terminal flowers lilac with long pedicels. Habitat: Uncultivated arable land at a low altitude. Flowers April-May.

Group B. Flowers all similar or a few terminal ones sterile, in which case they are a different colour and smaller in size.

1. Muscari neglectum. Leaves linear or linear-lanceolate, 6-40cm. X 1,5-8mm., light green, slightly reddish towards base. Stem 4-30cm., equal in length with the leaves. Crowded raceme with dark blue or blue-black flowers. Terminal sterile flowers (about 20) are smaller and lighter-hued than the others. Habitat: In cultivated and fallow fields. Flowers April-May. **2. Muscari commutatum.** Similar to 1 but leaves broader, up to 15mm.; flowers a very dark violet, almost black. Sterile flowers absent, if any only 4 smaller and lighter in colour than the remainder. Habitat: Hills, uncultivated land, at a low altitude. Flowers April-May. **3. Muscari parviflorum.** Similar to 1 and 2 but the leaves are narrower, 1-3,5mm. Raceme very lax. Flowers light blue. Sterile flowers usually absent. Habitat: Low altitude hills.

Allium (Onion or Garlics)

Bulbous perennial plants, usually smelling strongly of garlic or onion. 6-segmented small flowers in terminal umbellate inflorescences, enclosed in a membraneous spathe when buds. Inflorescences with or without bulbils at their base. Leaves filiform, strap-shaped tubular or ovate, parallel-veined.

Group A. Leaves like narrow straps. Flowers more or less wide open, starlike, or broadly campanulate.

1. Allium roseum. 2-4 strap-shaped, leaves 12-35cm. long and 1-14mm. broad. Stem 10-65cm. high, cylindrical. Umbels up to 7cm. across, with 5-30 flowers, without bulbils. Flowers pink, 7-12mm. long. Habitat: Cultivated or uncultivated land at a low altitude. Flowers March-May. **2. Allium neapolitanum.** Very similar to 1 but flowers white, stem with triangular section, slightly winged, leaves as a rule 2. Flowers March-May. **3. Allium longanum.** Similar to 1 but leaves up to 8mm. wide, more or less ciliate, umbel smaller, flowers white tinged with pink, inner perianth segments smaller and rounded. Habitat: North-East Crete and the surrounding islets. Flowers March-May. **4. Allium subhirsutum.** Similar to 2 but smaller, with a slender cylindrical stem up to 30cm. 2-3 leaves, 2-10mm. wide, ciliate. Small flowers, white with long pedicels up to 40mm. Habitat: Low and middle altitude rocky places. Flowers March-May. **5. Allium trifoliatum.** Similar to 1 but flowers smaller, up to 10mm., white, with a pink midvein. Leaves sparsely haired. Umbel up to 4cm.

Group B. Leaves like springs.

1. Allium circinatum - subsp. circinatum. A dwarf plant with a hairy stem up to 10cm., rarely higher, and threadlike leaves coiled like springs. Few-flowered inflorescence, flowers white with a pink midvein. A rare endemic. Habitat: Arid situations at a low altitude. Flowers March-April.

Group C. Leaves usually threadlike with broad sheaths at their base. Flowers stellate or broadly campanulate.

1. Allium hirtovaginatum. Stem up to 30cm. 3-5 leaves, up to 8cm. long, and 0,5mm. wide. Umbel with 3-15 flowers, whitish or pink, up to 9mm. long. Flower pedicels up to 40mm. Rare in East Crete. **2. Allium callimischon - subsp. haemostictum.** Similar to 1 but a little

Muscari commosum

Muscari neglectum

Muscari commutatum

Allium roseum

taller, up to 38cm. Leaves threadlike up to 30cm. Umbel with 8-25 flowers. Pedicels up to 25mm. Flowers 5-7mm. Perianth segments white with a brown or pink midvein, and purple dots on the outer surface. Endemic to Crete.

Group D. Flowers closed, cylindrical, or narrowly campanulate. Canaliculate or filiform leaves.

1. Allium paniculatum - subsp. paniculatum. 3-5 leaves up to 25cm. long and 2mm. wide. Umbel up to 7cm. with many, tightly-packed flowers without any bulbils. Flowers up to 7mm., pinkish-violet or almost white. Habitat: Low altitude. Flowers April-May. **2. Allium staticiforme.** Similar to 1 but 2-4 leaves up to 13cm. long, and 0,5-2mm. broad. Flowers up to 35mm., pink with red midvein, or white with green or violet midvein. Endemic to Greece. Habitat: Low altitude. Flowers April-May. **3. Allium tardans.** Similar to 1 and 2 but leaves filiform, 0,5mm. wide, flowers bell-shaped, erect, up to 6,5mm., light pink with a green midvein. Endemic to Crete. Habitat: Rocky sites at an altitude of 400-800m. Flowers March-April. **4. Allium ampeloprasum.** Stout stems, 45-180cm. 4-10 leaves canaliculate, 5-40mm. broad. Umbel up to 9cm., spherical, crowded with a great many flowers and bulbils. Flowers white, pink, or dark red. It is considered the wild ancestor of the leek. Habitat: Commonly found in tilled fields. Flowers May-June.

Group E. Umbels with bulbils. Leaves flat strap-shaped or canaliculate.

1. Allium bourgaei - subsp. creticum. Stem up to 115cm. 4-11 leaves up to 25mm. wide. Umbels 3-6cm. across, almost spherical or semispherical. Flowers small, 4-5mm., elliptic, either pink or red with yellow anthers. Umbel bulbils yellowish-brown. Endemic to Crete. Habitat: Low altitude slopes and rocky places. Flowers April-May. **2. Allium commutatum.** Similar to one but stems sturdier and up to 180cm. tall. Leaves up to 50mm. broad, canaliculate, without a keel, umbels with pale pink or light purple flowers. Habitat: Bare situations near sea. Flowers May-June.

Group F. Leaves narrowly tubular, canaliculate or filiform.

1. Allium amethystinum. 3-7 leaves up to 50cm. long and 8mm. wide, tubular or canaliculate. Stem 20-120cm., frequently reddish at its upper section. Umbel 2,5-6,5cm., rather spherical in shape, and many flowered. Flowers small 3-4,5mm., cylindrical, purple, with stamens projecting. Habitat: Fields and stony sites at a low altitude. Flowers May-June. **2. Allium dilatatum.** Similar to 1 but leaves filiform-tubular, up to 2mm. wide. Hemispherical umbels up to 4cm., with 15-25 flowers. Flowers white with midvein green. A Cretan endemic. Habitat: Rocky localities in South-West Crete. Flowers May-June. **3. Allium rubrovitatum.** Similar to 1 but much smaller. 3-4 filiform-tubular leaves, 2-5mm. broad. Stems shorter, 2,5-20cm., striated. Umbel up to 2cm., hemispherical or broadly ovoid, dense, with 5-30 flowers which are campanulate, reddish with white edges. Endemic to Crete and Carpathos. Habitat: Dry, rocky locations. Flowers April-May. **4. Allium chamaespathum.** Similar to 1 but shorter, up to 30cm., seldom up to 60cm., with leaves up to 4mm. wide, tubular-canaliculate. Umbel up to 4.5cm., its flowers white or light green. Habitat: Rocky sites. Flowers in autumn.

Group G. Leaves like broad straps.

1. Allium nigrum. 3-6 leaves up to 50cm. long, and 8cm. wide. Stem 60-90cm. high. Umbels 5-10cm., hemispherical, and many-flowered. Flowers either white or lilac with a green midvein. Habitat: Cultivated land at a low altitude. Flowers May-June.

Asparagus (Asparagus)

Insignificant plants from a decorative point of view, better known for their edible tender stems. Rhizomatous perennials, leafless or with tiny leaves that look like scales and have a spine at the base. From the axil of each such leaf a bunch of linear, and usually, acute-spiny branchlets (cladodes) arise. Insignificant 6-segmented flowers. Fruit a red or black berry.

1. Asparagus acutifolius. Dense stems, whitish or greyish in colour, up to 2m. Cladodes green, up to 8mm. long, rarely reaches 10mm. Fruit black. Habitat: Dry, stony places. **2. Asparagaus aphyllus.** A very spiny, rough plant. It is of a uniform dark-green colour, with hard cladodes as well as pointed, 10-20mm. long. Fruit a black berry. Habitat: Arid, barren places. **2. Asparagus stipularis.** This is a smaller plant, up to 60cm. high, dense, with cladodes 15-30mm., solitary or in bundles of 2-3. Fruit a black berry. Habitat: Barren spots at a low altitude.

Allium neapolitanum

Allium longanum

Allium subhirsutum

Allium commutatum

Ruscus (Butcher's Brooms)

Perennial rhizomatous herbs or shrubs with main stems tough. The main stems produce secondary ones which have the shape of a leaf and are called 'cladodes'. On the cladodes there ae small membraneous leaves from whose axils the flowers and fruit arise. 6-segmented, tiny flowers. Fruit a red berry.

1. Ruscus aculeatus. Stems 10-100cm., crowded. 1-4 rigid, pointed, cladodes, spiny at tip. Habitat: Found in barren, rocky, and stony localities, and in woods and forests of montane and sub-montane zones. Flowers in springtime. Fruotuation in summer or autumn.

Smilax

Perennial spiny, climbing plants with alternating leaves, arrow-shaped. Small flowers in umbels. Fruit berries.

1. Smilax aspera: Long stems up to 15m. Leaves, up to 10cm., but as a rule smaller, leathery, spiny. 5-30 small pink flowers to each umbel. Berries 1cm., dark red in colour.

Amaryllidaceae Family

Plants resembling the **Liliaceae** but flowers with inferior ovary always enclosed in a membraneous spathe before the flowering. In many of the species the stamens are surrounded by the corona. All the leaves are always to be found at the base.

Narcissus (Daffodils)

Flowers with a corona of variable shape. The flowers may be solitary or clustered in umbels. Leaves strap-like or cylindrical.

1. Narcissus tazetta - subsp. italicus: Stem 20-45cm. high, with 3-15 sweet-smelling flowers 2,5-3,5cm. across. Perianth segments cream-coloured, and cylindrical corona yellow, 3-6mm. high. Leaves 5-20mm. broad. Habitat: Damp localities and gardens at a low altitude. Flowers February-March. **2. Narcissus serotinus:** Very slender stem with a single flower, on rare occasions 2 flowers. Perianth segments white. Corona tiny, orange-coloured. 1-2 cylindrical, 1mm. wide leaves on flowering bulbs, or they may be absent, appearing later after flowering is over. Habitat: Bare situations and heaths at a low altitude. Flowers August-October.

Pancratium (Sea Daffodils)

Plants with large scented flowers. Corona fused with the filaments of the stamens, at least towards their base.

1. Pancratium maritimum: Plants with large bulb, and glaucous-coloured, strap-shaped leaves, 1,5-3cm. broad, which appear when flowering is over. Stout flattened stems. Flowers in an umbel at the apex of the stem; large, 10-15cm., with a very long funnel-shaped tube, 60-80mm. long; perianth segments narrow almost linear 30-50mm. Corona 20-45mm. with the stamens at its margin. Habitat: Sandy beaches. Flowers August-September.

The occurrence of **Sternbergia lutea - subsp. sicula** that used to be mentioned as existing in West Crete, has not been confirmed in recent years.

Dioscoreaceae Family

Dioeceous perennials with undergroud tubers and 6-segmented small flowers arising in clusters or spikes from the axils. Leaves more or less cordate.

Tamus (Black Bryony)

Climbing stem. Alternating leaves. Flowers in axillary racemes. Male flowers campanulate; female ones with 6 very small segments.

1. Tamus communis: Leaves 8-15cm., broadly ovate, and acute. Fruit a red berry 1cm. across. The Cretan plants as a rule have trilobate leaves and are frequently considered as a separate species under the name of **Tamus cretica.**

Allium nigrum

Smilax aspera

Narcissus tazetta - s. sp. italicus

Narcissus serotinus

Iridaceae Family

Perennial plants with bulbs or rhizomes. Leaves linear, graminaceous or gladiate. 6-segmented flowers actinimorphic or zygomorphic with inferior ovary and 3 stamens. Trilobate style (with 3 stigmas). Flowers enclosed at base by one or more spathes.

Crocus (Crocuses)

Bulbous plants; corms small, spherical or ovoid, enclosed in tunics of varied texture and shape. Stem very short, below ground. Flowers with long tube whose lowest part is underground. Leaves narrow, linear usually with white midvein. Leaves appear either simultaneously with the flowers or later on. Flowering is in autumn, winter or spring.

277

1. Crocus sieberi - subsp. sieberi. Flowers in spring. Flowers entirely white, or tinged with lilac at the tips of the segments; it is rare for them to be uniformly lilac-coloured. 4-8 leaves, 1,5-6mm. wide; they appear simultaneously with the flowers. Throat yellow or orange. Anthers yellow. Style yellow or orange, divided into 3 short cuneate lobes. A Cretan endemic. Habitat: The montane, sub-alpine and alpine zones of all the high mountains of Crete. **2. Crocus laevigatus.** Similar to 1 but flowers in winter, November-January. Flowers as a rule white, violet-coloured ones are rarer, they usually have 1-3 vertical, dark veins on outer segments. Anthers white. Style divided into many short, linear lobes. 3-4 narrower (1-2,5mm.) leaves. Endemic to Greece. Habitat: Middle montane zone. **3. Crocus boryi:** Similar to 2 but flowers in October-November always white with no dark outside veins. 3-7 leaves slightly wider. Style orange or reddish. A Greek endemic. Habitat: South-East Crete. Very recently met with in West Crete as well. Flowers in autumn (October-November). **4. Crocus tournefortii:** Similar to 2 but flowers bluish-violet, seldom white. Style orange or yellowish, with longer and denser linear lobes. Leaves 5-10, narrow. Endemic to Greece. Habitat: North-East Crete. Flowers Autumn. **5. Crocus cartwrightianus:** Similar to previous species but flowers of various colours ranging from white to dark mauve, and dark veined. Anthers yellow and style reddish, divided into three very long lobes which are broader at tip, and project from the flower, usually hanging over. Narrow leaves, 7-12 in number. Endemic to Greece. Habitat: On low hills around Chania. Flowers Autumn. **6. Crocus oreocreticus:** Similar to 5 but with 7-15 leaves; flowers violet or purple with darker veins; outer surface of petals with a silvery or yellowish tint, throat yellow and style lobes shorter. Endemic to Central and East Crete. Habitat: Montane zone. Flowers Autumn.

Romulea

Plants resembling Crocuses but leaves appearing always before the flowering. Perianth segments slightly fused at base or forming a very short tube. Stem prominent, quite long but its greater part is underground.

1. Romulea bulbocodium: Two basal leaves, up to 2mm. in breadth. Stem leaves up to 5mm. wide. Flowers 2-3,5cm. (rarely any bigger) from 1 to 6 to each stem, with a small tube at base, and colours varying from white to yellowish or violet. Throat yellow. The outer perianth segments with a greenish hue, otherwise with 1-5 dark lines. Stigmas longer than anthers. Habitat: Bare and sandy places at a low altitude. Flowers February-March. **2. Romulea ramiflora - subsp. ramiflora:** Similar to 1 but flowers smaller (1-1,8cm.), violet-blue, yellowy-green outside, and with a white or yellow throat. Stigmas smaller than anthers. Habitat: Low or middle altitude hills. Flowers March-April. **3. Romulea columnae - subsp. columnae.** Similar to 1 and 2 but flowers like those of 2, lilac-coloured, with a yellow throat and dark veins. Stigmas as long as anthers. Habitat: At a low altitude, as a rule close to coast. Flowers February-March. **4. Romulea columnae - subsp. rollii.** Like 3 but flowers darker-coloured, and throat yellowish. Habitat: Sandy beaches. Flowers February-March.

That **Romulea linaresii - subsp. graeca,** with uniform violet flowers occurs in Crete is stated with some doubts.

Iris (Irises)

Bulbous or rhizomatous plants. Flowers actinomorphic with two kinds of perianth segments, the 3 segments spreading or nodding, and the other 3 erect and frequently smaller in size. The style is divided into 3 large petal-shaped stigmas which cover the anthers.

Pancratium maritimum

Crocus sieberi - s. sp. sieberi

Crocus laevigatus

Crocus boryi

Group A. Leaves gladiate, distichous. Thick rhizome. Outer perianth segments with beard at base. Large plants with branched stems.

1. Iris albicans: Stems up to 80cm., branching and with many flowers. Big snow-white flowers about 10cm. high. Leaves up to 45mm. broad and 50cm. long. This is a plant of unknown origin naturalised in Crete. It probably comes from South Arabia. Habitat: On rocky and stony slopes, often cultivated or semi-subspontaneous. Flowers March-April. **2. Iris germanica:** Very similar to 1 but stems reach 90cm. in height, leaves up to 35mm. in breadth and 70cm. in length; Flowers a bluish-violet. Another plant of unknown origin (probably a native of the East Mediterranean). Habitat: Rocky sites and slopes of middle and low altitude. Flowers March-May. **3. Iris pseudacorus:** Stems 60-120cm. Leaves up to 90cm. long and 30mm. wide. Big yellow flowers. Habitat: Low altitude marshes. Flowers February-April.

Group B. Linear graminaceous leaves. Thin rhizome. Outer perianth segments without beard. Stem simple.

1. Iris inguicularis: Flowers violet-blue, solitary, with a very long tube and a short, almost absent stem. The three outer perianth segments with an orange-coloured spot surrounded by a white band. All the leaves at the base. The Cretan plants used to be considered a separate species, or at least a local variety whose chief characteristics were its smaller flowers. **(Iris cretica or Iris cretensis).** Habitat: Rocky and stony places of the montane and sub-montane zones. Flowers January-April.

Group C. Leaves canaliculate. Bulbous plants. Bulb with fleshy roots. Outer perianth segments without beard, stem simple and hollow.

1. Iris planifolia. Numerous leaves, undulate and rolled inwards, 10-30mm. broad. Flowers single, rarely 2-3, together, blue or violet, very occasionally white, with a very long tube 10-20cm. Perianth segments 50-80mm. long, the outer ones, and 20-25mm. the inner. Stem very short, underground. Habitat: At a low altitude. Flowers in winter.

Iris lutescens, with stem 3-3,5cm. long, leaves gladiate and distichous, up to 30cm. and flowers violet or yellowish, bearded. It is mentioned as occurring in Crete with some reservations.

Gynandriris (Barberry Nuts)

Plants similar to Irises but the stamens are attached to the stigma styles. Bulbous plants.

1. Gynandriris sisyrinchium: Blue or blue-violet flowers 4cm. across. Stems 10-30cm. 1-2 canaliculate leaves, 3-8mm. wide. Habitat: Bare hills and slopes at a low altitude. Flowers March-April. **2. Gynandriris monophylla:** Plants similar to 1 but much smaller. Only 1 leaf. Flowers about 2cm. Habitat: Hills and slopes at a low altitude. Flowers February-March.

Gladiolus (Gladioli)

Plants with round, bulb-like rhizome. Gladiate, distichous leaves. Zygomorphic flowers in a one-sided spike.

1. Gladiolus italicus: Stem 50-100cm. high. 3-5 leaves. 6-16 flowers circa 5cm. long, a purplish-pink. Habitat: Low altitude uncultivated and cultivated fields. Flowers April-May.

The **Juncaceae** and **Gramineae** Orders and their species, which are part of the Cretan flora, are not described in this book.

Principes

Palmae Family

Trees or large shrubs, usually with a simple trunk. Leaves very large. Inflorescence a simple or branched spadix. Perianth as a rule 6-segmented. Fruit a berry or drupe.

Phoenix (Palms)

Dioecious trees. Leaves pinnate with numerous linear-lanceolate, acute leaflets, those

Crocus cartwrightianus

Romulea bulbocodium

Iris albicans

Iris germanica

nearest the base smaller and spiny. Flowers yellow. Fruit drupes with flesh edible or not.

1. Phoenix theophrastii: Tree with trunk as a rule not surpassing 10m in height, producing other lateral trunks as well from the same root. Leaves glaucous-green, with the middle leaflets 30-40cm., stiff, while, those that are nearer the base are spiny and yellowish. Fruit about 1,5cm., a brownish-yellow, and when ripe blackish, fibrous and inedible. It is a rare tree, endemic to Crete. Habitat: Sandy damp valleys near the sea.

Spathiflorae

Araceae Family

Plants with perennial rhizomes and all the leaves at the base. Flowers tiny, clustered in an oblong spadix, enclosed in a spathe which is of varying colours. The spadix flowers are of two kinds: the lower ones female and the upper male.

Arum (Lords-and-Ladies or Cuckoo-pints)

Tuberous plants. Large arrow-shaped leaves, with long petiole. Spadix and spathe variously coloured. The lower spadix flowers are female developing into red berries at maturation.

1. Arum concinatum: The leaves which appear at the end of autumn or beginning of winter are large with a 15-35cm. blade. Spathe yellowy-green and spadix yellow. The fruiting spadix dense, 10-15cm. long. Habitat: Fields and olive-groves at a low altitude. Flowers April-May. **2. Arum creticum:** Leaves dark green, appearing in autumn with a 8-15cm. blade. Spathe 10-20cm., yellow, fused up to middle and opening abruptly at upper end. The yellow spadix projects greatly from the spathe. Endemic to Crete, Cassos and Carpathos. Habitat: Montane zone. Flowers in spring. **3. Arum idaeum:** Similar to 2 but spathe 5-8cm. a milky colour, more fused and spadix purple or blackish-purple, not protruding from spathe. A Cretan endemic. Habitat: Montane zone. Flowers Spring. **4. Arum alpinum:** Spathe greenish, oblong, slightly purple at lips, and deep inside. Spadix blackish-purple. Habitat: Montane zone. Flowers Spring.

Arisarum (Friar's Cowls)

Small plants with the spathe fused, curved forwards at its tip. Slender spadix.

1. Arisarum vulgare - subsp. vulgare: Leaves 6-12cm., ovate or almost sagittal. Spathe 3-5cm., light green with parallel brownish-purple stripes. Habitat: A common plant in fields and gardens at a low altitude. Flowers March-May.

Biarum

Small plants with oblong leaves. Spathe with fused lips at its lowest part thus forming a tube.

1. Biarum tenuifolium: Spathe brownish-black, whitish at base, very oblong, up to 20(-30)cm. long. Spadix brownish-black, very slender, somewhat longer than the spathe. Leaves linear or lanceolate, undulate with short petiole, appearing immediately after flowering is over. Habitat: Middle and low altitude pastures. Flowers October-November. **2. Biarum davisii:** Spathe whitish or greeny-white, often with dots of brownish-purple hue, short and thick, swollen with curved tip, and up to 5cm. long. Leaves ovate-lanceolate, appearing long after flowering is over. Endemic to Crete. Habitat: Low altitude pastures and stony sites. Flowers November.

Zantedeschia

Perennial plants similar to **Arum** in appearance.

Iris pseudacorus

Iris inguicularis

Gynandriris sisyrinchium

Gynandriris monophylla

1. Zantedeschia aethiopica: Sagittal, long-petioled leaves. Large white spathe. Yellow spadix. Habitat: Banks of streams, in ditches, along roads, etc. Flowers April-May. A native of East Africa widely cultivated in Crete. The writer has noted that in certain localities on the island it has become subspontaneous as well.

Dracunculus (Dragon Arums)

Plant similar to **Arum** but leaves pedate.

1. Dracungulus vulgaris: Tall plant up to 100cm. Leaves 15-20 X 25-35cm. Spathe large up

283

to 40(-55)cm., brownish-purple inside, greenish on the exterior. Spadix brownish-purple. The flowers have a nauseating smell. Habitat: Common in fields, ditches, and roadsides, at a low altitude. Flowers In springtime.

The **Lemnaceae** Family, together with some insignificant aquatic plants are not described here. Similarly the Cretan species of the **Pandanales**, which are in the main aquatic plants and insignificant from a decorative point of view, have also been omitted.

Microspermae

Orchidaceae Family

Perennial plants with tubers or fleshy roots at their base. Leaves entire. Inflorescence a spike or a raceme. Flowers zygomorphic, 6-segmented, composed of 3 identical coloured sepals, and 3 dissimilar petals, the bottom one which is called a labellum greatly differing from the other two, of strange shapes and colours, also usually larger.

Ophrys (Orchids)

Perennials with two small spherical or ovoid tubers. 4 or more leaves, mainly basal. Flowers with a large labellum, variously coloured, colours and shapes reminiscent of different insects. Few-flowered, lax inflorescence.

Group A. Sepals pink or purple.

1. Ophrys tenthredinifera. 6-9 leaves. Flowers on the whole large, up to 3cm. Pink or purple broad sepals. Petals small, pink. Labellum big, quadrangular, orange-coloured along edges, brown in the centre, with a small, upcurved middle lobe. Habitat: Grasslands and hills at a low altitude. Flowers March-April. **2. Ophrys fuciflora - subsp. candica.** Similar to that of 1. Flowers March-April. **3. Ophrys scolopax - subsp. heidreichii.** Similar to 1 but labellum narrower and longer (14-17mm.), with brownish upturned tip and white and purple patterns on it, and two short, lateral, pointed lobes arising from its base. Habitat: Hills and meadows at a low altitude. Flowers March-April. **4. Ophrys argolica.** Resembling 1, flowers, however, are smaller, sepals narrower, and labellum rather orbicular, brown, with two light-coloured spots in the centre. Endemic to Southern Greece right down to Crete and Carpathos. Habitat: Low altitude grasslands and hills. Flowers March-April. **5. Ophrys ferrum-equinum - subsp. ferrum- equinum.** Similar to 1 but sepals narrower, petals bigger, and labellum brownish-purple, with a horse-shoe-shaped pattern, in a light colour, in the centre. Habitat: Meadows and stony sites at a middle altitude. Flowers April-May. **6. Ophrys spruneri - subsp. spruneri.** Like 1 but petals a light purple, or light brown, labellum brownish-black with two light-coloured, parallel, lengthwise stripes in the centre. Habitat: Hills and grasslands at middle and low altitudes. Flowers March-May. **7. Ophrys apifera.** Small flowers, labellum brownish with white patterns, and two hairy lateral lobes. Sepals pink, petals green. Habitat: Found at a low altitude. Flowers March-April.

Group B. Greenish sepals.

1. Ophrys fusca - subsp. omegafera. Leaves 3-5. Flowers few with broad, greenish sepals, narrow, greenish petals, and labellum rather wedge-shaped, brownish-black, with two small lateral lobes,, and a light-coloured pattern of a calligraphic small W in the centre.

Gladiolis italicus

Phoenix theophrastii

Arum ideum

Biarum tenuifolium

Habitat: Middle and low altitude meadows, hills, and hillsides. Flowers March-May. **2. Ophrys fusca - subsp. iricolor.** Similar to 1 but petals a brownish-green, and labellum with a bluish patch. Habitat: Low and middle altitude meadows and hillsides. Flowers March-April. **3. Ophrys lutea - subsp. lutea.** Similar to 1 but with 4-8 leaves, and a smaller labellum, brownish in the centre and yellow along edge. Habitat: Grasslands and hills at middle and low altitudes. Flowers March-May. **4. Ophrys lutea - subsp. murbeckii.** Similar to 3 but a smaller plant. Flowers smaller, labellum 9-12mm., dark brown except for the margins that are yellowish. Habitat: Meadows, slopes, and hills at medium and low altitudes. Flowers March-May. **5. Ophrys sphegodes - subsp. litigiosa.** Like 1 but flowers

285

small, circa 12mm. in breadth, and labellum small, brownish, yellowish at lower part, and with two light-coloured bands in the centre. Habitat: Low altitude hills and meadows. Flowers March-April. **6. Ophrys sphegodes - subsp. mammosa.** Similar to 5 but labellum broad, a browny-purple, with two parallel pale-coloured stripes, or an H-shaped pattern in the centre, and two rounded bosses at the sides. Habitat: Low altitude hills and meadows. Flowers February-April. **7. Ophrys sphegodes - subsp. parnassica.** Similar to 6 but lips of labellum yellowish. Flowers February-April. **8. Ophrys bombyliflora.** Flowers small (about 1,5cm.). Sepals green and broad. Petals small and green. Labellum more or less rotund, brown, with two lateral projections like mammae. Habitat: Meadows and hills at a low altitude. Flowers March-April. **9. Ophrys cretica - subsp. cretica.** Sepals greenish-violet or greenish. Petals light brown or brownish-green. Lip oblong, brownish-black, with two narrow, lateral lobes, and a lighter-coloured H-shaped pattern. Endemic to Crete. Habitat: Grasslands, heaths, and hills at a low altitude. Flowers March-April.

Orchis (Orchids)

Plants similar to **Ophrys** but lower petal (labellum) spurred at its base, and usually of the same colour. Perianth segments similar, except for the labellum which is larger and differs in shape.

Group A. Yellow flowers

1. Orchis provincialis - subsp. provincialis. Leaves with blackish spots. Dense inflorescence with 5-20 bright yellow flowers. Labellum 3-lobed. Spur upward-pointing. Habitat: Middle altitude meadows, glades, and slopes. Flowers April-June. **2. Orchis provincialis - subsp. pauciflora.** Similar to 1 but leaves unspotted and flowers larger in size but fewer in number. Labellum longer with reddish dots. Habitat: Grasslands, clearings, and heaths at a middle altitude. Flowers April-June.

Group B. Flowers more or less pink, purple, or pinkish-violet. Labellum entire or divided into three short, broad lobes.

1. Orchis quadripunctata. Leaves with dark spots. Flowers pink or purple. Labellum three-lobed with 2 or 4 dark spots at its base. Spur long and slender pointing downwards. Habitat: Montane zone. Flowers April-May. **2. Orchis anatolica.** Resembles 1 but flowers are larger, purple, pink, pale pink, and on rare occasions white. Labellum with many spots, and spur pointing upwards. Leaves with dark spots, though sometimes they are unspotted. Habitat: Scrub and uncultivated ground at a low altitude. Flowers March-April. **3. Orchis boryi.** Similar to 1 but leaves narrow and without any spots. Flowers few, small, pink, purple, or purplish-violet, with slender spur. Labellum with 2 or 4 dark spots. Habitat: Low altitude heaths and hills. Flowers March-April. **4. Orchis laxiflora - subsp. elegans.** Leaves unspotted. Flowers uniformly purple or purplish-violet. Medium-sized spur. Labellum almost entire. Habitat: Damp situations and stream-banks of montane zone. Flowers May-June. **5. Orchis patens.** Leaves without any spots. Flowers pink or purple, except for the lateral sepals which have a greenish interior. The three-lobed labellum has dark spots. Habitat: Montane grasslands and glades. Flowers April-May. **6. Orchis papilionacea.** Leaves with no dark spots. Flowers pink or purple with an entire labellum, lighter-coloured than the other segments and, as a rule, with dark veins. Habitat: Low altitude scrub and uncultivated land. Flowers February-April. **7. Orchis tridentata - subsp. commutata.** Leaves unsullied by dark spots. Flowers only a few, pink-coloured. The three-lobed labellum has dark spots all over. The remaining perianth segments very acute, with parallel purple veins. Habitat: Montane glades. Flowers April-May. **8. Orchis lactea.** Very similar to 7 but with smaller, almost white green-veined flowers. Habitat: Clearings at a low altitude.

Dracungulus vulgaris

Ophrys scolopax - s. sp. heldreichii

Ophrys ferum equinum -
s. sp. ferum equinum

Ophrys lutea - s. sp. murbeckii

Group C. Flowers either pink or violet in colour. Labellum with four-lobes. The lobes of labellum are long and narrow giving it a distinct human shape with arms and legs.

1. Orchis italica. Flowers in a dense spike, big, pink with purple spots on the labellum. Thick stem. Leaves unspotted. Habitat: Grasslands and scrub of middle and lower zones. Flowers March-April. **2. Orchis simia.** A slenderer plant with smaller flowers. Labellum lobes violet-coloured. Leaves are without spots. Habitat: Montane zone. Flowers April-May.

287

Group D. Flowers greenish, reddish, or brownish-black.

1. Orchis coriophora - subsp. fragrans. A small plant with unspotted leaves. Flowers small, greenish or a greenish-red. The labellum with red spots or rarely red all over. Habitat: Heaths and hills at a low altitude. Flowers April-May. **2. Orchis sancta.** Like 1 but flowers always red or reddish, and labellum dentate. Habitat: Heaths and bare localities at a low altitude. Flowers March-April. **3. Orchis saccata.** Flowers brown, purplish-brown, or brownish-black. Spur white and puffed like a small sack. Leaves unspotted. Brown labellum which is white towards its base. Habitat: Bare stretches and scrub at a low altitude. Flowers February-April.

Dactylorhiza

Plants very similar to **Orchids** but differing in tubers which have fleshy projections like fingers.

1. Dactylorhiza sulfurea - subsp. pseudosambucina. (Old name **D. romana**) About 10 unspotted leaves gathered at base. Flowers yellow or pink and labellum broad, and shallowly divided into three lobes. Habitat: Middle and lower montane zone.

Anacamplis (Pyramidal Orchids)

Plants greatly resembling **Orchids** with flowers in dense, ovoid spikes, and large labellum, deeply cleft into three lobes.

1. Anacamptis pyramidalis. Leaves without dark spots on them. Flowers pink, with very long and slender spur pointing downwards. Habitat: Calcareous slopes, and meadows of middle and lower zones. Flowers March-May. The Cretan plants correspond to the brachystachys variety with pale pink flowers, and all parts of the plant smaller than those of the typical form.

Neotinea

Plants very similar to **Orchis** but flowers small, with very small spur and perianth segments converging, except the labellum which is 3-lobed.

1. Neotinea maculata. Leaves 3-6 with dark spots, rarely without spots. Flowers pink or purple, rarely greenish-white, in a dense spike, 2—6cm. along. Habitat: Woods and bushes at montane and sub-montane zone. Flowers March-May.

Aceras

Plants similar to **Orchis** but flowers small, without spur. Labellum with 4 linear lobes and other perianth segments converging.

1. Aceras anthropophorum. Leaves without dark spots flowers at elongated spike, greenish-yellow, often tinged with red. Labellum oblong with 4 lobes. The flowers resemble to a little man. Habitat: Middle and lower zone. Flowers April-May.

Ophrys spegodes - s. sp. mammosa

Ophrys cretica - s. sp. cretica

Orchis provincialis - s. sp. pauciflora

Orchis quadripunctata

Barlia

Plants with globulan tubers and strong stem. Leaves large. Spike dens and flowers with small spur. Labellum very similar at **Orchis.** The other parts of perianth curved but not converging.

1. Barlia robertiana. Stem 25-50cm. Lower leaves about 25cm. length and 10 cm. width, without dark spots. Flowers fragrant, purple-brown, purple-violet or violet-brown. Labellum with 3 lobes. The middle lobe divided at 2 smaller lobes. Habitat: Montane and sub-montane zone. Flowers March-April.

289

Himantoglossum

Plants with 2 spherical tubers. Flowers in long spike. The 5 segments of perianth converging. The lubellum 3-lobed. The middle lobe linear, very long. Spur short.

1. Himantoglossum hircinum - subsp. caprinum. Stems 20-90cm. Leaves without dark spots. Labellum pale pink. Middle Lateral lobes very short. The other perianth segments greenish. Habitat: Rare at montane and sub-montane zone. Flowers May-June.

Epipactis (Helleborines)

These plants have fleshy, perennial roots. Flowers in spikes, patent or drooping, and perianth segments free. Both petals and labellum smaller than the sepals. Spur absent.

1. Epipactis helleborine. Dark green ovate-elliptic leaves. Greenish sepals. Pink petals and labellum, the latter pointed at its apex. Habitat: Montane woods and forests. Flowers June-August. **2. Epipactis microphylla.** Minute leaves resembling green bracts. Sepals greenish. Petals and labellum whitish. Labellum pointed. Habitat: Found in montane and sub-montane forests and woods. Flowers May-July.

Cephalanthera

Plants with fleshy, perennial roots like those of **Epipactis.** Leaves without dark spots. Flowers of uniform colour, and with all segments converging. Labellum surrounded by the other perianth segments. Very small spur.

1. Cephalanthera rubra. Few florets in a lax spike, rose-purple in colour. Narrow, lanceolate or filiform-lanceolate leaves. Habitat: Montane forests and woods. Flowers May-June. **2. Cephalanthera cucullata.** Flowers white or whitish-pink, few but in a dense spike. Leaves small, scale-like. Habitat: An extremely rare endemic to be found in the montane zone forests of Central and East Crete. Flowers May-June. **3. Cephalanthera damasonium.** Sparse, snow-white flowers arising from big, green bracts. Leaves ovate or lanceolate. Habitat: Montane zone. Flowers May-June.

Limodorum (Limodores)

Violet-coloured plants lacking chrolophyll, saprophytes with small rhizome. Bract-like leaves. Sepals violet, spreading. Petals narrower than the sepals. Labellum acute at apex. Spur present.

1. Limodorum abortivum. Its rhizome is covered with thick roots. Stem 40-80cm. high. Raceme with 4-25 flowers, 3-3,5cm. across. Labellum of equal length or shorter than the sepals. Habitat: Montane, lowland and littoral woods. Flowers May-June.

Listera (Twayblades)

Plants with many, fleshy roots, and two opposite leaves at their base. Spike with small flowers. Elongated labellum with two lobes that look like a man's legs. The other perianth segments smaller.

1. Listera ovata. Stem 20-60cm. high. Leaves 2,5-20cm., ovate or elliptic. Flowers with a greenish, two-lobed labellum. Petals and sepals green-violet. Habitat: Montane and submontane zones. Flowers May-June.

Orchis anatolica

Orchis papilionacea

Orchis tridentata - s. sp. commutata

Orchis italica

Spiranthes (Lady's Tresses)

Root with two or more oblong tubers. Flowers small, segments converging. Labellum of equal length, and the same colour as the other segments.

1. Spiranthes spiralis. Flowers whitish-green, small in a spiral, or one-sided, leafless spike. Leaves all basal, appearing after flowering is over. Habitat: In glades, heaths, and meadows, at middle and low altitudes. Flowers August-October.

Serapias

Plants with 2-5 round tubers at the roots. Leaves rather narrow, canaliculate. Labellum elongated, drooping, with acute tip. Sepals ovate-lanceolate, pointed, coming together to form a 'helmet'. Petals smaller.

1. Serapias vomeracea. Tubers two. Stem 10-55cm. Flowers 15-30mm. long. Labellum brown with two dark-coloured lobes at its base. The other segments pink or reddish, with darker-coloured parallel veins. Leaves very narrow. Habitat: Meadows, scrub, and woods at middle and low altitudes. Flowers March-May. **2. Serapias orientalis.** Very similar to 1 but a shorter plant, reaching up to 25cm; leaves broader, and flowers a lighter colour and labéllum wider, cream or light brown. This species is often thought to be some subspecies of the previous plant. Habitat: Sub-montane zone. Flowers March-May. **3. Serapias lingua.** Similar to 1 and 2 but flowers smaller, a black patch at the base. Tubers 2. Habitat: Middle and low altitude heaths, meadows, and olive-groves. Flowers March-April. **4. Serapias parviflora.** Similar to 3 but flowers smaller, not surpassing 20mm. Labellum smaller, and without black patch missing from its base. Habitat: Uncultivated land, olive-groves, and ground along the coast. Flowers March-April.

The writing of this book was finished and the MSS were in the printer's hands when the author was informed of some of the latest findings regarding Cretan flora published recently. These have added another 32 species and subspecies to those already known of in the flora of Crete. It was no longer possible for these species to be intercalated in the appropriate chapters of the book, therefore, only a brief list is given below. In any case, this goes to show that Crete has many more surprises in store for us.

Adrachne telephioides - subsp. oreocretensis. Endemic to the alpine and sub-alpine zones of the mountains of Crete.

Aeteorhiza bulbosa - subsp. microcephala. Its occurrence in many localities has been confirmed.

Ajuga orientalis has been discovered in the gorge Poropharango, in the eparchy of Kissamos.

Artemisia herba-alba has been located on the islet of Gavdhos. This is the first time it has been observed in Greece.

Asperula arvensis has been noted in the districts of Lassithi and Mirabello.

Asperula crassula. This is a new species and endemic to Crete. It was found on the Mavros Promontory in North-East Crete.

Athamantha macedonica. Seen in the montane zone of the White Mtns.

Blackstonia acuminata - subsp. acuminata. Observed at Skiès of Kydonia, in the district of Chania. This is the first time it has been noted as occurring in the Aegean.

Calepina irregularis In the Petres Gorge at Rhethymnon.

Cephalanthera longifolia It has been come upon in West Crete.

Cirsium creticum - subsp. dicaeum A new endemic, discovered in the montane zone of the East Crete mountains.

Cirsium vulgare Discovered in the eparchy of Kydonia.

Conyza albida An alien, established in Crete.

Epipactis cretica A new Cretan endemic of the montane zone.

Orchis simia

Orchis saccata

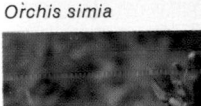

Dactylorriza sulfurea -
s. sp. pseudosambucina

Aceras anthropophorum

Erigeron glabratus A European and Mainland Greece species, it has been found in the alpine and sub-alpine zones of the White Mtns.

Gallium canum - subsp. ovatum. Seen in North-East Crete. It is a West Asia plant, formerly known to grow as far west as Carpathos only.

Hypericum jovis. A new endemic of the mountains of Central Crete.

Lepidium virginicum A North American alien discovered in the eparchy of Kydonia.

Malcolmia nana It has been met with at Malia and Seteia.

Barlia robertiana

Himantoglossum hircinum - s.sp.caprinum

Epipactis helleborine

Cephalanthera rubra

Ophrys fleischmannii Discovered to occur on Mt. Youchtas, in the eparchy of Temenos.

Orchis laxiflora - subsp. palustris. Found at Frangocastello of Sphakià, and at the Yeropotamos Delta, near Phaistos.

Orchis spitzelli - subsp. nitidifolia. Found in many districts but always in the montane zone.

Ornithogalum nivale In the montane and sub-montane zones. Formerly known, to occur on the mountains of Turkey.

Ornithogalum nutans Found in sub-montane meadows.

Cephalanthera damasonium

Limodorum abortitum

Spiranthes spiralis

Serapias vomeracea

Orobanche hederae Discovered to occur in the district of Rhethymnon, Malevizion, and Pedhiadha. Parasitic on Ivy.

Rosa agrestis Its occurrence on the Cretan mountains has been confirmed.

Rosa dumalis (also called r. vosagiaca, and R. caesia) Found in West Crete on the White Mountains.

Ruscus hypophyllum Cultivated in Crete since long ago, it has now been found to grow subspontaneously at the Sabbathiana Mone (Convent or Monastery) in the district of Malevizion.

Salvia pratensis - subsp. haematodes South of the village Armeni, Rhethymnon.

Serapias orientalis   *Serapias orientalis (form with dark flowers)*

Serapias lingua   *Serapias parviflora*

Sinapis alba - subsp. mairei Formerly considered a Moroccan endemic.

Tusillago farfara In the Sphacoriaco Valley, south of the Prassiano Gorge, in South Rhethymnon.

Vitis vinifera - subsp. sylvestris In the eparchy of Kydonia. This is the genuine, native form of the vine.

As it was stressed also in the beginning of this book, the existence of a large number of species in the Cretan flora is in inverse ratio to its small populations. That is why it is necessary to stress the fact that we must not pick the lovely wild flowers we come across in the country. Doing so we add one more threat to already badly injured Nature in Crete.

cream or creamy		dark green	
pale yellow		light green or grass-green	
lemon-yellow		glaucous	
golden-yellow		grey-green or greyish-green	
orange		silvery	
red		white	
crimson		pale pink	
blackish-red		pink	
dark brown		purple	
light brown		dark violet or mauve	
grey		violet	
blue		lilac	
dark or deep blue		pale blue	

Because in the text colours and hues of flowers or leaves alluded are difficult for the reader to comprehend fully, a list of colours and their names has been provided.

GLOSSARY

glandular 1

flower (sex)
 male 2
 bisexual
 or hermaphrodite 3
 female 4

ray floret 5
tubular or disk flroret 6
fusiform or spindle - shaped 7
apical 8

flowers (shape)
 actinomorphic 9
 zygomorphic 10
 butterfly-like
 or papilionaceous 11

anther 12
pedicel 13
arachnoid lanate 14
distant 15

stem (shape)
 quadrangular 16
 cylindrical 17
 hollow 18
 winged 19

stem (position)
 ascending 20
 creeping 21
 erect 22
 arcuate or arched 23

bract 24
bracteole 25
woody short-shoot 26
cluster 27
dioecious 28 ★
terminal 29
sessile or stalkless 8b
blade or lamina 8c
petiolate 32
caducous or falling early 33
depressed (hairs
 or other parts) 34
papillose or warty 34b
catkin 35
calyx 10b

fruit (type)
 achene 6b
 drupe 38
 carpel 39
 nut 40

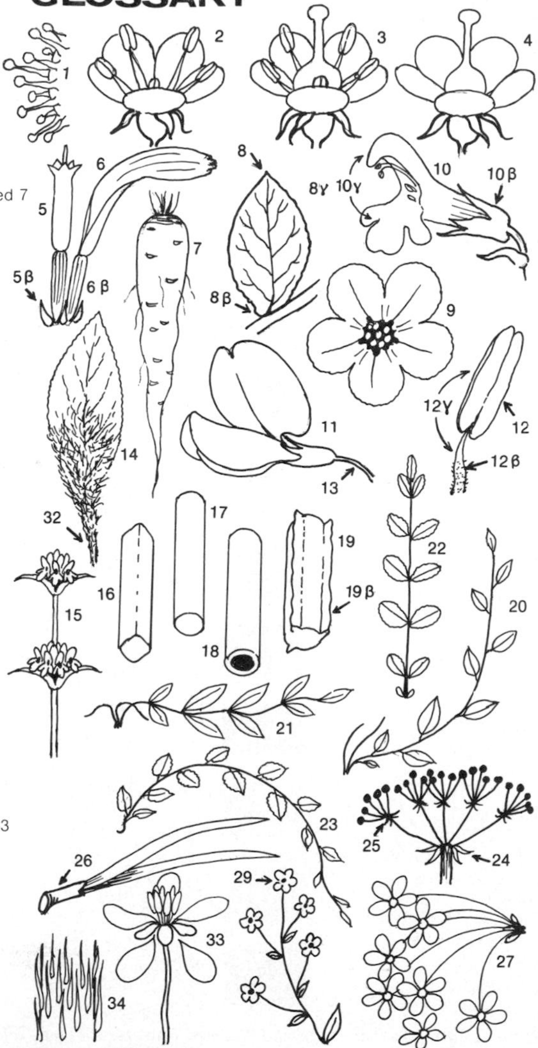

★ 28. Having male and female flowers on different plants

298

capsule 41
siliqua or silicula 42
pod 43
berry 44
samara 45
legume or pod 46
legume articulate or jointed 47
legume constricted 48

sheath 49
tuber 50
cup or cupule 51
decurved 52
deflexed 53
incurved 54
recurved 55
reflexed 56
scale 5b
hairless or glabrous 58
lobe 59
lanate 60
axil - axillary 61
loaf stolk or petiole 02
solitary 63
monoecious 64 ★
vein 65
filament 12b
claw 67
corona 68
stipules 69
perianth 70
perianth segment 71
spur 72
wing 19b
pyramidal crown 74
beak 75
rhizome 76
rosette 77
clavate or club-shaped 78
spathe 79

corolla or calyx
  two-lipped 10c
  bell-shaped or campanulate 52
  cup-shaped or crateriform 81
  tubular 82
  rotate or wheel-shaped 83
  funnel-shaped 84

stamen 12c
stolon 86
tube 87

★

inflorescence or infructescens
  curl 88
  raceme 89
  dichasium 90
  catkin 91
  head or capitulum 92
  corymb 93
  cyme or cymose 94
  cone 95
  umbel 96
  secondary umbel 97
  spike 98
  spikelet 98 b
  panicle 99

hairs (shape)
  simple 100
  star-shaped 101
  forked or bifurcate 102

hairy 103
saccate 104
epicalyx 105
epicalyx scales 106
leaflet 107

leaves (position)
  opposite 108
  perforate 109
  distichous 110
  alternate 111
  whorled or verticillate 112

leaf or other part of plant (tip)
  aristate or awned 113
  emarginate or notched 114
  obtuse 115
  mucronate 116
  truncate 117
  acute 118

leaf or other part of plant (margins)
  entire 119
  ciliate 119b
  fimbriate 120
  undulate or wavy 121
  dentate or toothed 122
  crenate 108b

leaf or other part of plant (shape)
  obcordate 124
  oblanceolate 125
  obovate 126
  shield - like or peltate 127
  canaliculate or chanelled 128
  sagittal or arrow - shaped 129
  needle 130

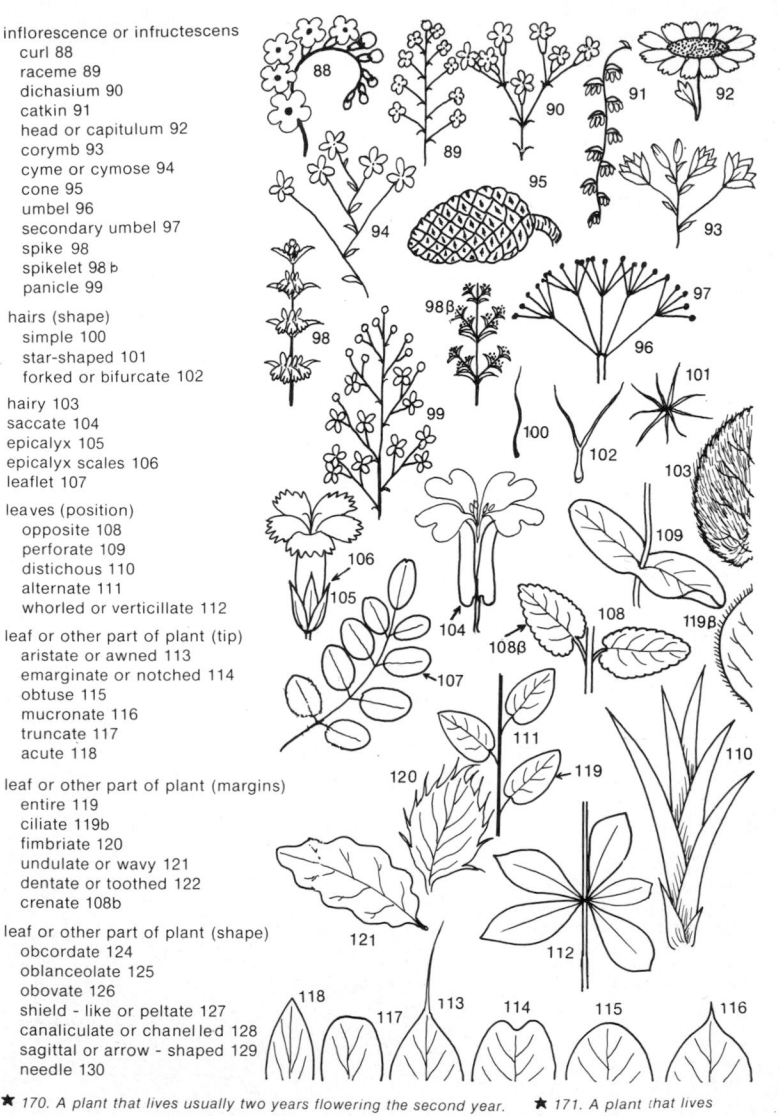

★ 170. A plant that lives usually two years flowering the second year.   ★ 171. A plant that lives

decurrent 131
bractlike 132
lingulate
or tongue - shaped 133
linear 134
deltoid 135
bilobed 136
orbicular 137
bipinnately lobed 138
bipinnate 139
bifid or bipartite 140
bifurcate 141
elliptical 142
semitubular 143
cordate
or heart - shaped 144
lanceolate
or lance - shaped 145
lyrate 146
reniform
or kidney - shaped 147
filiform 148
subulate
or awl - shaped 149
palmately - lobed 150
palmatifid or palmate 151
amplexicaul
or stem - clasping 152
pedate 153
oblong 154
pinnately - lobed 155
pinnate or pinnatifid 107
rhomboidal 156
gladiate or sword - shaped 110
spathulate 159
cuneate 160
tubular 161
strap - shaped 162
trifoliate 163
ovate or egg - shaped 164
plant (shape)
  tree 74
  shrub 166
  cushion - shaped
  shrublet 168 or pulvinate 167
  caespitose 169
plant (duration of life)
  biennial 170 ★
  annual 171 ★
  perennial 172 ★
pubescent or downy 173
ovary (position)
  superior 174
  semi-inferior 175
  inferior 176
auricle 177
only one year or less.

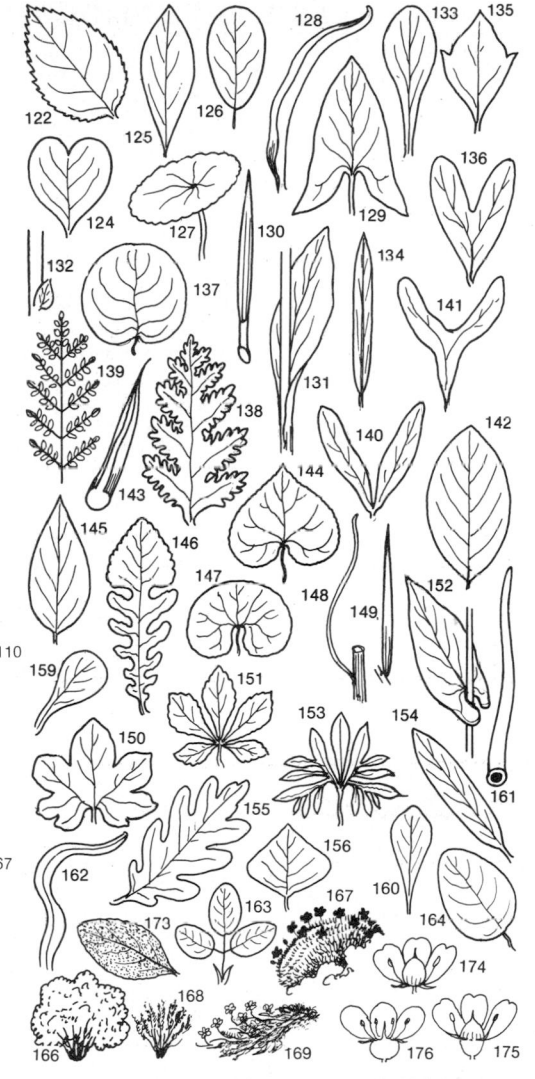

★ 172. A plant whose underground parts, at least, live for several years.

FOREIGN BIBLIOGRAPHY

Bothmer R. von — Cytological Studies in Allium - I Chromosome numbers and Morphology in Sect. Allium from Greece.

Bothmer R. von — Studies in the Aegean Flora XV - Chromosome numbers in Labiatae - Botaniska Notiser - 1970

Broussalis P. — Greek species of Fritillaria - Annales Musei Goulandris 4

Erben M. — Cytotaxonomische Untersuchungen an südosteuropäischen Viola - Arten der Section Melanium München 1985

Garbari F. - Greuter W. - Miceli P. — The "Allium cupani" group, a preliminary taxonomic, caryological and anatomical study. "Webbia" 34(1) 1979

Gldblata P. — Systematics of Gynandrinis (Iridaceae). A Mediterranean - Southern African disjunct. - Botanisca Notiser 133 - 1980

Greuter W. — Med - Checklist Notulae, 3 Willdenovia 11 - 1981

Greüter W. — Les Arum de la Crète - Botanica Helvetica - 94/1 - 1984

Greüter W. — Beiträge zur Flora des Sudagais-Candollea 1-7-1965

Greuter W. — Additions to the flora of Crete 1938-1972 Annales Mus. Goulandris - 1973

Greuter W. — Beiträge zur Flora der Südägäis 1-7 Candollea 20-1965

Greuter W. — The endemic flora of Crete and the significance of its protection

Greuter W. — Contributiones floristicae austro-aegaeae 10-12 - Candollea 22-2-1967

Greuter W. — Contributio floristica austroaegaea - Candollea 23-1-1968

Greuter W. - Matthäus U. - Risse H. — Additions to the flora of Crete, 1973-1983 (1984) - III - Willdenowia 15-1985

Greüter W. - Matthäs U. - Risse H. — Notes on Cardaegean plants 3. Medicago strasseri, a new leguminous shrub from Kriti - Willdenomia 12-1982

Greuter W. - Matthäus U. - Risse H. — Additions to the flora of Crete, 1973-1983 (1984) - II - Willdenowia 14 - 1984

Greuter W. - Miage J. — Nombres chromosomique de quelques plant recoltees en Crète. Athène 1979

Greuter W. - Raus T. — Med - Checklist Notulae 11 - Willdenowia 15 - 1985

Greuter W. - Strid A.

Notes on Cardaegean plants 2. A new species of Ranunculus sect. Ranunculus from the mountains of W. Kriti.

Gustafson M. - Bentzer B. - Bothmer R. von - Snogerup S.

Meiosis in Greek Brassica of the Oleracea group. - Botaniska Notiser 129 - 1976

Gustafson M. - Snogerup S.

A new subspecies of Brassica from Peloponnisos, Greece - Botanica Chronica 3 (1-2) 1983

Huxley A. - Taylor W.

Flowers of Greece and the Aegean

Huxley A.

Flowers in Greece - An outline of the Flora

Kamari G. - Georgiou U.

Cytological notes on two Ornithogalum species from Crete - Votanica Chronica 1/1 - 1981

Mathew B.

The Crocus - London 1982

Mathew B.

The Iris - London 1981

Mathew B.

The greek species of Crocus (Iridaceae). A toxonomy survey - Annales Musei Goulandris - 6 - 1983

Mathew B. - Baytop T.

The Bulbous Plants of Turkey

Papanikolaou K. - Kokkini S.

A taxonomic revision of Sideritis I - section Embe doclia (Rafin.) Bentham (Labiatae) in Greece

Phitos D.

Die quinquelokulären Campanula - Arten - Österreichischen Botonischen Zeitschrift - 1965

Polatschek A.

Die vertreter der Gattung Erysimum auf Kreta - Annales Musei Goulandris 113-126/1973

Polunin O.

Flowers of Europe - Oxford - 1969

Polunin O.

Flowers of Greece and the Balkans

Polunin O. - Huxley A.

Flowers of the Mediterranean - London 1965

Rechinger K.H.

Flora Aegaea

Runemark H.

Studies in the Aegean Flora - XIII - Tordylium L. (Umbeliferae) - Botaniska Notiser - Lund - 1968

Runemark H.-Greüter W.

Notes on Cardaegean plants 1. - The Sedum litoreum group - Willdenowia 11-1981

Runemark H. - Snogerup S. - Nordenstam B.

Studies in the Aegean Flora - I Floristic Notes - Botaniska Notiser - Lund - 1960

Sfikas G.

Flowers of Greece-Athens - 1984

Snogerup S.

Studies in the Aegean Flora - VIII - Erysimum, sect. Cheiranthus. A´ Taxonomy - Opera Botanica - No 13

Snogerup S.

Studies in the Aegean Flora - IX - Erysimum, sect. Cheiranthus B´. Variation and evolution in the smallpopulation system. - Opera Botanica - No 14

Snogerup S.

Studies in the Aegean Flora - IV - Bupleurum flavum and related species - Botaniska Notiser - Lund 1962

Stearn W.   Allium longanum. A species for the South - eastern
                                       Aegean region. Annales Musei Coulandris 3 - 1977

Stearn W. - Davis P.   Peonies of Greece - A taxonomic and historical sur-
                                       vey of the genus Paeonia in Greece - Goulandris
                                       Museum - 1984

Stork A. - Snogerup S. - Wüest J.   Seed character in Brassica, section Brassica and
                                       some related groups - Candollea - 1980

Strid A.   Variation in the satellite chromosomes of Nigella
                                       doerfleri (Ranunculaceae) - Botaniska Notiser -
                                       1969

Tzanoudakis D.   Karyotypes of the taxa of Allium, section Scorodon,
                                       from Greece - Caryologia - vol 36 n. 3 - 1983

Williams J. - Williams A. - Arlott N. Orchids of Britain and Europe, with N. Africa and
                                       the Middle East

Yannitsaros A.   Tagetes minuta in Greece - Candollea No 34 - 1979

Zahariadi C. - Stamatiadou E.   Geographical distribution of species of Ornithoga-
- Dima A.   lum (Libiaceae) in Greece including two new taxa -
                                       Annales Musei Goulandris 5 - 1982

The main help was the series of five books of "Flora Europaea" publication of the University of Cambridge which co-operated with the most famous Botanists in Europe.

BIBLIOGRAPHY IN GREEK

Calopisis J.   Cephalanthera cucullata. The Cretan Cephalan-
                                       therum which is threatened with extinction. The dire
                                       message to mankind.

Chandrinos G. - Dimitropoulos A.   Birds of Prey of Greece.

Cavadhas D.   Botanic and Plant Dictionary.

Dimitropoulos A.   Ecological Travels in Crete. (May-June 1980-Vol. 42
                                       of the journal "Taxidevontas" (Travelling)

Foitos D.   The genus Bolanthus (Caryophyllaceae) in Greece.
                                       Botanica Chronica (Chronicles) 1/1 1981.

Ganiatsas C.   The Flora of Crete. 1974.

Grispos P.   The forest History of Modern Greece. Athens 1973.

Hawks J.   History of Mankind. UNESCO Vol. I, Part I - Prehi-
                                       story.

Heldreich Th.   Dictionary of the popular names of the plants of
                                       Greece.

Hermjakob G.   Orchids of Greece and Cyprus. 1. Ophrys Genus.
                                       A Goulandris Museum Publication. Kifissia 1974.

Kokkini S. - Gouzgouni S.	Classificationary Studies on the genus Mentha in Greece.
Sfikas G.	Trees and Shrubs of Greece.
Sfikas G.	Greek Nature through the Centuries.
Simopoulos C.	Foreign Travellers in Greece.
Spanakis C.	Crete
Tzanoudakis D.	Popular names of Cretan Plants. - from the journal "Cretologia" June-December 1980.
Tzanoudakis D.	Cyttotaxonomical study of the genus Paeonia I. in Greece - 1977.

Information was also taken from the Encyclopaedia 'Domé' and 'The world of plants and animals'

INDEX OF LATIN NAMES

CONTENTS